LANDMARK COLLECTOR'S LIBRARY

WELSH CATTLE DROVERS

Agriculture and the Welsh cattle trade before and during the nineteenth century

RICHARD MOORE-COLYER

A Tour through England & Wales
D. Defoe

"*for from hence they send yearly great herds of black cattle to England,
and which are known to fill our fair and markets, even that of
Smithfield itself*"

Letter IV

Published by

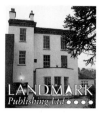

Ashbourne Hall, Cokayne Ave
Ashbourne, Derbyshire DE6 1EJ England
Tel: (01335) 347349 Fax: (01335) 347303
e-mail: landmark@clara.net
web site: www.landmarkpublishing.co.uk

2nd Landmark edition

ISBN 1-84306-222-4

Printed by Bath Press Ltd, Bath

Design & reproduction by able design

Cover by James Allsopp

Opposite: Cilgerran Fair, late in the 19th Century
Cover captions:
Front: The drovers' road between Blaendoethie and Soar-y-Mynydd at Ty' ncornel Youth Hostel.
Back: The drovers' road above Cwmystwyth

LANDMARK COLLECTOR'S LIBRARY

WELSH
CATTLE DROVERS

Richard Moore-Colyer

CONTENTS

With the exception of the Frontispiece and photographs on pages 12 and 70, which appear by courtesy of the National Library of Wales, and page 152, courtesy of Barbara Holl, all photographs are by Lindsey Porter. The author and publisher wish to thank the University of Wales Press, the original publishers, for permission to produce the present volume.

Tables

Figures

Maps

PREFACE

FIRST EDITION

Until relatively recently social historians have tended to concentrate their attention either upon the attempts of the upper echelons of society to resist social change or upon the activities of the representatives of the people to initiate or to accelerate alterations in society. Finally, after a long and brilliantly successful reign, Goldsmith's princes and lords have faded and the common man stands supreme.

Apart from the princes and the people, however, another class, hitherto largely neglected by historians, was instrumental in the evolution of our present society. This was the artisan class; the blacksmith, the wheelwright, the butcher and the cattle dealer, to name but a few. Though often numbered among the *"labouring poor"*, these people were possessed of considerable skills, were usually self-employed and were frequently fiercely independent. By virtue of their specialist skills, this class occupied a position in the social hierarchy above that of the landless, unskilled labourer whose sad plight lay heavy upon the conscience of Victorian Britain. In Wales particularly, where divisions between social classes had always been more blurred than in England, and where craftmanship and manual skills were held in high regard, the artisan class played a fundamental role in the social, cultural and economic evolution of society.

The principal objective of this book is to examine some aspects of the activities of one group of this class, namely the cattle dealers and drovers whose pursuits resulted in the inflow of much needed cash to the remote valleys of western Wales. Before the large scale development of iron and coal production in the mid-nineteenth century, livestock constituted the major "export" from Wales to England. Accordingly, any consideration of the cattle trade must not neglect some reference to the farmer, and thus the first two chapters of the book concern the farmer and the animals which, by his exertions, were available for driving to England.

Although there have been numerous general, and often ephemeral contributions to the subject, there have been but few attempts to examine the nineteenth century Welsh cattle trade in depth via the primary sources. However, the early studies of Professor Caroline Skeel, Dr. R.T. Jenkins and Mr. Llefelys Davies are notable exceptions, while the more recent work of Dr. Richard Phillips has emphasised the relevance, and indeed the importance, of utilising personal reminiscences and local tradition. The lack of such detailed works may reflect the paucity of primary source material and the questionable reliability of much of the contemporary printed material. The available manuscript sources comprise, in the main, the account books of drovers and dealers, together with legal cases recorded in Great and Quarter Sessions material and isolated references in manuscript letters and diaries. Among the secondary sources, the works of nineteenth century agriculturalists and antiquarians such as Edmund Hyde Hall, Walter Davies and John Bannister may be cited, while many of the Parliamentary Com-

missions and Select Committees sitting at various stages of the nin⸌
cerned, albeit peripherally, with facets of the Welsh cattle trade.

A search of the depositories throughout Wales has yielded only f
counts encompassing the latter part of the eighteenth and a considerab
ries. Four of these accounts provide a mere snapshot of the situation
accounts of the Jonathan family contain a detailed record of transactio ⸍⸍⸍⸍ued period. It
is because these Jonathan papers are concerned with the operation of the cattle trade in the central
and southern counties of Wales, that the following chapters tend to concentrate upon the activities of
the drovers in these areas. This applies particularly in Chapter V which is concerned with the location
of the principal drove routes from mid-Wales to the English border. In view of Phillips' success in
reconstructing part of the droving story on the basis of the personal interview, I felt that a great deal
of valuable information could be accumulated by contacting individuals known to have had family
connections with the trade.

These interviews I normally carried out during the course of the fieldwork undertaken to trace the
drove routes. Time limitations and other physical restrictions dictated that this fieldwork, and thus
the interviews, be conducted within a reasonable distance of the University College of Wales,
Aberystwyth. In consequence I decided, rather than to attempt a necessarily superficial coverage of
the drovers' roads throughout the Principality, to effect a detailed investigation of the routes in mid-
western Wales, many of which could be corroborated by manuscript evidence. Thus the tracing of the
drove routes of north Wales awaits the advent of a local historian equipped with a stout heart and an
unlimited fund of patience. Notwithstanding, much of the background material and information
relating to the basic "mechanics" of the cattle trade has been gleaned from manuscript, printed and
occasionally verbal sources from northern and southern as well as central Wales.

It is, of course, virtually impossible to acknowledge individually the assistance I have received from
friends, colleagues and correspondents throughout England and Wales. However, I wish above all to
express my gratitude to Emeritus Professor E.G. Bowen, Dr. Richard Phillips and Mr. Frank Emery
for the invaluable advice and criticism which they have offered during the preparation of this book.
My thanks also go to the staffs of the National Library of Wales and the various Records Offices both
in the Principality and in England, and to Mr. A.J. Bird of the Department of Geography in the
University College upon whose cartographic expertise I have drawn heavily. Where I have used information from my correspondents and verbal material collected "in the field", appropriate
acknowledgements are given in the footnotes.

During the course of my fieldwork I have spoken with numerous people whose profound knowledge of local matters has been a source of great delight to me. I am deeply indebted to these many
people throughout the length and breadth of Wales, not only for the benefit of their knowledge and
scholarship, but also for the gastronomic pleasures I have often enjoyed at their tables. I am grateful
also to the Editor of the Agricultural History Review for allowing me to print material from Chapter
II which originally appeared in that journal and to the Librarian of the National Library of Wales for
kindly authorising the republication of some of the material in Chapters III and IV which appeared in
the pages of the National Library of Wales Journal. Finally I wish to record my thanks to Professor W.
Ellison of the University College of Wales, Aberystwyth, for providing me with the facilities to carry
out this work as a member of staff in his Department.

R. Moore-Colyer, February 1975

SECOND EDITION

In the twenty five years that have elapsed since the first edition appeared the corpus of historical writing on rural Wales has expanded dramatically. Major works on the agricultural and social history of rural Wales from the pens of such scholars as David Howell, Melfyn Humphreys, Matthew Cragoe, John Davies, Geraint H Jenkins and David Pretty (to name but a few) have significantly broadened and deepened our understanding of the *mores* of the farmers, landowners and rural labourers in the nineteenth and earlier centuries. Similarly a broad raft of specialised contributions to the periodical literature provided by myself and many other historians, historical geographers and social anthropologists have laid (and continue to lay) a solid platform for the interpretation and reinterpretation of the past, be it in the field of rural technology, economy or social life.

In the context of *The Welsh Cattle Drovers* some of this work, coupled with my own more recent studies of the agrarian history of nineteenth century Britain, has made Chapter I of the original edition seem decidedly dated and I have accordingly excised much of the first part of that chapter and substantially restructured the remainder, together with part of Chapter II. Much of the material setting out the 'general' background to the farming industry in nineteenth century Wales originally appeared in the 1850-1914 volume of the *Agrarian History of England and Wales* (Cambridge, 2000) and I am most grateful to the editor of that volume, Professor E.J.T. Collins, for permission to make use of it. The historiography of droving itself has been amplified by several articles in the periodical literature and a handful of books and booklets of a non-scholarly nature. However, little has appeared to persuade me of the need to modify the overall findings reported in *The Welsh Cattle Drovers*, and although I have added material here and there, Chapters III to VI remain more or less as they originally appeared.

The first edition of *The Welsh Cattle Drovers* was marred by the lamentably poor quality of the maps and diagrams (largely hand-drawn by myself), and by a variety of inaccuracies in both text and footnotes consequent on my being abroad when the proofs became available. It goes without saying that I am most grateful to Mr Lindsey Porter of Landmark Publishing for the opportunity to rectify the latter, and to publish a second edition wherein the maps appear in a form both clear and elegant. Rereading the Preface to the first edition I note that not only are those individuals whose assistance I acknowledge no longer in the land of the living, but that most of the many correspondents cited in footnotes have also passed on. As they have faded away so the final thread of contact with the droving past has been severed.

Concurrently the agricultural world, even that of the 1970s, has changed beyond recognition with intensification, changes in field boundaries and other aspects of farm rationalisation consequent upon economic exigencies. This inevitably means that some of the drovers' routes which I was able to pursue on foot and by car in the seventies may now be less easy to trace on the ground, while to my certain knowledge, several of the drovers' pubs, cattle shoeing compounds and other physical evidence of the drovers have disappeared without trace. Meanwhile, Northampton market, which I described in my Epilogue as still being a venue for Welsh cattle dealers in the 1970s, has long succumbed to a miasma of carparks, offices, and commercial developments.

R. Moore-Colyer, June 2001

Land & Agriculture in Nineteenth Century Wales

The physical landscape of Wales essentially comprises a central highland mass embraced, on all sides, by a fringe of lowland. Bare, exposed mountains in excess of 2000 feet are generally limited to the counties of Caernarvon and Merioneth, while the bulk of the highlands are made up of wet acidic moorlands from 600 to 2000 feet in elevation. Here, rainfall levels may reach eighty inches annually, and the dominant vegetation of cotton grass and purple moor grass occasionally gives way to upland peat bog, with bracken infesting the drier slopes extending as high as 1500 feet in favourable conditions. To the west, steep-sided river valleys dominated by oak, ash and birch cut through the upland and flow into Cardigan Bay, their lower reaches flanked by broad tongues of lowland of variable relief, creating what is essentially an undulating coastal plateau where rainfall rarely exceeds fifty inches. As with the Rheidol, Dyfi, Mawddach and Teifi in the west, the Clwyd, Dee and Conwy rivers flow through extensive lowlands in the north, while the River Severn traverses a great swathe of fertile farmland extending through Welshpool to Newtown and Llanidloes.

Further south, the Black Mountains separate the valleys of the Usk and Wye and numerous smaller rivers drain from the central uplands into the Bristol Channel. Apart from the low-lying fields of Anglesey (traditionally *Môn mam Cymru*, the granary of Wales) and the extensive lowlands of the Llŷn Peninsula, the predominant agricultural lowlands of the Principality lie to the south. Favoured with a mild Atlantic climate and relatively well-drained soils of low acidity, the Vale of Glamorgan, the Gower Peninsula in Carmarthenshire, and the geologically complex parishes of South Pembrokeshire comprise some of the finest farmlands in Wales, although even here the undulating relief imposes some restrictions on the practical business of farming.

Whether he lived in the lush counties of the south, or attempted to wrest a living from the unprom-ising northern uplands, a farmer lucky enough to survive from the end of the Napoleonic Wars to the closing years of the nineteenth century would have witnessed considerable, if generally undramatic, changes to the farmscape. He would have noted, in particular, significant alterations both to national and local demographic structures which may have impinged upon his social life and would almost certainly have influenced his farming system. At the national level, population was steadily increasing, and as the rate of increase accelerated during the final half of the nineteenth century, the population of Wales advanced from 0.587 millions in 1801 to a total of 2.421 millions in 1911.

But this was by no means a uniform increase, and many rural areas experienced either population stagnation or absolute decreases with each decennial census, so that Radnorshire, in 1801 the only county with less than 5 per cent of the population, was joined in this category by seven other rural counties in 1911. By contrast, the southern counties of Glamorgan and Monmouth, with 20 per cent of the population in 1801, accommodated over half the souls living in Wales at the turn of the twentieth century.[1] Locally, demographic patterns changed in proportion to industrial development. In Carmarthenshire, for example, despite a 23 per cent increase in total population between 1841 and 1891, country people were drawn away from agricultural underemployment towards the industrial areas around Llanelli, leading to a decline of almost one third in the agricultural workforce in the same period.[2] A similar situation applied in neighbouring Cardiganshire where the agricultural population of the southern parishes tended to peak in 1841, after which migration more than balanced the natural increase.[3]

Overseas emigration from the rural west in the 1830s and 1840s, and urban-orientated migration in later decades had far-reaching repercussions for all aspects of life, and a major effect on the rôle of farming in the economy of many parts of Wales. In Glamorgan, in particular, agriculture had declined to the status of a minor industry by 1911, employing less than one quarter of those engaged in the metal trades, and a mere one thirteenth of the coalmining workforce.[4] As early as the mid-century, the gathering of the harvest in this, and other parts of south Wales, had become dependant upon migrant labour from England, while the loss of indigenous rural craftsmen and labourers was supplemented by arrivals from the depressed agricultural parishes of south-west England, together with mass immigration of Irish families.[5]

In the Principality as a whole less than 20 per cent of the male population worked on the land in 1911, although the proportion remained at close to 50 per cent in the agrarian counties of Radnor, Montgomery and Cardigan, and at around one third in Merioneth and Anglesey. Since the decline in the agricultural workforce tended to be highest among young, mobile labourers, there were obvious implications for what still remained an occupation demanding of much physical labour. On the other hand, given the inexorable trend towards pastoral farming characteristic of the period, family and hired labour was more meaningfully employed and the seasonal underemployment common in Wales in earlier decades probably disappeared. This point is largely substantiated by the declining role of women on the land. Women had traditionally been employed as day labourers during the growing and harvesting seasons, but as cereal acreages decreased so did opportunities for field work diminish, with what remained being the prerogative of permanent farm staff. As a labourer's wife from Wenvoe in Glamorgan explained in 1869:

> *"Women are not employed in the fields. My mother used to work regularly, and I went weeding as a girl with other women. The weeding is now done by men and boys".*[6]

The Census Returns reveal a decline in the female agricultural labour force in Wales from some 27 per cent of the population in 1851 to slightly over 9 per cent in 1911, although it is significant that in the counties of Cardigan, Carmarthen and Pembroke where there was increasing emphasis on dairying enterprises, employment of women on the land remained in excess of 20 per cent.

By the penultimate decade of the nineteenth century the farmscape of Wales remained overwhelmingly dominated by the estate system to the extent that a mere 10 per cent of the land was under owner-occupation in 1887. If the vast Wynnstay and Tredegar estates, the former including 142,000 acres in north and mid-Wales, and the latter holding more than 1000 farms in three southern counties were exceptional, estates in excess of ten thousand acres were widespread.[7] In Cardiganshire alone the estates of Nanteos, Gogerddan and Trawscoed embraced over 100,000 acres, while Edwinsford in Carmarthenshire and Stackpole in Pembrokeshire are representative of more modest properties of between 10,000 and 15,000 thousand acres.[8] Taken as a whole, however, the majority of Welsh estates were less extensive in scale, as indicated in Table I, derived from Bateman's survey of the 1873 ownership returns.

Table I
Percentage distribution of estates of over 3,000 acres, 1873

Acres	%
3,000-5,000	48
5,001-8,000	21
8,001-11,000	11
11,001-14,000	6
14,001-17,000	4
17,001-20,000	2
over 20,000	8
	100

Bateman's figures reveal that only 31 per cent of the farmed area was held by owners of more than 3000 acres, and if the data is presented on a county basis, the effect of proximity to areas of urbanisation and industrialisation on the rent burden of tenants is highlighted. (Table II)

Table II Areas and rents per acre of land on estates over 3,000 acres, 1873.		
Area	*Percentage in estates over 3,000 acres*	*Rent per acre*
Glamorgan/Monmouth	15	£2.5
Pembroke/Cardigan/Carmarthen	31	£0.7
Brecon/Radnor/Montgomery	15	£0.7
Merioneth/Caernarvon/Anglesey	32	£0.8
Denbigh/Flint	7	£1.4

It will be clear from the evidence set out above that mid-nineteenth century Wales was essentially a land of small estates owned, by and large, by an Anglicised and Anglican gentry whose traditional rôles as guardians and patrons of the ancient culture had all but disappeared, and whose relationship with a predominantly Nonconformist tenantry was becoming increasingly strained. The combined effects of earlier generations of profligacy, crippling family settlements which had necessitated heavy mortgaging, and total or partial absenteeism, meant that in many cases estates teetered close to the verge of bankruptcy and provided rich pickings for a host of generally incompetent lawyers and agents.[9] Alongside these smaller estates lay the properties of the yeomen freeholder. Of these, some had purchased their freeholds in the 1870s while others, resisting the blandishments of richer neighbours, had held hereditary property for many generations, their deep personal attachment to the land enabling them to overcome hard times and financial stress. In general, the distribution of smaller freeholds was more common in areas where no single landlord dominated, so that in the Cardiganshire parishes of Blaenpennal, Nantcwnlle, Llanbadarn, Lledrod and Llangeitho, between 22 and 48 per cent of the land was in freehold occupation in the 1890s.[10]

Leaving aside problems of undercapitalisation on the part of both landlord and tenant, the advance of farming throughout much of Wales was inhibited by cultural and social factors. To begin with, the growing sense of alienation between landlord and tenant created a climate of mutual suspicion whereby the former became disillusioned by the "hereditary prejudices" widespread among their tenantry, while the tenants themselves, in deriding (and largely ignoring) the efforts of the estate home farm to demonstrate modern practices, believed that such improvements were in many cases irrelevant to the economic realities of farming, besides which, if put into practice on their own farms, they would merely result in advanced rent demands.[11] Moreover, as David Parry-Jones demonstrated, in describing the Welsh countryside in the years preceding World War I, an innate conservatism permeated rural society to the extent that security was considered vital and change dangerous:

"We valued very much an orderly settled social structure... perhaps too many movements up and down might endanger its equilibrium and poise... The old ways were always the best; the old order, the old customs, the old methods..."[12]

A sort of fatalistic conservatism hung like a heavy pall over much of the farmscape, and when allied to the fact that communal cooperation was considered essential for the discharge of a whole range of farming activities, it would have served as a potent disincentive to individual initiative and technological innovation.[13]

Language too, was a formidable obstacle, since, despite the increasing use of English in the industrial valleys and the eastern counties, a high proportion of the working people in the north and west were monoglot Welsh speakers.[14] Meanwhile, landlords and their agents retained but a hazy under-

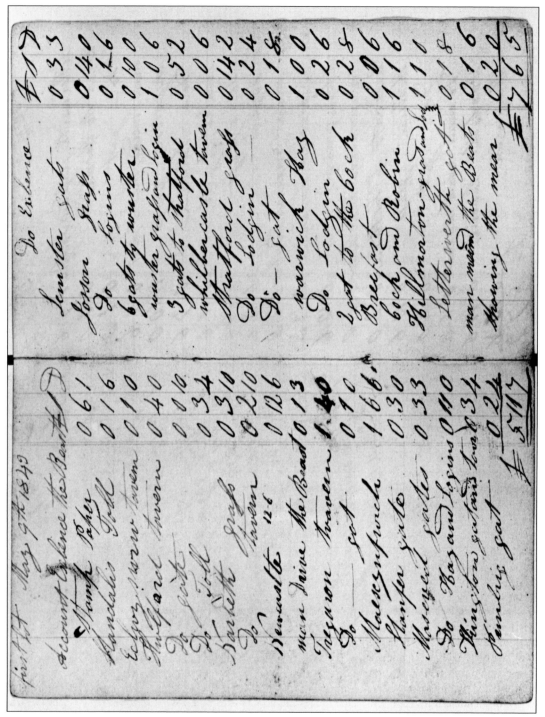

Extract from the accounts of David Jonathan, a cattle dealer and drover, from Dihewyd, Cardiganshire, 1849

standing of Welsh, while Welsh language material on the technical aspects of agriculture was largely limited to occasional newspaper columns and pamphlets sponsored by local *eisteddfodau*. For all the growth of specialist publications dealing with farming matters in the final half of the nineteenth century, there were no more than four Welsh language volumes concerned with practical agriculture.[15] In recognition of the problem the Board of Agriculture began to publish Welsh versions of its advisory pamphlets in 1893 and bilingual forms for the official June Returns in 1907, concurrent with the efforts of the University of Wales to compile glossaries of technical terms for use in future Welsh-language publications involving agricultural matters.[16]

If the large upland sheepwalks which had already evolved from the ancient transhumance system of *hafod* and *hendre* are excluded, the farm structure of Wales by 1850 was essentially one of small units.[17] Some of these enjoyed access to the bracken, rush and bilberry-infested upland commons, with obvious implications for stocking capacity, while others were self-contained holdings with management profiles ranging from semi-subsistence to fully-commercial, according to the aspirations and individual abilities of their tenants. By the outbreak of the Great War some 70 per cent of farms in the Principality were of less than 50 acres in size, with only 2 per cent exceeding 300 acres, a pattern which had not changed significantly since the early 1870s.[18] Although the traditional view that the economic lot of the smaller tenant was little better than that of the day labourer is probably sustainable, the much-vaunted notion that the Welsh farmer and his workers formed a unified class standing shoulder-to-shoulder against a predatory gentry can no longer be accepted, and there remains no doubt as to the clearly-defined social differences between farmer and labourer in the closing years of the nineteenth century.[19]

Yet, both classes shared a common interest in the land, and while pastoral farming was to make an increasingly significant contribution to farm output as the century progressed, the production of arable crops, especially in the more fertile lowlands, remained an important preoccupation in 1850.[20] Of the three major cereals, wheat was only grown extensively in the vales of Glamorgan, Clwyd and Usk and the light lands of Pembrokeshire, while barley, an important element in the rural diet, was more widely cultivated, usually as the second successive white crop.[21] In agronomic terms, neither of these cereals was ideally-suited to Welsh conditions, in contrast to oats, which, being relatively tolerant of high soil acidity, high rainfall and low summer temperature, were well-adapted to both upland and lowland areas. Of equal importance, the unexacting oat crop can thrive under indifferent management, so it is not surprising to find that it was the most common cereal in Wales by the later nineteenth century, providing nourishment for household, stable and byre.

Beyond taking account of the observations of contemporary commentators, it is virtually impossible to guage the extent of the success of the gentry in promoting a rational approach to crop rotation. The overall impression, however, is that outside the more agriculturally sophisticated southern and northern vales, tenants paid scant regard to the notion of rotations and only in "rare and isolated" cases, imposed a turnip or green crop between runs of cereals.[22] In mitigation, the turnip crop was both difficult and expensive to grow and regularly subject to the unwelcome attentions of the flea beetle.[23]

Traditionally, the various cereal crops had been manured with a variety of composts including farmyard manure, seaweed, seasand, ditch-scrapings and lime. Lime, in particular, was extensively used and was carted many miles inland from the several hundreds of limekilns dotted along the Cardigan Bay coastline to which shiploads of limestone and culm were delivered from South Pembrokeshire.[24] The misguided belief that lime was a "fertiliser" when, in reality, it was a soil conditioner and a buffer against acidity, did little to promote its effective use. This meant that in some areas overliming was common, while elsewhere the high cost of carting to farms remote from a kiln meant that lime use was often minimal and soils remained unresponsive to other fertilising materials.[25]

Lime spreading went into steep decline with the decay of the coastal kilns and with the growing availability of guano, and superphosphates, although, it must be emphasised, these could never be effective substitutes.[26] The development of inorganic sources of phosphate and the importation of

German potash and Chilean nitrates in the mid-century prompted a shift in emphasis away from guano, rape dust and other organic plant nutrients throughout Great Britain as a whole.[27] How far these vital components of Thompson's second agricultural revolution impinged upon crop husbandry in Wales is an open question deserving of further study.[28] Home farm account books and other estate documents reveal unequivocally that the gentleman farmers of Wales followed the national trend, not only using new sources of fertilisers on cereal and root crops, but continuing with the well-established practice of feeding oil cakes to livestock at pasture.[29]

Again, although estate bailiffs experienced some difficulty in persuading tenants of the virtues of guano, farm diaries from the 1850s onwards contain frequent references to dissolved bones and superphosphates. But, on the assumption that the diarists were among the more technically "advanced" farmers, their writings tell us nothing of the general situation. The balance of probability is that the smaller tenant farmers, chronically starved of working capital, deeply suspicious of change and, in the main, reliant on livestock farming for their income, made relatively little use of these materials before 1900. Whether or not such reasoning also applies to the use of basic slag, a cheap source of phosphate ideally suited to the encouragement of nitrogen-fixing wild white clover in pastures, and widely available after 1890, must await the results of more detailed investigation.

The preparedness or otherwise of Welsh farmers to substitute the newer agricultural technology for the wide range of hand tools traditionally used in crop husbandry depended upon a variety of factors, of which capital availability, farm size and the relative abundance or scarcity of labour were among the most important. Of significance too was the degree of literacy in the local society, the willingness of landlords to use the institutional framework of estate management to encourage innovation, and the vigour and persuasiveness of opinion-leaders, be they tenants or freeholders. In the Vale of Glamorgan and the arable areas of the English border, for example, mechanisation was well advanced by the 1860s and access to skilled craftsmen allowed for the maintenance of increasingly complex cultivation and harvesting equipment.

While the traditional crafts of the wheelwright, blacksmith and cooper continued to thrive, progressive farmers in these areas had access to the ploughs, corn and turnip drills and threshing equipment produced by men like William Tilley of Cowbridge and Henry Yorath, who not only manufactured their own equipment, but served as retailers of machinery produced by the large-scale English manufacturers.[30] At the same time, arable farmers of the northern vales could purchase ploughs and other cultivation equipment from producers in Corwen, Llanwrst and Denbigh, and as Hodges and Wright of Brecon sold their newly-patented barn machinery in the south and east, hay and straw-cutting equipment was available to vale-land livestock men from the factory of Thomas Bright of Carmarthen by the 1860s.[31]

Whereas iron ploughs, drills, threshers and winnowing machines were widely-adopted in the arable dominated vales, the sickle, reaping-hook, and scythe remained in use long after the introduction of Bell's reaper and its various modifications. Indeed, it was only in the late 1880s when the fortunes of arable farming began to plummet in parallel with a steady advance in the real value of wages that the reaper, and subsequently the reaper-binder, came to replace the harvest gang. Thus, in 1898, the owner of the Highmead estate in Carmarthenshire, reckoning the cost of mowing by hand at 10 shillings per acre, and reaper-binding at 2 shillings and 6 pence, considered that capital invested in a reaper-binder could be amply justified on one hundred acres of arable land.[32]

With the widespread adoption of the reaper-binder after 1900 or, at least, its availability through the services of contractors, came the end of the tradition of family work in the fields. Henceforth the harvest would be gathered by permanent farm staff, and as the binder rendered anachronistic the itinerant harvest gang, it also reduced the potential for gleaning, thereby severing a centuries-old bond between community and village.[33] On the other hand, however, for the breeder of horses, often operating in the fringes of the uplands, the use of increasingly-sophisticated agricultural machinery in the low-lying vales offered positive economic advantages. Essentially, more machinery meant more demand for draught power, and between 1871 and 1921, a period when the arable acreage of Wales was in absolute decline, the number of working horses per hundred acres of cultivated land advanced from 2.6 to 3.2.[34]

In terms of the adoption of machinery, the situation on the lowlands contrasted markedly with that of the pastoral uplands. Mowers with reciprocating blades, improved farm wagons and later, hay elevators, were available for his use, yet the upland farmer, short of capital and often isolated from the nearest craftsman, continued to make and maintain his own simple equipment before 1900. Poor roads, and the undulating and often boggy terrain enforced the continuation of the use of pack-horse and sled for transport purposes until a relatively late date, and in addition precluded the use of the reciprocating mower in the hay harvest.[35] Besides, in the context of an overwhelmingly pastoral economy dominated by family-run farms, agents for the manufacturers of the new farm machinery viewed upland Wales rather despairingly as a lost cause and did little to promote the sale of their products in these remote localities.[36]

With their mild climate and abundant rainfall both the uplands and lowlands of the Principality were well-suited to the growth of forage for grazing animals.[37] Yet, despite the establishment of legumes and ryegrasses in some of the climatically-favoured lowlands in the late seventeenth century, many of the innovative approaches to grassland management which had become commonplace in England were comparatively rare in Wales by 1850.[38] The problem of obtaining sources of grass seeds of reliable purity and germination (which was to remain, by and large, the case until the end of the century) together with a widely-held view that pasture adequate for most purposes could be readily obtained by allowing nature to take its course at the end of a run of cereal crops, meant that grasslands and their management remained in a relatively primitive condition.[39] Both open hill and re-cently-enclosed upland common remained much as nature intended, while broad acreages of lowland were largely innocent of improvement; the province of rush and matt grass, couch and buttercup.

In parts of Brecknockshire, Cardiganshire, Carmarthenshire and Montgomeryshire, the gentry and some of the more substantial tenants had attempted to introduce the flooded water meadow in the early 1800s, but in most cases their efforts had foundered on the shortage of skills required to carry out necessary maintenance of the infrastructural works.[40] Since little effort was made to rationalise grazing practices, either by reseeding policy, manuring, or the control of stocking, pasture was prob-ably in surplus during the early and mid-season and in deficit towards the autumn, so that the latter part of the year posed problems for the sustenance of grazing animals. To some extent these were circumvented by the use of "foggage", or autumn-saved pasture, and of gorse (*Ulex europaeus*), fed in combination with hay or straw after being bruised with hand, and later, horse and water-powered gorse mills.[41]

Regardless of whether he occupied a self-contained lowland holding, a hill sheepwalk, or an upland farm with access to common grazing, the farmer's overriding concern was to produce sufficient for-age to sustain his ruminant livestock over the winter months. His spring and summer stocking capac-ity would inevitably reflect his assessment of how many animals he could maintain for what was essentially a six month winter and because his inwintering facilities were often inadequate, most livestock remained out of doors with clear implications for maintenance energy requirements. Thus was the hay harvest of paramount importance. Indeed, saving a crop of hay of sufficient bulk and quality meant the difference, in farming terms, between survival and failure, and it is no surprise that the hay harvest was undertaken in an atmosphere of high seriousness, aided by the prayers and ap-peals in church and chapel alike.[42] Whatever the level of technology employed, and numerous low-land tenants had adopted the horse-drawn mower by the 1870s where the terrain permitted, haymaking was the vital task of the livestock farmer's year and, given the unreliable weather conditions in Wales, remained a high-risk operation in the pre-silage years.

The rather bleak sketch of the Welsh pastoral landscape outlined above was to change little during the nineteenth century, and the wholesale improvements of lower-lying grasslands and the dramatic transformation of the moribund hills and uplands would need to await the ingenuity of R.G.Stapledon and his colleagues when the Welsh Plant Breeding Station was established shortly after the Great War.

FOOTNOTES FOR CHAPTER 1

1 C.Thomas, "Rural Settlement in the Modern Period", in D. Huw Owen, (ed), *Settlement and Society in Wales*, Cardiff, 1989, p. 249.

2 D.W. Howell, "Rural Society in Nineteenth Century Carmarthenshire," *Carmarthenshire Antiquary*, XIII, 1977, p. 72.

3 D.Jenkins, *The Agricultural Community in South West Wales at the turn of the Twentieth Century*, Cardiff, 1971, pp. 158-9.

4 J.Davies and G.E. Mingay, "Agriculture in an Industrial Environment", in A. John and G. Williams (eds), *Glamorgan County History, 1800-1970*, Cardiff, 1980, p. 284.

5 E.Scourfield, "Rural Society in the Vale of Glamorgan" in P. Morgan (ed), *Glamorgan County History*, 1780-1980, Cardiff, 1988, p. 277.

6 *Royal Commission on the Employment of Women and Children in Agriculture*, Third Report, B.P.P.1870, p. 72.

7 J. Davies, "The End of the Great Estates and the Rise of Freehold farming in Wales," *Welsh History Review,* VII(2), 1974, pp. 186-20; R. Phillips, *Tredegar: The History of an Agricultural Estate, 1300-1956*, Tredegar Memorial Trust, 1990, p. 242. Since this book was completed, two major volumes concerned *inter alia* with landownership and the agrarian activities of the Welsh gentry have appeared, namely, M Humphreys, *The Crisis of Community: Montgomeryshire, 1680-1815* (Cardiff. 1996), and M Cragoe, *An Anglican Aristocracy - the Moral Economy of the Landed Estate in Carmarthenshire, 1832-1895*, Oxford, 1996.

8 R.J. Moore-Colyer, "The Edwinsford Estate in the Nineteenth Century," *Bulletin of the Board of Celtic Studies XXVI(2)*, 1975, p.p. 200-217 *Ibid.*, "The Gentry and the County in Nineteenth Century Cardiganshire", *Welsh History Review*, 10(4), 1981, pp. 497-535.

9 R.J. Moore-Colyer, "The Land Agent in Nineteenth Century Wales," *Welsh History Review, 8(4),* 1977, pp. 401-25; *Ibid.*, "Nanteos; a landed estate in decline", *Ceredigion*, 9(1), 1980, pp. 58-77.

10 B.P.P. XV. 1894, pp. 580-97.

11 For some of the more absurd notions of home farm activities see, R.J. Moore-Colyer, *A Land of Pure Delight; Selections from the correspondence of Thomas Johnes of Hafod, 1748-1816*, Gwasg Gomer, 1992.

12 D. Parry-Jones, *My Own Folk*, Llandysul, 1972, pp. 91-2.

13 Jenkins, *op.cit*, passim; J.T. Schlebecker, "Farmers and Bureaucrats: Reflections on Technological Innovation in Agriculture," *Agricultural History*, 61(4), 1977, pp. 650-55; A.H. Bunting (ed), *Change in Agriculture*, London, 1970, pp. 762-63.

14 R.C.L.W.M., *Report*, 1896, p. 288.

15 N. Goddard, "The Development and Influence of Agricultural Periodicals and Newspapers," 1780-1880, *Ag. Hist. Rev.* 31(2), 1983, p.117; A.O. Evans, "Some Agricultural Writers," *Welsh Journal of Agriculture*, VIII, 1932, pp. 71-84. The Welsh Journal of Agriculture, which ran from 1926 until 1943, reflects the research interests of the biologists and social scientists working at the University Colleges of Bangor and Aberystwyth and at the recently established Welsh Plant Breeding Station. However, the volumes contain a number of articles, notes, and statistical data referring to the period between the end of the 'Great Depression' and World War I (see R J Moore-Colyer, "Farming in depression: Wales between the wars, 1919-39", *Ag.Hist.Rev*, 46, 1998).

16 L.Phillips, "Prominent Welsh Agriculturists: Cadwaladr Bryner Jones, 1872-1954," *Journal of the U.C.W. Agricultural Society*, LX, 1978, pp. 143-9.

17 Howell, *op.cit*, passim; R.J. Moore-Colyer, "The Size of Farms in early Nineteenth Century Wales", *Bulletin of the Board of Celtic Studies XXVll, (2)*, 1976, pp. 200-17.

18 Agricultural Returns, 1875-1914.

19 D.A. Pretty, *The Rural Revolt that Failed: Farm Workers' Trades Unions in Wales 1889-1950*, Cardiff, 1989, passim.

20 For details of crop husbandry systems see, R.J. Moore-Colyer, "Crop Husbandry in Wales before the onset of mechanisation," *Folk Life, Journal of Ethnographic Studies*, 21, 1983, pp. 49-90.

21 W.B. Wall, "On the Farming of Pembrokeshire," *J.R.A.S.E.* Ser ii. 1887, pp. 86-7.

22 T Morgan, *An Essay on the System of Agriculture of Carmarthen*, Carmarthen, 1852, p.19.

23 J. Gibson, *Agriculture in Wales*, Aberystwyth, 1879, p. 61.

24 R.J. Moore-Colyer, "Of Lime and Men; aspects of the coastal trade in Lime in the eighteenth and nineteenth centuries," *Welsh History Review*, 14(1), 1988; *Ibid.*, "Coastal Limekilns in Southwest Wales," *Folk Life Journal of Ethnographic Studies*, 28, 1990.

25 R.C.L.W.M., *Minutes of Evidence III*, 1895, p. 434.

26 J.G. Jenkins, *Maritime Heritage: The Ships and Seamen of South Ceredigion*, Llandysul, 1982, pp. 49-50.

27 L.J. Peel, "Science, Energy and Agriculture since 1800," *Acta Museorum-Agriculturae* XII, 1977, pp. 60-3.

28 F.M.L. Thompson, "The Second Agricultural Revolution, 1815-1880," *Ec.H.R.* Ser ii, 21, 1968.

29 See, for example, National Library of Wales MSS Lucas 631-43; Picton Castle 44-46.

30 Scourfield (1988), *op. cit*, pp. 228-29.

31 E. Scourfield, "The Interpretation of the history and development of farming techniques in Wales as illustrated by the collection at the Welsh Folk Museum," *Acta Museorum Agriculturae*, 1978, pp. 118-31.

32 National Library of Wales, Highmead MSS, Box Y.

33 D.H. Morgan, *Harvesters and Harvesting, 1840-1927; a study of the Rural Proletariat*, Croom Helm, 1981, pp. 17-21.

34 J.L. Davies, "Horse Labour on Welsh Farms, 1871-1927" *Welsh Journal of Agriculture*, VI, 1930, p. 44.

35 J.G. Jenkins, *Agricultural Transport in Wales*, Cardiff, 1962, p. 13.

36 Gibson, *op.cit.*, p. 98.

37 For details of grassland and grassland management see, R.J. Moore-Colyer, "Aspects of the Pastoral Economy in pre-Industrial Wales," *J.R.A.S.E.*, 144, 1983, pp. 46-60.

38 F.V. Emery, "The Early Cultivation of Clover in Gower", *Gower* XXV, p. 459; W. Davies, *A General View of the Agriculture of South Wales*, I, 1815, p. 588.

39 C.S. Read "On the Agriculture of South Wales", *J.R.A.S.E.* X, 1849, passim.

40 J. Clark, *General View of the Agriculture of Breconshire*, London, 1794, p.15; C. Hassall, *General View of the Agriculture of Carmarthenshire*, London, 1794, p.12; Anon, "A Sketch of the Parish of Llanfechain", *Montgomeryshire Collections*, 5, 1872, p. 218.

41 R.O. Roberts, *Farming in Caernarvonshire around 1800*, Caernarvon, 1973, p.11; H. Evans, *The Gorse Glen*, Liverpool, 1949, p.138.

42 D. Parry-Jones, *My Own Folk*, Batsford, 1952, p.100.

The quiet revolution in livestock breeding which played so significant a part in the evolution of English farming during the eighteenth century, created among farmers and landowners an awareness of the financial benefits to be gained from adopting an enlightened approach towards animal husbandry. The increased demand for meat from an expanding population, coupled with the "fashionable" aspect of cattle breeding, encouraged farmers to follow the lead of such men as Webster, Bakewell and Canley in taking a rational and critical view of livestock improvement.

In general, though, the gentleman farmers of Wales did not share the enthusiasm of their English counterparts, with the inevitable result that the bulk of the native stock remained unimproved until the latter part of the nineteenth century. As late as 1853, R.H. Jackson wrote to Edward Jones of Glansevern complaining bitterly about the attitude of Welsh landlords towards stock improvement:

> *"had the attention of the Welsh gentry been given to the improvement of the native breeds, we should ere this have had a description of cattle indigenous to Wales far superior to any of the Highland or Ayrshire... our attention to breeding has been literally worse than nothing; the best stock being invariably sold out of the country, added to which a great deal of prejudice has existed among people of capital and influence against anything Welsh."[1]*

More than twenty five years later an anonymous essayist still complained that the Welsh farmer was forced, by reason of lack of capital, to sell his best beasts instead of retaining them as breeding stock.[2]

It is perhaps worth pausing at this stage to consider some of the technical problems confronting the Welsh farmer who may have considered embarking upon a programme of breed improvement. Whilst the technical capacity to develop a superior strain within a breed of cattle may be available, the effort expended in so doing is justified only if the nutritional environment is modified so as to exploit the enhanced genetic potential of the "improved" animals. Thus as the genetic potential for growth rate and capacity for fattening increases, so must the level of nutrition improve; a fact recognised by Bakewell. In the harsh upland environment of Wales, the capital cost of improving grassland was often prohibitive, particularly where the major proportion of farm income was derived from such low output enterprises as store cattle production. This was the first obstacle to the improvement of native stock.

The second obstacle was also based largely upon economic considerations. The principles of improvement advocated by Bakewell and his associates aimed to fix breed type by concentrating all the desirable characteristics as a result of close inbreeding. During the process of any close-inbreeding programme many of the progeny exhibit undesirable characteristics, notably of reduced vigour. In order to prevent the spread of this inferior genetic material throughout the animal population such individuals must be rigorously culled. If this were not so, inbreeding depression would rapidly reduce the vigour of the race to the extent that its very survival would be threatened. Had Welsh farmers been sufficiently affluent to undertake long-term inbreeding programmes of the Bakewellian type and to sustain the expense of rejecting undesirable material, then the process of inbreeding could have been used to establish a uniform type, while at the same time preserving among indigenous cattle the important characteristics of hardiness and ability to withstand adverse environmental conditions.

However, the majority of Welsh improvers preferred to follow the cheaper method of cross-breeding with English or Scottish stock as a means of upgrading the value of native stock, a policy often unsuccessful due to lack of consideration for environmental factors. Thus, although the imported breeds would theoretically introduce desirable production traits, crossbreds by these animals out of unimproved native dams would not necessarily be able to tolerate the harsh climatic conditions of upland Wales.

The absence of attention to the improvement of indigenous Welsh cattle is reflected in their lack of success in an exhibition held at Gloucester in 1853:

"... The Welsh breed was a complete failure: £70 was offered, for which only five animals were shown and these were not worth the amount of the prizes."[3]

As indicated above, gentleman farmers seem to have been more interested in experimenting with the introduction of improved English stock than selection within the native breeds. This practice was condemned by contemporary agricultural writers, who realised that no significant advances could be achieved by cross-breeding unless the native breeds were initially improved by close inbreeding followed by the culling of animals exhibiting undesirable characteristics.

In general terms, the performance of cross-bred animals tends to average that of the parental stock. In certain characteristics, however, particularly those associated with fertility and hardiness, the cross-bred is superior to its parents. This phenomenon, known as "hybrid vigour", has probably been appreciated, in an unconscious manner, since time immemorial. Obviously the quality of the hybrid animal will be largely a reflection of the qualities of the parent material, so that genetic improvement from cross-breeding is only possible if the foundation stock are of satisfactory quality. This was realised by Murray in 1866, who drew attention to the extensive crossing of native Glamorgan cattle with Devon and Hereford bulls, which apparently met:

"... with so little success that the breeder will here best promote his interest by attending to the improvement of the existing races."[4]

Other nineteenth century writers deplored the loss of local "type" which followed an unsophisticated breeding programme based, perhaps, upon the purchase of scrub bulls of non-local origin. Hall W. Keary found that the mixed breeds of Cardiganshire and the western parts of Brecknockshire and Radnorshire completely lacked uniformity by virtue of having been crossed, on an *ad hoc* basis, with bulls from North Wales.[5] Morgan Evans disapproved of attempts to improve Anglesey cattle by crossing with English breeds:

"... the colour becomes destroyed and the type broken and the produce cannot be reduced to a uniform standard." [6]

However, although Edward Williams (Iolo Morganwg), had declared that nine out of every ten attempts at crossbreeding in Wales were doomed to failure, some breeders were successfully using English bulls within their herds.[7] The Rev. J. E. Vincent noted that in 1832, an Anglesey dealer in a substantial way of business:

"... gave the greatest price for three year old half-bred Shorthorn x Anglesey cattle and that they were the only lot in that drove that he made money of." [8]

Unfortunately many landowners attempted to introduce English blood into regions which were environmentally unsuited, and the performance of subsequent cross-breds was considerably below potential. It is hardly surprising then that small farmers became highly suspicious of the supposedly superior English stock and religiously adhered to their own native breeds. Thomas Rees found that in Cardiganshire particularly, farmers enthused about their own breed of cattle:

"... no argument can prevail upon them to substitute another kind in their stead, although many weighty objections be against them, particularly as respects the dairy."[9]

The indiscriminate introduction of Longhorn blood to the cattle of Pembrokeshire did little to improve the attitude of the Welsh farmer towards English cattle. Thus:

"These cattle crossed with ours made them altogether ill-calculated for stocking in this district. By this fatal error our farmers became more than ever attached to their own breed and prejudiced

Llanddewibrefi from where the drovers crossed the Elenydd via Soar-y-Mynydd on the way to Abergwesyn

against anything that bore the name English."

An anonymous marginal note in this particular edition of Hassall's Pembrokeshire comments: *"I procured the names of the introducers of the new breeds of cattle, but I do not think it necessary to publish them. When they got their oxen fat for market they could find no purchaser. The drovers come into this country for pure Pembroke cattle and for them only."* [10]

A similar argument applied to the cattle of Merioneth, where the introduction of English bulls had generated little enthusiasm on the part of farmers or drovers.

The influence of the cattle trade with the English Midlands upon the development of local Welsh breed types has yet to be fully investigated, but contemporary evidence would seem to indicate that where a constructive breeding policy was operated, animals tended to be selected on the basis of their meat-producing rather than milking potential. In Cardiganshire, Lloyd and Turnor found the local cattle:

"... to be less milchy than most breeds, but as the country in general places more dependence on the drover than on the dairies, this objection may be not great disadvantage to the farmer." [11]

Ironically enough, the drovers, who formed a key link in the chain of trade between Wales and England, have often been cited as obstacles to livestock improvement. One example of this may be seen from a letter written to John Kay, compiler of the *General View of Caernarvonshire:*

"The drovers, I was informed, are great enemies to the improvement of stock; and the reason assigned for it is that were larger and finer cattle reared, they might meet with more rivals in the trade, which is at present in a very few hands by which means they have both credit and prices on their own terms." [12]

In north Wales the drovers tended to prefer the small hardy native breed, which would thrive not only on the rich old fattening pastures of the English midlands, but also on the heavy clay vales of Essex. Writing to the *Farmer's Magazine* in *1859,* Samuel Arnsby, a noted Northamptonshire grazier, highlighted the great variability in performance of the north Wales cattle fed on the Midland grass-lands. However, he concluded that:

> *"... the North Welsh cattle are second to none in strength of constitution which is the foundation of sound and profitable breeding."*[13]

Nevertheless, there seems little doubt that the selective introduction of English bulls into areas which were environmentally favourable would have improved the potential of local breeds of native stock. Indeed, in the lowland areas of Caernarvonshire the introduction of English breeds was highly successful and crossbred animals were fetching £2 – £3 per head more than native pure-breds when sold at three years old. Such a situation, apparently, did not appeal to the drovers, for as one of Kay's correspondents pointed out:

> *"The general improvement of stock by the introduction of English blood would be a great inducement to many other drovers to come into the country to purchase cattle with ready cash, instead of credit which is at present the practice whereby many an honest farmer is duped out of his property in whole or in part."*[14]

This observation corroborates the views of John Lawrence (1805) who noted that:

> *"... the drovers it seems are averse to the improvement, preferring the inferior breed and price."*[15]

In spite of the importance of the store cattle trade to the rural economy of Wales, it is difficult to accept that the drovers' rather negative attitude was a serious barrier to stock improvement in the nineteenth century. It is probably more realistic to suggest that a combination of adverse climatic conditions, shortage of capital, lack of mutual confidence between landlord and tenant and reluctance on behalf of many farmers to accept new concepts of arable and livestock husbandry were some of the more important obstacles to stock improvement.[16]

Stock improvement may be most rapidly and effectively achieved by selection of superior male animals. In view of this the widely adopted practice of selling the best male animals to the drovers and keeping back the poorest calf to rear as a stock bull would have the effect of progressively worsening the quality of the animals in a given herd. Read observed:

> *"... that there is not much prospect of the cattle in the interior of the Principality improving as too little attention is generally paid to the selection of the male animal."*[17]

Commenting on the state of cattle production in Wales in 1879, John Gibson emphasised the lack of attention paid to the selection of sires, particularly in Cardiganshire. He found that the unwilling-ness on the part of farmers consciously to select superior bulls from within their herds had resulted in a preponderance of 'mongrel' bulls which were allowed to mate with female animals in a totally indiscriminate manner to the inevitable detriment of livestock quality. While he realised that capital for livestock improvement was in short supply, Gibson maintained that by careful selection much improvement could be achieved without excessive expenditure. Moreover, he castigated landlords for not adopting the practice of breeding superior male stock for the use of their tenants. Having weighed up the evidence, Gibson was forced to conclude that some improvement had taken place, yet:

> *"One of the greatest hindrances to improvement is the deeply seated notion that bad farming is more profitable than good farming; and that the herd of mongrels, though it sells for less money, is still more profitable than the same number of pure-bred animals."*[18]

Contemporary commentators attached a great deal of value to the hardiness and adaptability of the native breeds to local conditions. They rightly argued that quality cattle could not be produced unless priority was given to land improvement and the provision of better grazing and winter feed. Accord-ing to Thomas Rowlandson:

> *"The first object ought to be to produce nutrient capable of sustaining superior breeds; until then the old breed will maintain its ground and under the present circumstances will prove the best."*[19]

John Clark railed against the poor quality of the local cattle in Brecknockshire. In a marginal note in his copy, however, Walter Davies commented that:

> *"the breed of cattle in the country are not despicable...nothing is wanted but to cultivate more*

The road into Tregaron, which must have witnessed many thousands of cattle making the journey to England. Here they were shod behind the Talbot Hotel.

turnips. *The turnip crops are shamefully neglected not one acre in thirty being down to the Norfolk system."* [20]

In view of this it is hardly surprising that the cattle of superior type were found in areas favourable to grass growth and in which the turnip husbandry had been accepted and incorporated into the farming system.

Notwithstanding the relatively favourable physical environment of Pembrokeshire and the Vale of Glamorgan, the proportion of good grazing land to that of total pasture was very small. Even so, these regions produced cattle held in high regard by English graziers. In particular there was a steady demand for store cattle of the Pembrokeshire breed:

"The Pembrokeshire ox always finds a ready market in the feeding counties. Kent and Sussex have usually been the principal places of sale with our drovers; and of late years great numbers of our cattle are driven to the Midland counties." [21]

John Bannister saw many Pembroke cattle on the rich lands of Sussex, particularly in the region of Pevensey, while later in the century, Pembrokeshire cows were highly prized by London dairymen. [22,23] According to Read the Pembrokes were coal black, having a clean light head and a bright prominent eye. [24] Youatt's statement that: "... a few have white faces or a little white about the tail or udder" was strongly contested by Evans who insisted that any such marking indicated the influence of "strange blood." [25] Observers of the Pembroke breed agreed unanimously that, given good management, the cows possessed excellent milking qualitites, being capable of giving six or seven pounds of butter per week during the summer months. Charles Hassall felt that this performance could be further improved by careful attention to feeding. The Pembroke cattle of the poorer regions of Carmarthenshire were considerably inferior, however, "being a short-bodied coarse kind of beast, ill-shaped and unprofitable to the pail." [26]

It is possible that these were the Pembrokeshire cattle observed by Lawrence to have deteriorated due to crossing with the Longhorn in an unsuccessful attempt to improve milk yield "... thereby making the carcase coarse and long." [27] In view of the prevailing local conditions the Pembroke cow could be fed and bred 15 per cent cheaper than the Hereford or Shorthorn breeds, which in Evans's experience had to be housed for three weeks longer than the Pembroke during the winter months. Contemporaries expressed enthusiasm over the meat producing qualities of the breed which, in spite of its deficiency in width and roundness of rib, would weigh between seven and eight hundredweights at four years old. Although his praise for the Pembroke was unbridled, Evans admitted that:

"... *Capitalists holding sheltered or luxuriant pastures, having extensive farm buildings, and who aim at producing large prime fat beasts may there, as elsewhere, keep Shorthorns to greater advantage than any other breeds...*" In the main, however, "... *persons of limited means, living on poor land, and with small farmyards, cannot do better, I think, than maintain and cultivate the indigenous breed of the country.*" [28]

Within the Pembrokeshire breed, which extended throughout Pembrokeshire, Carmarthenshire and south Cardiganshire, were two important sub-varieties. These sub-varieties arose in the areas of Castlemartin in south Pembrokeshire and Dewsland in the northern part of the county. Due perhaps to the enterprise of the farmers in the anglicised Castlemartin district, the local breed achieved greater popularity than the cattle of the Welsh speaking area around Dewsland, particularly for their capacity to fatten. Evans, however, insisted that by the late nineteenth century the larger Dewsland type was of equal, if not greater, merit than the Castlemartin. Eventually both these sub-varieties, together with the Anglesey and north Wales types, were amalgamated in the Welsh Black breed for which a herdbook was opened in 1874.[29] Mr. Buckley of Penyfai was optimistic as to the future of the new breed when he spoke to the Carmarthenshire Farmers' Club in 1879:

"... *now that the breed has been taken in hand by those that have the means and skill to carry out improvement... the steers will be splendid beasts and bring the drovers to our farms and monthly markets in droves.*" [30]

Lord Cawdor of Stackpole Court, whose enthusiastic efforts had been largely responsible for the Welsh Black Cattle Herd Book, lamented the fact that North Wales Black cattle were permitted to be entered into the herdbook. He believed strongly in the idea of "pure-blood", and felt that the cause of the north Wales livestock improvers would only be properly served if they opened a herd book for their own cattle. According to a letter written by Cawdor in 1879, most gentlemen in south Wales accepted the importance of preserving "purity" of blood. Mr. Lewis of Henllan, however:

"... *told me the other day that we should spoil the Welsh breed of cattle by our herd book... if we found such an opinion entertained by a gentleman of his position, education, etc., it certainly shows that a similar opinion may be held by a person less enlightened and in a humbler position.*" [31]

Notwithstanding the views of Mr. Lewis, evidence of the popularity of the "*South Wales Blacks*" is provided by the fact that some 25,000 of these animals were annually being taken to England towards the close of the century. This indicates the potential of the breed under a high standard of management:

"*instead of the old course of leaving them almost from birth to struggle into dwarfed maturity by neglect and semi-starvation.*" [32]

The influence of English farming practices and accordingly of English cattle breeds was strongly felt in the border counties of Wales where, by the closing years of the nineteenth century, the pure local breeds had all but disappeared. As early as 1797 Clark noted that in the border counties:

"*the native small black breed is mostly out in consequence of a mixture with that of Hereford and Shropshire. The Herefordshire breed, it is true, always dwindle away and grow smaller in proportion, as they are carried higher into the mountainous country.*" [33]

There are abundant descriptions of a distinct Glamorgan breed during the mid and late nineteenth century, yet the Rev. John Evans protested that in 1804 he was unable to notice any difference between the cattle of Pembrokeshire and those of Glamorgan; indeed, "... *many Pembrokes are purchased and sold as the breed of Glamorgan.*" [34] But the true Glamorgan was generally of a muddy brown colour, having white streaks along the back and belly, and if Glamorgan cattle with white faces were observed from time to time, it is likely that such animals contained some Hereford or Devon blood. The Glamorgan breed was widely distributed throughout Glamorgan, Monmouth and Brecon, but was only rarely to be seen west of the River Dulais where the Pembroke breed predominated.[35] The cows, which were particularly good milkers, averaging sixteen to eighteen quarts per day, were held in high regard by George III. This notable judge of livestock maintained a herd of Glamorgan cows on his Windsor farm, for which he frequently drew replacement stock from Welsh country fairs. These cattle, in addition to providing milk, were also used for all the carting, rolling and harrowing tasks in Windsor Park.[36] Iolo Morganwg placed great emphasis on the docile qualities of the Glamorgan cattle which made them particularly suitable as draft animals. Moreover, they had "longer steps" than Herefords and Devons, characteristics which Iolo contended to be invaluable in draft animals. He went on, somewhat paradoxically, to declare that while Glamorgans were in great demand from graziers, they were unable to withstand journeys of long distances and in consequence lost more condition than "the black western breed" on being driven to England.[37]

Neither Davies nor Read were particularly enamoured of the beef potential of the Glamorgan which:
"... are commonly handsome in the fore-quarters but want for symmetry from the loins backwards."[38]

Read complained also that the Glamorgans "... had too often flat backs and high rumps." [39] These deficiencies in conformation apart, Glamorgan oxen were capable during the early years of the century of achieving weights of 12-14 scores per quarter and providing meat of very high quality. Indeed, in the fertile parishes of St. Athan, Gilestone and Llantwit, Glamorgan cattle had been noted for their large size, some animals weighing, when fat at six years old, no less than 400 pounds per quarter.[40] This undoubtedly accounted for their popularity among the graziers of Northamptonshire and Leicestershire.

Notwithstanding Iolo's comments on the iniquities of crossbreeding, it is clear that crosses by Hereford, Ayrshire and Shorthorn bulls became more common as the century wore on. Hassall was amazed at the "extraordinary prices" paid for the hiring of Hereford bulls in Abergavenny. When these bulls were put to Glamorgan heifers, the progeny produced a greater weight of beef at 5-7 years of age while preserving the essential "activity" of the pure Glamorgan, a vital characteristic if the animal was to perform well at the yoke.[41] Other observers agreed that meat production was increased in the hybrid, although reservations were held about the quality of this meat which it was contended had been reduced as a result of early maturity.

With the expansion of industrial activity in south Wales, local demand for milk and milk products was stimulated, encouraging some farmers to experiment with the introduction of the Ayrshire breed, noted for its capacity to produce milk of high butterfat content. The experiment met with considerable success. Not only was milk yield and quality enhanced in the crossbred animal, but also a more acceptable beef carcase was produced when the cow was eventually slaughtered. By the close of the century the effect of cross-breeding had been such that no pure Glamorgan herds remained. However, repeated cross-breeding was not the sole cause of the decline, and it seems that many farmers, particularly the more affluent ones, were selling up their Glamorgan herds and restocking with Hereford or Shorthorn cows quite early on in the century. Thus in a letter to the *Farmer's Journal* in 1824, J.S. Smythe predicted that Herefords and Shorthorns would soon completely supersede the Glamorgan. In support of this prediction he pointed out that two-year-old Hereford steers had fetched between £5 and £10 more than six-year-old Glamorgans at Tredegar Show.[42]

That a price differential existed is certainly true, although contemporary farm accounts indicate that its magnitude was considerably less than that suggested by Smythe. The boom in corn production which accompanied the Napoleonic Wars was also partially responsible for the eventual disappearance of the breed. So profitable was cereal growing that farmers in Glamorgan ploughed every available and readily croppable acre so that the stock were relegated to the less fertile corners of the farm where they remained while the boom lasted. Thus stock improvement was largely ignored, and existing animals forced to eke out a precarious existence on the poorer pastures of the holding. This situation was aggravated by the advanced demand for hay from the pit owners of the south Wales coalfield, and according to Samuel Lewis it was more profitable for a farmer to sell his hay for the sustenance of pit ponies than to use it for cattle production.[43] Given that the yield of hay from the meadows of the Glamorgan lowlands would have been unlikely to exceed 7-8 hundredweights per acre, and that the best of this hay was then sold off to the pit owners, it seems that overwintered stock languished under conditions of considerable nutritional deprivation.

The cattle shoeing enclosure, Abergwesyn, Brecknockshire

Edwin Bradley wrote in 1842 to Sir Charles Morgan of Tredegar expressing his thanks to Sir Charles for the interest the latter had taken towards restoring the once "far famed breed" of Glamorgan cattle. Bradley's enthusiasm for the breed was such that he had entered several animals in Sir Charles's livestock show at Tredegar, explaining, perhaps rather optimistically, "...that we shall not have any disposition of being frightened by the Great Bloods of the island." [44] But, despite the survival of isolated herds of Glamorgan cattle into the closing years of the century, even the enthusiastic efforts of devoted individuals could not prevent the final eclipse of the breed.

Beyond the mountains of Brecknockshire which supported "an innumerable store of oxen which are well stocked and return thousands to the country", the "Radnor" or "Builth" breed held sway.[45] Of these cattle, little appears to be known apart from the fact that they were of a red or brindled colour, and were superior to those of most of the mountain districts of South Wales[46]. It is unlikely that Clark was referring here to purebred local animals for the local type lacked uniformity and was characterised by lightness of flesh consequent upon indiscriminate matings with North Wales cattle. William Youatt, an eloquent advocate of crossbreeding, declared that the introduction of Hereford bulls to these "scrub" cattle had produced a second cross, which although too large to be finished on local grasslands, was in considerable demand from graziers in possession of good quality fattening land.

Some years later, Hall W. Keary wrote that the cattle of these upland areas had markedly improved due to the introduction of West Highland blood by the efforts of the fourth Duke of Newcastle.[47] The small, light-fleshed animals typical of the Radnor hills were also widely distributed throughout the uplands of Carmarthenshire, Cardiganshire and west Brecknockshire. In the low-lying southern areas, however, Pembroke cattle were widespread, and by the 1830s Devon beasts were frequently seen in the southern part of Carmarthenshire, while on the grazing lands around Llandovery and Llangattock the influence of the Hereford was already being felt. It appears, nevertheless, that the bulk of the farmers, particularly in the uplands of Cardiganshire and Carmarthenshire, preferred their native "runts", not only for sale to the drovers but also for dairying and draft purposes.[48]

In the early part of the century, Walter Davies noted that a new type; "... of the long legged high red colour without any spots and with smoky or dun faces", was assuming some importance in the area around the Severn Vale.[49] These cattle, known as the Montgomeryshire Smoky Faced breed, were believed to have come originally from Herefordshire, and through the Bishop's Castle area into Montgomeryshire. Smoky Faces were also found in the uplands of Radnorshire in the earlier part of the century, for as Read noted:

"There were formerly some good red smoky faced cattle in the hilly parts of Radnor, but they have lost much of their distinctive character by crossing with the Shropshire and Hereford cattle."[50]

The breed was apparently adaptable to a wide range of conditions, being both extremely hardy and of good fattening potential. Writing after the dispersal of the last herd in 1886, J.B. Morgan observed that the breed had been preferred by butchers and graziers above all other Welsh cattle.[51] Seventy years earlier, a Mr. Croxton of Oswestry, "a grazier of good judgement and great experience", preferred the Montgomeryshire cattle from the Vales of the Severn and Vyrnwy to any other breeds of Welsh cattle:

"... because they collect bulk on the most valuable parts after nine months feeding with hay or turnips they will add about three score pounds weight to each of their quarters."[52]

A four-year-old ox of the Montgomeryshire breed would apparently weigh 6-7 scores per quarter if reared on the hill, and 9-11 scores per quarter if reared in the vales.[53] The disappearance of this breed, which apparently possessed so many good qualities, came about largely from cross-breeding with Hereford cattle. In the early 1860s an attempt was made to stem the inflow of Hereford blood, as it was believed by many that the offspring of the crossbred animal were too "coarse" to meet the requirements of the dealer. It is doubtful that breeders were successful in this endeavour, for when the Montgomeryshire Agricultural Society offered prizes for the breed in the 1870s it was found that good examples of the Smoky Face were restricted almost entirely to the herd of Colonel Heyward of Guilsfield.[54] Repeated crossing with Hereford blood, then, had gradually diminished the numbers of purebred Smoky Faces until eventually the breed was crossbred out of existence.

Of the cattle of north Wales, the Anglesey and Llŷn types were undoubtedly of the greatest importance. Indeed, the cattle of the remainder of Caernarvonshire and the highlands of Merioneth and Denbigh were in the main diminutives of these two types. Davies stated that:

"an Anglesey runt should be of coal-black colour with white appendages, remarkably broad ribs, high and wide hips, deep chest, large dewlap, flat face and long horns turning upwards."[55]

The fact that Anglesey calves were not weaned until almost twelve months of age was held to be the cause of the "bull-like" appearance of the steers.[56] In many respects the Anglesey was not dissimilar to the Castlemartin, although the former was:

"coarser in the forepart, but having better hindquarters and broader loins than their southern rivals."[57]

As late as 1870, W.H. Beever was extolling the virtues of the Anglesey breed, of which many still found their way to Northamptonshire and the eastern coastal counties of England "... where they fatten on the scraps of more favoured and fastidious kine."[58] The majority of these animals would be two and three year olds and after a twelve month period at grass, would fatten at between 8 and 11 scores per quarter. Where the cattle had been used for draught purposes and subsequently fattened at eight to nine years old, they were reputed to be capable of achieving weights of 11-15 scores per quarter. Cattle which had been previously worked at the yoke were preferred by many graziers as these could not only be purchased more cheaply, but also gained weight more rapidly than animals which had not been used for draught purposes. The performance of the Anglesey and Llŷn types could not be matched by their diminutives in other areas. Indeed, the cattle of Merioneth, Denbigh and the uplands of western Montgomeryshire:

"have little to recommend them save their extreme hardiness and consequent cheapness of rearing."[59]

However, Mr. Corbet of Ynysmaengwyn, near Towyn, had successfully crossed native Merionethshire cattle with (unspecified) English stock to considerable advantage. Having subjected purebred natives and crossbreds to similar conditions of management, he was able to sell the latter for twice the sum fetched by the local purchased stock. [60] In view of Youatt's comment that the native cattle of Merioneth "were at the very bottom of the list and disgracefully neglected ", this is perhaps hardly surprising.[61]

Along the north eastern coast between Abergele and Holywell, and towards the Cheshire border, the native cattle were of a more productive type, many fattened animals being seen in the Vales of Flint and Denbigh.[62] Walter Davies quoted the case of a farmer:

"who, having worked his oxen until after turnip sowing in June, sold a pair of them to a neighbouring grazier. By December they had fattened on grass and were sold at double their cost." [63]

In the hilly areas of north Wales, large quantities of butter and cheese were made for sale in the markets of Holywell, Chester, Shrewsbury and Bridgenorth. Consequently the milking potential of the Angleseys and their diminutives was of considerable importance. Milk yield apparently ranged from five to fifteen quarts daily according to locality and quality of food. It was believed that cattle which did not give above five quarts of milk per day:

"...generally manifest a greater disposition to fattening than milking, and should not be kept a week longer on a dairy farm."[64]

To illustrate the potential of the North Wales cattle, Davies instanced a cow in Flintshire which produced 4,026 quarts of milk and 358 pounds of butter over a period of 183 days. Cows continued to be profitable milkers for 8 to 10 years, although in the herd of Mr. Wynne of Ryton were three cows which continued to give milk in abundance until they were each eighteen years old. Their productive life over, the cows were dried off, shod, and eventually driven to the fattening lands of the border counties or the English Midlands.[65]

Despite Corbet's successful introduction of improved English cattle to Merionethshire, other attempts to do so were largely doomed to failure. Scottish cattle had been introduced on the west coast, particularly around Llwyngwril in Merionethshire, although with little success, for as Rowlandson pointed out:

"Several gentlemen have introduced the Ayrshire and Galloway breeds, but the cattle are looked upon as whims of the gentry."[66]

During the first decade of the century improved English cattle had been brought into west Caernarvonshire. This importation improved the indigenous stock to a limited degree, but Davies was sceptical regarding the future of such a policy:

"The difference of climate and of quality of pasture, will at length dwindle the mixed breed, after repeated crossings, nearly to the original native size."[67]

There is little doubt that with few exceptions the adverse environmental conditions of both north and south Wales operated against the effective implementation of an improvement plan based upon importation of English stock. Such stock improvement which did take place was achieved almost entirely in the lowland regions of Wales where pasture quality could be enhanced at a relatively low cost and the improved stock thereby supported. It is difficult, however, to escape the conclusion that the neglect of local stock in upland and marginal areas, so deplored by contemporary writers, resulted largely from an unwillingness on behalf of the larger farmers to commit their limited capital to expensive programmes of stock improvement based upon the principles pioneered by Bakewell. Moreover, even if the more progressive landowners had succeeded in achieving some degree of improvement within their own herds, it is likely that the rather reactionary and suspicious nature of the impecunious small farmer would have severely reduced the chances of facilitating a widespread and permanent upgrading of native stock.

Throughout the century, the relative merits of the different cattle breeds were hotly disputed at the meetings of local Agricultural Societies and in the columns of farming magazines. In many cases, the supporters of a breed, driven by a fervour at times almost religious in its intensity, chose to make claims regarding the qualities of their breed which were often totally unsupportable. Thus it is necessary to treat with caution some of the rather more extravagant claims made on behalf of certain breeds. It is nevertheless possible to obtain some estimates of cattle weights from the writings of the more objective and impartial observers of the agricultural scene.

In 1929, George Fussell maintained that while the size and weight of cattle increased throughout the eighteenth century, the total size of the cattle population did not advance dramatically. Accordingly he concluded that the expansion of meat supplies arose largely as a result of increased slaughter weight coupled with earlier maturity.[68] The latter factor reflected the increasing use of horses as draught animals and hence the release of oxen for earlier fattening. There is certainly little doubt that by the turn of the eighteenth century many British farmers were beginning to realise the advantages, in terms of efficiency of food utilisation, to be gained from providing animals which reached slaughter condition at a relatively early age. In 1805, Charles Gordon Grey explained to the Bath Society:

"... that in the rich soils of the kingdom where large oxen have usually been fed, the graziers there (generally) are feeding Scotch, finding the smaller most profitable."[69]

Five years later, Richard Parkinson wrote that on good quality pasture land, "a large ox with quick aptitude to fatten some-times increases in twelve months as much as a small ox weighs." Even so, he held the view that if smaller beasts did not make the same profit on good land, on poorer land, they would fatten earlier in the year thereby coming to market before the autumn "glut."[70]

In the early nineteenth century consumers were beginning to react against the fat, and often enormous, cattle which were arriving at Smithfield. The *Farmer's Magazine* of January 1800 mentions the arrival in London of a bullock from Buckinghamshire weighing 300 stones live weight, and of such bullocks being slaughtered in the streets around Blackfriars Bridge, being unable to stagger on to Smithfield. Numerous correspondents to the *Gentleman's Magazine* witnessed the arrival of these monsters, and in their comments they echoed the aversion of many people to the excessive quantities of fat on butcher's meat at the time. One correspondent, signing herself as: "A friend of the Golden Days of Good Queen Bess", declared, that the cattle produced:

"are in general so loaded with blubber that we may suppose, and with reason, that their feeders are more in the interest of the tallow chandler than the butcher. To introduce the custom of killing sheep or oxen so enormously fat and in consequence rendered almost useless for the table can never be attended with any good effect."[71]

If contemporary reports and contemporary prints and lithographs are to be trusted, this apparent demand for more lean meat was not satisfied during the first half of the century. J. B. McDonald, for example, wrote of an ox of four and a half years of age being slaughtered in Smithfield in 1829, the internal fat of which constituted one quarter of the carcase weight; while at the Christmas fatstock show of 1893, Welsh runts of between 2,240 and 3,000 lbs. were exhibited.[72,73] The fat content of such animals must have been extremely high. However, the later reports of Smithfield fatstock shows may not provide entirely realistic average weights of cattle of the day. The "prize" animals arriving at Smithfield were carefully chosen and hand fed, and were hardly typical of the average beasts of the time. Accordingly, weights of cattle from the Metropolitan Market and Smithfield Club Shows should perhaps be regarded as atypical.

The following list (see page 29) compiled from contemporary sources, show the weights of some of the Welsh cattle types throughout the century. All weights have been converted into pounds.

It is clearly necessary to exercise considerable caution in drawing conclusions from the subjective estimates of contemporary observers. Very few cattle were weighed before the latter half of the nineteenth century so that the accuracy of his assessment depended entirely upon the skill and judgement of the observer. The figures shed little light on the question as to whether there was any significant change in Welsh cattle weights throughout the century, for the wide variation in dead weights within a period render inter-period comparisons relatively meaningless. Furthermore, since contemporary observers saw and assessed these cattle under a broad spectrum of management conditions it is probably impossible to draw firm conclusions about the genetic potential for meat production of the various breeds.

Some Welsh Cattle Weights

Breed	Age	Date	Dead Weight (lbs)	Source	Comments
Anglesey	3-4 years	1805	480-960	J. Lawrence, *A general treatise . . . on livestock* London, 1805.	*"No cross would improve, these islanders."*
Anglesey	3-4 years	1810	640- 880	W. Davies *(North Wales).*	
Anglesey	8-9 years	1810	1,040-1,200	W. Davies *(North Wales).*	*Oxen worked at the yoke.*
Anglesey	4 years	1849	784-89	C.S. Read *J.R.A.S.E.* Ser I IX, 1849.	
Cardigan +	3-4 years	1814	480- 560	W. Davies *(South Wales).*	*"When crossed with Herefords-Carmarthen weigh 800-960 lbs."*
Cardigan + Carmarthen	?	1848	504-664	H. Keary, *J.R.A.S.E.* 'Ser. i, IX, 1848.	*"'Little propensity to fatten."*
Glamorgan	3-4 years	1814	640-900	W. Davies *(South Wales).*	*Cows.*
Glamorgan		1814	960-1,120	W. Davies *(South Wales).*	*Oxen (some heavier).*
Glamorgan	4-5 years	1848	784-896	H. Keary, *J.R.A.S.E.* Ser. 1, IX, 1848.	*"Coarser than the Pembrokes and inferior in early maturity."*
Montgomery ?	1800	784		Anon.	*Montgomery cow beef 560-800 lbs.*
Montgomery	4 years	1810	480-660	W. Davies *(North Wales).*	*Cattle reared on hills.*
Montgomery	5 years	1810	640	W. Davies *(North Wales).*	
Montgomery	4 years	1810	720-880	W. Davies *(North Wales).*	
Montgomery	5 years	1810	880-1,040	W. Davies *(North Wales).*	*Cattle reared in vales.*
Radnor ?		1800	520-720	N.L.W. *1695B.*	*"Superior to most mountainous districts of South Wales."*
Pontypool ?		1810	800-1,600	T. Rees, 1810 *(A Description of the counties of Glamorgan, Pembroke and Radnor).*	
Pontypool ?		1809	480	W. Pitt *(Northants).*	
Pembroke	4 years	1805	640-1,120	J. Lawrence, *A general treatise ... on livestock,* London, 1805.	*"... comes early ripe."*
Pembroke	4 years	1814	720-800	W. Davies *(South Wales).*	*Oxen.*
Pembroke	4 years	1814	480-560	W. Davies *(South Wales).*	*Cows.*
Pembroke	4 years	1848	700-784	H. Keary, *J.R.A.S.E.,* Ser. i, IX, 1848.	*"Best found in Castle-martin and Roos hundreds."*
Castlemartin	4 years	1814	800-960	W. Davies *(South Wales)*	
North Wales	6-7 years	1800	1,120	Youatt, *(Cattle),* 1834,	*"beautifully veined and marbled."*
	4 years	1848	560-700	H. Keary, *J.R.A.S.E.,* Ser. i, IX, 1848.	
Welsh Runts	?	1805	720	A. Young.	
Welsh Runts	4years	1889	658	A. Pell, *J.R.A.S.E.,* Ser. ii, XXV, 1889.	*55% of liveweight.*
Welsh Runts	?	1889	776	"The Times." November 4th, 1889.	*Good second quality cattle shown at the Metropolitan Meat Market.*

Thus the figures probably reflect environment and plane of nutrition rather than genetic potential. This is well illustrated by a comparison of the dead weights of cattle from upland Wales with those of Pembrokeshire for a given period. The superiority of carcase weights of the Pembroke breed may reflect a more amenable nutritional regime and an environment capable of producing a store animal which would feed to heavier weights than similar animals reared in the harsh upland regions of Wales. A further complication arises from the fact that most of these weights relate to animals reared in Wales, but fed in England. Accordingly, the final weight of the animal would depend as much if not more on the quality of the Northamptonshire fattening pasture or the expertise of the Essex stall fattener as it would upon the genotype of the store beast.

Despite the various limitations to livestock improvement, the trade in Welsh cattle with the English Midlands, which had expanded dramatically following the *Irish Cattle Act* of 1666, continued to play a vital part in the rural economy of Wales during the nineteenth century.[74] Indeed, the demand for hardy Welsh stock, both from the graziers and the yard feeders of the midland and south eastern counties, persisted throughout the century. That these "unimproved" Welsh beasts were so highly prized, suggests that their performance, in terms of growth rate and ability to fatten on the superior nutritional regime of the Midland grazing pastures, may reflect the stimulus of compensatory growth arising from previous nutritional deprivation. It might be claimed with some justification that within the general framework of Welsh social history, this fortuitous biological phenomenon was of major significance, in that the growth and persistence of demand for Welsh cattle stimulated continuing cultural contact between Wales and England via the agencies of the drovers and dealers whose activities form the subject matter of much of the remainder of this book.

Pasture Management and Cattle Production

The rate of progress of pasture husbandry and management in Wales lagged behind the arable sector in both the lowland and upland areas. Relative to the total grass acreage of the Principality, there were few pastures upon which cattle could be effectively fattened for slaughter. Fattening pastures occurred in the Vales of the Severn and the Vyrnwy in Montgomeryshire, along the banks of the Dee and Clwyd in Denbighshire and in the hundred of Castlemartin in Pembrokeshire. In general, however, pasture quality was adequate only for the support of sheep, store cattle, and in some areas, dairy animals. The ancient system of *hafod* and *hendre,* by which cattle were depastured on the uplands throughout the summer and brought to the lower-lying land during the winter months, had all but disappeared by the turn of the eighteenth century. John Kay found little evidence of this practice in north Wales, while any isolated occurrences finally disappeared as the uplands were enclosed and self-contained hill farms established.[75]

The creation of these upland farms had been gradually taking place over several centuries. By the beginning of the nineteenth century, pressure of population was pushing the frontiers of cultivation further up the Welsh hillsides, so that although there were 1,696,827 acres of unenclosed waste in 1795, the Tithe Commissioners estimated that the proportion had declined to 521,098 acres by 1843.[76] This enclosure of the uplands, either by encroachment, "common consent," or Act of Parliament, had been accelerated during the early decades of the century.[77] Originally the open common grazings had been administered by the manorial courts, and custom dictated that the number of stock depastured on the commons by a given parishioner was related to the number of stock which could be overwintered on the holding. Accordingly, many smaller proprietors who were without adequate overwintering facilities, were unable to make full use of the upland common grazings, and understocking resulted.

This was clearly a problem of some antiquity, for as Leland wrote in 1536:

"... the pastures of the mountains of Cardiganshire be so great that the hunderith part of hit rottith in the ground and maketh sogges and quicke more by long continuance for lak of eting of hit." [78]

In his deposition to the Select Committee on Commons Inclosure of 1844, Frankland Lewis held

The drovers' road to Abergwesyn from Tregaron crossing the Elenydd. This route was abandoned by the Jonathans in 1856 in favour of turnpike roads

that lack of wintering facilities precluded many of the smaller farmers in Radnorshire from fully exploiting common grazings. In Brecknockshire, where by 1833 one third of the land area was still open mountain with common grazing rights, the number of sheep and cattle stocked in common was estimated to be three times below carrying capacity owing to limitations on the availability of winter fodder.[79] Frankland Lewis and other witnesses before the Select Committee drew attention to the many abuses of the common system. T. Davies, steward to the Duke of Beaufort, complained that many farmers living close to common grazing land tended to over-stock the pastures, much to the detriment of tenants living further afield. In South Wales, explained Davies, it was frequent practice for a man to take a small farm in the parish for depasturing a few cattle and then to heavily overstock the common grazings with large flocks of sheep, thereby reducing the availability of grazing for other tenants.[80] Moreover, a correspondent of the *North Wales Gazette of* March 8th 1810 wrote of the over-stocking of grazing where right of common was unlimited, *"so that no large sized or generous animal can be fed upon it."* Where rights were limited: *"either frauds are committed or the stint is so large that the commons, though under limitations, are of little use."*

In spite of these abuses to the system, the enclosure of the upland commons was bitterly resented by many of the smaller occupiers for whom the availability of common grazing often played a vital role in the farming economy. Enclosure usually resulted in the Lord of the Manor being the greatest allottee, the allotments of smaller men far from compensating for the surrender of common rights. Indeed, Davies contended that the deprivation of common rights reduced the value of land previously abutting on to common grazings by as much as one third. He also expressed doubts as to the value of the newly enclosed farms, claiming that such farms were only superior to the open mountain by virtue of being surrounded by a grass baulk or dry stone wall. Such a farm was owned by his master, the Duke of Beaufort, and this farm, 360 acres in extent, was let for a mere £15 per annum.[81]

By all accounts, the large upland fields, luxuriant with ferns which were only cut at the end of the year for litter, provided little opportunity for controlled grazing and grassland improvement, so that enclosure did not appear to bring about any significant improvement in the standard of grassland management. Relatively little attention was paid to the development of leys and seeds mixtures for the hill situation, it being a widely held opinion that permanent pasture, while yielding less herbage than the ley, produced superior milk, butter and cattle. The laying down of "permanent pasture" generally implied leaving wild grasses and weeds to regenerate after ploughing.[82] Lloyd and Turnor reported that some farmers in the uplands of Cardiganshire sowed 12-14 lbs. of red clover and 2 bushels of rye grass as a break after three or four years of cereals. This practice was relatively rare however, most of the ordinary farmers being content "with the natural production of a worn out soil."[83]

In the lowlands and river valleys, grassland received rather more attention. In the more favourable areas, rye grass and clover in rotation had been introduced, while in the vales of the Tywi, Taff and Teifi, planted permanent pastures were thriving. In North Wales, oat grasses, fox, cat and dog's tails, holcus, sweet vernal, marsh bent, fescues, cocksfoot and trefoil were valued as pasture grasses, while some farmers on the moister meadow lands increased the bulk of their pastures by sowing vetches and tares. Leys on the lowland were commonly undersown in a barley or oat crop at the rate of 10 lbs. of red, 10 lbs. of white and 5 lbs. of yellow clover, together with a bushel of rye grass per acre, although in Denbigh and Merioneth, hay and plantain seeds from Anglesey were frequently sown.[84]

In Cardiganshire, red clover and rye grass "invariably" comprised the sown artificial grasses, while liberal dressings of lime and farmyard manure constituted the main fertilisers for the lowland grasslands.[85] In the coastal counties of Carmarthen and Cardigan, however, sea-sand and seaweed were frequently mixed with manure and spread upon the grass. Samuel Lewis relates one occasion when a storm in Cardigan Bay deposited two thousand cart loads of seaweed on the beach at New Quay, all being removed by farmers in the course of a fortnight.[86] In Pembrokeshire, a predominantly pastoral county by the nineteenth century, where: "many agriculturalists devote their land more to grazing than the production of corn," an abundance of thistles and ragwort was considered indicative of good land, while a multiplicity of weeds was regarded as being beneficial to a good ley.[87]

The practice of "fogging", extensively pursued in the counties of Carmarthen, Pembroke and Cardigan, simply involved leaving autumn grass ungrazed until the spring, with the inevitable result that a high proportion of the herbage was damaged over the winter months. Although English farmers considered this practice to be prejudicial to the production of good grass:

"The Welsh farmer is decidedly of the opinion on the contrary, that it keeps the young springing grass warm, and the following crop is by this means generally doubled."[88]

Although the bulk of herbage would certainly be increased, the additional material would be of dubious quality.

Pembrokeshire farmers also contended that the presence of abundant loose stones near the soil surface favoured the growth of cereal crops, it being held that such stones increased the rate at which the soil warmed during the Spring months. Accordingly when a ley was sown, stones were heaped in the fields "to give the grass room to grow," eventually being re-spread when the ley was ploughed out. By 1887, much of the grassland overlying limestone parent rock was of a highly productive nature, but a great deal of the total acreage of Pembrokeshire was impoverished and weed infested. By this time, notwithstanding the use of dissolved bones and superphosphate in some areas, farmyard manure, supplemented by a compost of manure, earth, sand, seaweed and road-scrapings, was still the most usually applied top-dressing for grassland.[89]

How far the oft-quoted "hereditary prejudices" inhibited the development of grassland farming in nineteenth century Wales is not clear. Demesne farm accounts and other estate material reveal that the value of the one year ley was appreciated by the squirearchy, and no doubt some of the larger tenants had also adopted this and other modern methods of grassland farming.[90] On the other hand many tenants realised only too well that novel methods of farming demanded scarce capital. As they

High above Llanbedr, Merioneth, on the London road from Harlech is Pont Scethin, now largely forgotten (above). In the valley below this bridge is Llety Lloegr (the English Inn), (below). Reminders of the old drovers' roads like these can be found all over Wales.

watched their landlords engaging in expensive experimental husbandry inappropriate to their circumstances, they took the view that any spare cash might be more sensibly used than in hare-brained farming schemes. But whatever the motives of the smaller tenantry, the overall impression gained from the printed sources is one of inhibition, by the persistence of traditional systems and attitudes, of the widespread adoption of the more sophisticated methods of pasture management.

By the close of the eighteenth century the upland grazings throughout much of Wales had become the preserve of sheep, cattle being grazed in the main on the enclosed lowland meadows. By Rowlandson's time, for example, the mountain pastures of Caernarvonshire were almost entirely devoted to sheep, cattle only being kept in areas where the soil was capable of providing a crop of hay which frequently comprised the sole winter forage.[91] The provision of adequate winter feed was of the utmost importance. The sale of butter, cheese and store stock formed the main components of the income of both hill and lowland farmers in many parts of Wales. The supply of winter feed determined the number of stock which could be overwintered on the holding, so that if supplies were inadequate for the winter months it became necessary to sell off stock in the autumn when demand was usually slack. This would result in severe financial loss to the farmer forced to sell off young cattle, while the dairyman selling off his cows would inevitably deplete his numbers of breeding stock and thereby reduce his income from butter and cheese sales over the next year. To a considerable extent, the standard with which cattle were managed during the winter determined their performance the following spring. In 1849, Hall W. Keary complained of the low standard of winter cattle management on Welsh farms. Frequently the animals remained exposed to the elements for the whole of the winter, while those fortunate enough to be housed were: "huddled together in dark, ill-ventilated hovels and entirely deprived of exercise."[92]

Such environmental conditions, coupled with a plane of nutrition often below the level required for normal body maintenance, would have resulted in both store and dairy cattle being in an extremely poor condition by the end of the winter months. In consequence, both milk yields and growth rates would have been low during the early spring months while animals were replacing their depleted body reserves.

Before relatively cheap "artificials" became available in the 1840s and 1850s, the housed animal provided the principal source of manure for both the arable and grassland acreages on the small farm. According to the *Cambrian Traveller's Guide* of 1813, farmyard manure was frequently mixed with lime, rotted ferns, headland and ditch scrapings before being spread on the land. The guide deplored the fact that the dunghill was "universally neglected" throughout Wales, a view echoed by other contemporary commentators. Evans, for example, complained:

"that the farmyards are generally on a declivity and destitute of a reservoir where the rains wash away everything valuable as a manure," while Hall W. Keary also recognised that continual exposure to rain and sun reduced the efficacy of farmyard manure as a fertiliser.[93]

While hay and barley straw, occasionally supplemented by turnips, were the principal feeds of the housed animal, many farmers, particularly in South Wales, included chopped furze or gorse in the ration. The furze was generally harvested from early September until Christmas, and fed to cattle and horses up to the end of April.[94] In the main, wild furze was cut, although in the Tywi Vale, furze was cultivated as a forage crop where yields of 12-15 tons per acre were not uncommon. Before being fed, the material was bruised and mixed with straw at the rate of one hundredweight of straw per ton of furze.

A letter written from Mostyn Hall in 1847 discusses the use of furze as a forage crop in North Wales.[95-96] It was contended that by growing French furze at the rate of 11 tons per acre (valued at 15s. per ton), the value of the output from light mountain land could be increased from 5s. to over £8 per acre. The furze, which was sown by being broadcast with oats in the spring months, was harvested after two years.

The furze bruising machine, driven by water power and attended by a boy at the rate of ls. daily, was capable of handling one ton of material in three and one quarter hours a total cost of 4½d. per ton. By the 1830s most furze bruising or crushing was carried out mechanically, and machines for this purpose feature prominently as "implements of husbandry" in the probate inventories annexed to the wills of farmers of this period. An interesting account of the growing and processing of furze occurs among the letters of the Rev. W. Williams of the Aberpergwm estate near Neath. Writing to Lady Hall in 1844 he complies with a request:

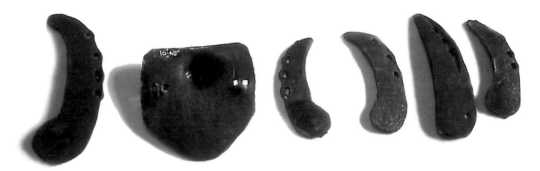

Cattle shoes exhibited in Llandovery Museum, (the second from the left seems questionable)

"to know how furze is served up to horses and cattle, the recipe is; first fence in an acre of ground, the most stony, gravelly and rubbishy you can find so that no quadruped epicure can break into it, especially horses and fell rabbits. Then sow French furze, sold by seedsmen and sometimes ironmongers, in drills about a foot asunder. When they appear have all the weeds hoed away for one year, after they will take care of themselves. When they are 18 inches high cut them close to the ground, that is each day the quantity required for consumption. (This) is to be put into a trough made of strong coarse wood and there chopped up small with a kind of long mallet at each end of which there are two pieces of iron fastened crossways and projecting about an inch beyond the iron hoop which encircles the ends of the mallet. This is work that women can perform unless they have something better to do. The furze is then mixed with chopped hay and straw. When this process is required on a large scale there is a mill and chaff-cutter used, but then considerably more than an acre is requisite. It is often let for 5 guineas an acre when the value of the ground is not more than 5 shillings." [97]

From the evidence available it would seem that the feeding of oil or cotton seed cake, which became so widespread in the grazing counties of England, was relatively infrequent in much of Wales. Few commentators refer to its use, while only sporadic references occur in farm diaries and notebooks. Indeed, the Welsh Land Commission of 1896 was informed that few tenants believed cake feeding to be a paying proposition, it being generally regarded as a "fad" only to be indulged by farmers with money to spare.[98]

Cattle Price Movements

The fortunes of the Welsh cattle producer were inextricably linked with those of the English grazier. In the days before the widespread use of oilcake, the demand for lean cattle from Wales was largely conditional upon the availability of forage in the English grazing counties. In this context, the expectancy of an early spring followed by a productive summer, increased the demand for, and hence the price of, Welsh store cattle.[99] The vagaries of the seasons, however, were only in part responsible for the fluctuation in store cattle prices, which were also strongly affected by the prevailing economic climate. Thus, even in an unfavourable season prices remained relatively high during an inflationary period, while in a favourable season, inflation tended further to enhance prices.

In his attempt to undermine the economic viability of Britain by way of the Continental system, Napoleon created a near monopoly for British farmers, setting into motion a trend in price inflation which persisted throughout the years of the French Wars. The dual effect of wartime inflation and the changing seasons on the store cattle producer in Wales may be gauged from the contributions of a Glamorgan farmer to *The Farmer's Magazine* in the early years of the century. The very dry summer of 1800 resulted in cattle being foddered with hay at pasture for some weeks before harvest.[100] In spite of a fair hay crop, so brisk was demand that in September of this year, hay was fetching between £4 and £6 per ton. Fortunately, however, a mild winter set in, so that by March 1801 hay could be purchased for as low as 50s.[101] In the same month, Cardiff fair was thronged with buyers:

"there were more Englishmen appeared to purchase cattle than ever known so early in the season, and every kind able to walk went off at high prices."

The demand for lean stock continued throughout the year, so that by October:

"cattle have been on the advance for several months, which has occasioned the country to be nearly drained." [102]

Indeed, the scarcity of cattle had so depressed the demand for hay that "reasonable" hay changed hands at 40s. per ton. Cattle prices had risen to unprecedented heights, with oxen of 40 scores selling for £20 while young heifers and steers were "proportionately higher." This happy state of affairs persisted throughout the autumn, and by January 1802:

"young heifers, which seven years ago would have drawn about 70s., went off at 10 guineas and upwards." [103]

The high prices continued to hold until April 1802, by which time a dry spring had set in, and demand from the desiccated Midland pastures had slackened. Twelve months later, prices were "low, but not to be complained of." However, the winter of 1804 -5 witnessed a continual decline in prices and:

"the want of sale forced farmers to thresh out more than the usual quantity of corn so money might be got to answer their payments."

Although the comments of the *Farmer's Magazine* correspondent only refer to the situation in Glamorgan, they do serve to illustrate the way by which seasonal changes induced fluctuating prices throughout an inflationary period.

The price movements in Figures I and II have been compiled exclusively from manuscript farm and estate accounts. This is a somewhat different approach to that adopted by other writers in this field. Edith Whetham, for example, has compiled a price index for store cattle based upon prices at the autumn fair held at Ballinasloe in Ireland between 1851/53.[104] A similar approach was adopted by David Howell who constructed an index using prices of store cattle at Carmarthen Market reported in *The Welshman* and *The Carmarthen Journal*.[105] These methods, however, might be criticised on the basis that the prices prevailing at isolated fairs and markets tended to reflect local supply and demand factors and thereby may not be entirely applicable over a broad area.

In a country like Wales, variation in climate between, for example, Welshpool and Haverfordwest, is sufficient to influence a considerable differential in herbage supplies, an important factor in the determination of both the supply of and the demand for cattle. Furthermore, many of the prices quoted in nineteenth century newspapers were provided by salesmen, and later by auctioneers, who

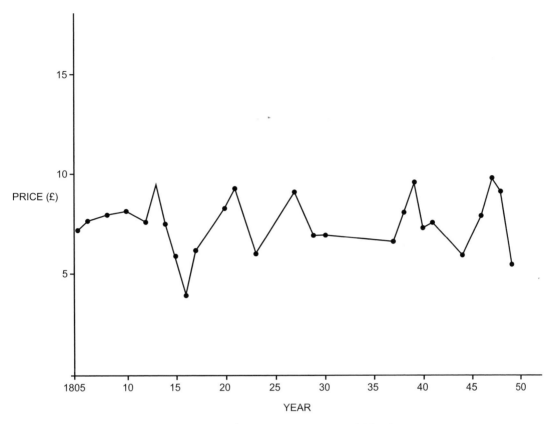

Figure I. Cattle Price Movements: 1800-50

would often tend to give an over-optimistic review. Despite these criticisms, the newspaper market reports have the singular advantage of providing a continuous and comprehensive price series over a given period. In using the farm accounts it was possible in most cases to differentiate between different classes of animals and then to calculate mean purchase and sale prices for each set of accounts for a given year. The points on the graphs, therefore, refer to the average of the mean prices from each account series. The use of farm and estate accounts, of course, imposes the problem of continuity, sets of accounts often covering only two or three years. Such material has been rejected and the figures are based upon accounts spanning at least ten years of transactions. This sort of approach has one great advantage in that it circumvents the problem of local price variation by providing material from a wide range of farms from different climatological and topographical regions.

Figure 1 illustrates the mean prices of barren cows and two, three and four year old cattle from a series of farms widely distributed throughout Wales. For any particular year the figure conceals a price variation of between five and ten per cent. This variation reflects local supply and demand factors, local variation in cattle type and the bargaining powers of individual buyers and sellers. Insufficient material was available to distinguish regional variations in prices, although there was some suggestion in the farm accounts that store cattle prices for the southern counties of Wales tended to be rather higher than those in the north.

The accounts illustrate dramatically the catastrophic fall in prices which accompanied the early post-Napoleonic War period, during which insolvency was widespread among the Welsh farming community. Prices had begun to drop after 1813, so that by July 1816 our Glamorgan correspondent reported:

The holding pens and ruins of the building of Ffŵrd-ar-Camddwr, six miles out of Tregaron.

"cattle are nearly unsaleable, no-one looking for them ... no money to be made out of livestock."[106]
There is little doubt as to the seriousness of the immediate post-war depression in Wales. Simon Lloyd, of Bala in Merionethshire, wrote to the Board of Agriculture maintaining that the paper money in circulation had been reduced by half and that:
"all agricultural improvements are in a great measure suspended, the ill effects of which must be felt in this and succeeding years."[107]
Another witness contended that one of the most striking features of the depression was the unparalleled frequency of sales of livestock by farmers under execution for rents and debts. He wryly commented:
"Sheriff's officers are the only class of men who in these days are fully employed and make their fortunes."[108]
Although some landlords were able to grant rent abatements ranging from 20 per cent to 50 per cent, many farms were unoccupied. In the countryside around Lampeter, for example, twelve of the largest farms were untenanted, while in Radnorshire many farms of £40-£250 rental were deserted. The prevailing atmosphere of gloom and despondency is illustrated by two letters written by Robert Jones from Garthmyl in Montgomeryshire to his brother. In January 1816:
"the distress of the less opulent farmers is beyond all example and in a country like this, fully agricultural, it must be universally felt ... God knows when it will end."
By March things had not improved, the country being:
"almost universally bankrupt, farmers on the very best farms are losing at least the annual rent ... such a state of things cannot last long."
Over the next few months conditions did not materially improve. The appalling summer of 1816

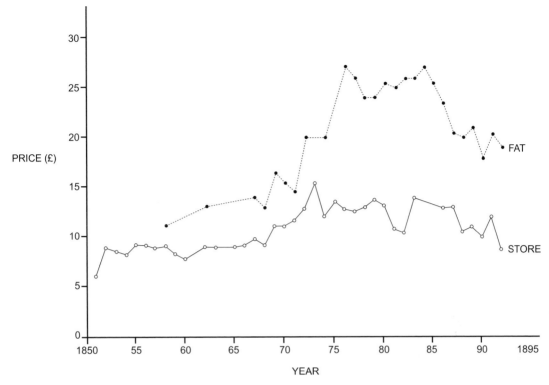

Figure II. Cattle Price Movements: 1850-95

resulted in a dearth of winter forage so that by January 1817, cattle were in such poor condition that many were unsaleable and had had to be slaughtered.[109] In his evidence to the Select Committee of 1821, John Maughan of Oswestry drew attention to the extreme poverty among farmers in 1817, when it had been necessary to sell cattle at any price, both to pay the rent, and to buy food. Moreover in 1818 the exceptional drought in England resulted in a great depression in cattle prices so that very few cattle sold at Narberth Fair changed hands at reasonable prices.[110] Ironically, the drought in England was matched by severe gales and floods in the Tywi Vale and elsewhere in Wales, reducing many people to destitution. Farmers, where they were able to do so, sold off their cattle for a fraction of the normal price in order to purchase everyday necessities. [111]

John Maughan took the view that by 1821 conditions had improved, largely due to better seasons and more favourable prices for livestock.[112] The following two years, however, witnessed a steep downward movement in prices which moved Thomas Prothero, Newport agent to Sir Charles Morgan of Tredegar Park to suggest rent abatements on the Newport estate. Having explained to Sir Charles that two year old Glamorgan heifers had sold for a mere £3. 1s. at Newport Fair, he opined:

"it may in general be said of all livestock that it is reduced considerably more than half. Under such circumstances you may suppose that the farmers are fast decaying in property and that the failures are numerous."[113]

After a period of recovery, cattle prices had declined to the 1822 level by 1829 as a result of lack of demand. Lord Kensington was informed on November 21st by his Haverfordwest agent of the stagnant condition of Welsh markets, yet:

"I am inclined to think that we are not quite so badly off as in the agricultural districts of England."[114]

If the Welsh farmer was less severely affected than his colleague in eastern England by the slump in grain prices which characterised the late twenties and the eighteen thirties, he was nevertheless exposed to a downward trend in livestock prices throughout this period. It may even be that these low livestock prices were among the many contributory factors responsible for the agrarian discontent eventually to culminate in the Rebecca Riots of the early forties. The data provided by the farm account books is insufficient to permit detailed comment upon livestock prices in the mid twenties and thirties. It is known, however, that prices of sheep, cattle and butter in Wales were severely depressed in 1836/1837 and again in 1842/43, while poor, highway and county rates were rapidly increasing, thereby adding to the costs of the already overburdened farmers.[115] The fodder shortage of 1836/37 occasioned the flooding of local markets with cattle. A letter to the *Farmer's Magazine* describes the situation in South Wales:

"outhouses have been unthatched to furnish food, and every description of vegetation, hitherto considered as refuse, has been brought from great distances..." [116]

The low livestock prices throughout the early 1840s reflects the effect of the series of poor summers on the demand for lean cattle. The run of "starvation seasons" eventually culminated in the catastrophic drought of 1844/45, when Herefordshire farmers were:

"selling their cattle of the finest description in the shape of walking skeletons for one half the price they cost them." [117]

The early spring of 1846 stimulated pasture growth in the English grazing counties, thereby pushing up the demand for store cattle, so that dealers like David Jonathan of Dihewyd in Cardiganshire were forced to pay up to £2 per head more for Welsh 'runts' than they had done in the previous year. [118] Prices remained at a satisfactory level over the next two years, when Elias Jones was able to record a profit of £4.10s. on the sale of three heifers at Abergele Fair in 1847, and £1. 8s. on two oxen the next year.[119] In 1849/50, however, prices slumped severely due to lack of keep. In the autumn of 1849, J. B. Annwyl lamented the low prices and vast numbers of cattle at the fairs of Dinas Mawddwy and Lledrod, while a disconsolate Pembrokeshire farmer valued his steers at £3 and his heifers at the derisory figure of £1.5s.[120,121]

Figure II represents a continuation of the cattle price series. The "store" line is constructed on the basis of the mean price of cattle of similar categories to those in Figure I. Although the number of accounts containing references to fat cattle was relatively small, in general terms price movements within this category tend to parallel those of store cattle for which a considerable volume of material was available.

The relationship between store cattle prices and the availability of forage has already been explored. From the mid-fifties to the late seventies, store cattle sold from Welsh farms increased in price. Until the late sixties, the rate of increase was relatively undramatic, a feature characteristic of a stable agricultural situation. The price troughs throughout this period may be almost entirely ascribed to the lack of forage availability and hence depressed demand from buyers. In 1859, for example, the dry spring resulted in very large supplies of cattle at the fairs of Haverfordwest and Hay-on-Wye, although demand was dull. At Hereford in the same year:

"had there been 24 hours rain immediately before the fair, stores would have realised fully 10 per cent more than they did and the sales would have been as quick as they were slow." [122]

By 1862, however, plentiful supplies of fodder as late in the year as September induced a brisk demand for lean stock. [123]

It is not possible to consider price movements during the latter part of the nineteenth century in isolation from the structural changes in Welsh agriculture conditioned by the vicissitudes of the "Great Depression." The evidence given before the Welsh Land Commission suggests that the full effects of the depression were first felt in some areas after the outstandingly wet year of 1879 when both arable and livestock producers suffered on account of the inclemency of the season. The agent for the Margam Estate in Glamorgan submitted to the Commissioners that:

"the depression has been going on and off since 1879; it is undoubtedly worse at the present time owing to the prices of everything being depressed." [124]

George Williams of Hayston in Pembrokeshire expressed a similar view. He also echoed the opinions of many tenant farmers when he pointed out that landlords were often not prepared to accept that any real depression in farming existed prior to 1885, and even then did not fully appreciate the plight of their tenants faced with the depressed conditions.[125] The bulk of the evidence given before the Commissioners indicates that the northern Welsh counties did not experience the full effects of the fall in prices until a somewhat later date. W. D. W. Griffiths, owner of the Garn Estate in the Vale of Clwyd concluded that in his view, agricultural depression was not evident in that area before 1885, when he had first received complaints from his tenants about the severity of the times.[126] The tenants of the Vaynol Estate did not consider it necessary to request a rent reduction until 1887, when they unanimously agreed to petition for a reasonable reduction:

"we have all been driven into such a state of penury, that we are utterly unable to pay (the rent) and at the same time to live honestly." [127]

This petition elicited a l0 per cent rent reduction, the tenants of the nearby Penrhyn Estate enjoying similar relief. By 1889, Lord Penrhyn's agent was writing to Captain Stewart, agent at Vaynol, suggesting the withdrawal of the 10 per cent reduction as he "had gained the impression that things are improving. [128] Lord Penrhyn, however, decided to retain the 10 per cent reduction on the understanding that rentals would revert to normal, "if things remain as at present."[129]

Edward Williams of Holywell had found many North Wales farmers in straightened circumstances, with landlords preferring to take farms in hand rather than give rent remissions. Although he himself had received a 15 per cent rent reduction, Williams considered this completely inadequate. Writing to T. E. Ellis at the House of Commons in 1888 he complained that:

"the greater number (of landlords) withhold their consideration too long and are still holding in too many instances the millstones of arrears round their tenants' necks." [130]

While he attributed the refusal to reduce rents to "selfish motives" in the case of some landlords, Williams fully realised that, as in the earlier part of the century, many landlords were themselves in straightened circumstances and accordingly were unable to reduce rents if they were to meet the demands of bank interest, marriage settlements and bequests.

The overall extent of rent reductions in the face of the depression varied markedly between eastern and western Wales. On the six predominantly pastoral counties of west Wales rents fell very little after 1878/9, remaining in 1883/4 at 18.5 per cent above the level of 1864/5, although at 2.1 per cent below the level prevailing in 1878/9. In the eastern counties, however, where corn-growing contributed more significantly to farm income, rents after 1878/9 fell almost to the level of 1864/5.[131] In general, the farm accounts used in the compilation of Figure II would seem to support the evidence on livestock prices given before the various commissions of enquiry.

The price index for two year old steers constructed by Howell and quoted by Davies reveals that prices increased during the 1870s, culminating in the peak price of 1883.[132] Figure II indicates a peak store price in 1883, although contrary to the indices of both Howell and Whetham it shows a price trough in 1882, which is perhaps surprising in view of the widespread liver-rot epidemic which decimated both the sheep and cattle population between the years 1880 and 1882.[133] However, the farm accounts confirm the findings of Howell, that store cattle prices in Wales did not seriously decline until after 1885. Davies' analysis of beef prices in the markets of Wrexham, Newtown, Monmouth and Cowbridge revealed that the year 1885 represented the beginning of the downward movement in beef prices, a finding which concurs with the movement of fat cattle prices in Figure II.

During the seventies and early eighties foreign imports had had relatively little effect upon domestic livestock prices which at this time were dictated to a considerable degree by the vagaries of the weather and the frequency and nature of disease epidemics. The cold, wet seasons which characterised the seventies had tended to reduce cattle supplies and thus maintain prices. The wet autumn of 1875, for example, was followed by high rainfall throughout the winter of 1876/7, while the spring of 1878 heralded the advent of three wet and cheerless years. By the mid-eighties, however, notwithstanding a series of summer droughts which depressed the demand for store cattle, the beef market was becoming influenced progressively more by foreign imports. The development of refrigerated ships enabling the cheap and rapid transit of carcasses from the United States and elsewhere, resulted in imported meat becoming a more important determinant of domestic prices than varying weather patterns.

Thus by the nineties witnesses before the Welsh Land Commission were almost unanimous in their belief that low cattle prices arose from the effect of the increasing volume of imported meat. Edward Perkins, for example, contended that the prices of inferior and average cattle had dropped by 75 per cent and 25 per cent since the mid-seventies.[134] Another witness, Thomas Hopkins of Llangattock, pointed out that between 1872 and 1893 fat cattle had lost 40 per cent of their value, while store cattle had declined in price by 50 per cent. Moreover, a farmer from Pwllheli was concerned not only by the low prices, but also by the fact that markets were saturated.[135] Thus farmers were being forced to hold back cattle in the anticipation of a more satisfactory market at a time when forage was both scarce and expensive. It is important, however, not to attach too much significance to the comments of these and other witnesses, whose observations tended to be limited to a restricted locality. Nevertheless, Figure II reveals a decline of some 30 per cent in the prices of fat cattle sold from farms in Wales between 1876 and 1892, while beef prices at the markets of Cowbridge, Newtown and Wrexham fell by 23, 28 and 28 per cent respectively between 1873/77 and 1892/96.[136]

Adjustment to the changing economic climate was effected to a large extent throughout the United Kingdom by a reduction in the cereal acreage with an increasing emphasis on low cost production, particularly of dairy and beef products. Dairying and cattle breeding required considerably less labour than cereal production, thereby permitting substantial reductions in the rapidly growing farm wages bill. Moreover, these enterprises could readily utilise the abundant supplies of cheap cereal products.

By 1875, the compilers of the Agricultural Returns had standardised their definitions of the various categories of land so that the Returns provide an opportunity for tracing the progress of conversion of arable land to permanent pasture on a county basis. Figure III, in which the Midland grazing counties are included for the purposes of comparison, indicates that between 1875 and 1890, all counties increased their permanent pasture acreage. This upward trend continued in all counties with the exception of Carmarthenshire, Caernarvonshire, Merionethshire, and Denbighshire until 1895 after which permanent pasture acreage tended to decrease in parallel with the decreasing intensity of the depression. The continuing expansion of permanent pasture in Montgomeryshire and Pembrokeshire throughout the latter part of the period may be attributed to the permanent substitution of dairying for corn growing in the low-lying areas of these counties. It is significant that with the exception of Carmarthenshire the increase in permanent pasture acreage was undramatic. This is attributable to the relatively small contribution of corn sales to farm receipts in most parts of Wales.

The decline in arable acreage was paralleled by an overall increase in the basic unit of the cattle population, the breeding herd. With the exception of Merionethshire, the size of the breeding herd increased in all the Welsh counties during the last quarter of the nineteenth century. Increases of the greatest magnitude took place in the counties of Flint and Glamorgan where demand for liquid milk from the northern border towns and the towns of the South Wales coalfield was rapidly expanding. Accordingly, out of a total increase of 30,458 breeding females between 1871 and 1900, 1857 came from Flint and Glamorgan alone, a further 6,629 being found in the counties of Pembroke and Carmarthen. By 1875, some degree of specialisation in dairying had developed in the border counties of North Wales and the counties of Glamorgan, Carmarthen and Pembroke.

Even at this early date, considerable capital resources were required to develop an efficient dairy farm, with the result that the depression in prices occasioned by the growing volume of imported dairy products was not followed by the wholesale abandonment of dairying in these areas where it had become an established part of farming practice. The early 1880s witnessed a hardening in butter prices paralleled by further expansion of herd size in the regions where dairy production was developing. This was particularly the case on farms in proximity to industrial centres where the point of consumption was close to the point of production and thus problems of transport and keeping quality were minimised.

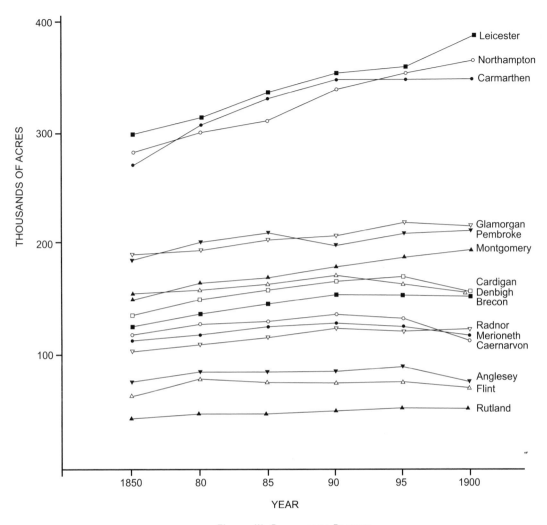

Figure III. Permanent Pasture

Beef prices did not collapse until 1885 so that breeding herd sizes in the store cattle rearing counties of Anglesey, Carmarthen and the English borders continued to rise into the mid eighties. After 1885 a series of dry seasons in England reduced the supply of fodder in the beef fattening counties. This was reflected in decreased demand for store cattle which halted the expansion of breeding cow herds in the Welsh rearing counties. It is significant that over the generally unfavourable quinquennium of 1885/1890, herd sizes in Glamorgan and Flint continued to increase owing to the buoyant demand for liquid milk. At this time the net return to farmers selling liquid milk was greater than the return from butter and cheese production, since the liquid milk market was, by its nature, protected from foreign competition. Hence there was no increase in herd size in the counties of Denbigh and Cardigan where butter sales had been a major source of income. By 1890, beef prices tended to stabilise and while butter prices moved upwards from 1885 there was still considerable annual fluctuation. This being so, the general trend in herd size was downwards. However, after the price trough of 1895/6 the upward movement in animal product prices which was to continue, with the occasional reverse,

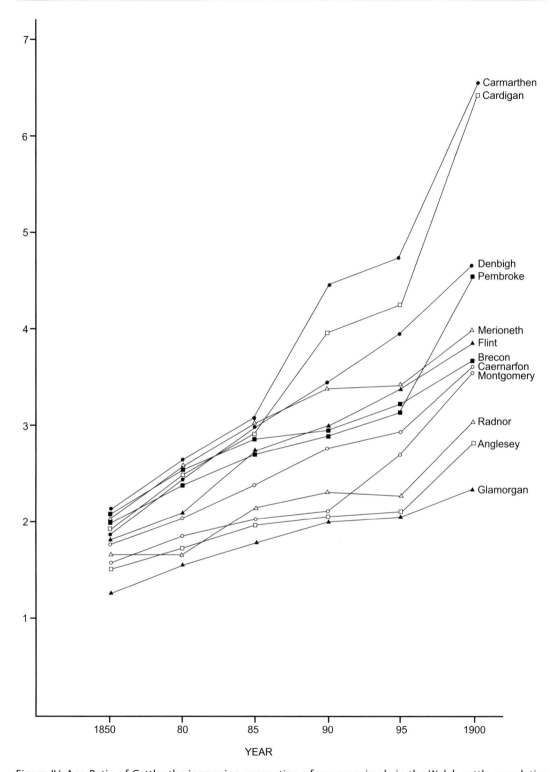

Figure IV. Age Ratio of Cattle; the increasing proportion of young animals in the Welsh cattle population

until 1920, was followed by an expansion in the breeding cow population in both dairy and beef sectors by the turn of the century.

The remainder of the cattle population comprised breeding herd replacements, together with store and fattening cattle, enumerated in the Agricultural Returns as "cattle of 2 years and above" and "cattle under 2 years." The changing proportions of cattle under 2 years old, relative to older animals, is of considerable significance. During the last quarter of the century there was a steady decline in the proportion of animals in the latter category, and although varying in degree this was a feature common to all counties. Thus from a ratio in 1875 of between 1:1 and 2:1 in favour of young cattle, the proportion of young cattle increased dramatically. This changing ratio reflects an important development in cattle production. Farm accounts and sale catalogues from the early 1860s bear witness to the fact that not only was it becoming less profitable to feed cattle to heavy weights, but consumers were showing a marked preference for lean smaller joints of meat from relatively early maturing cattle.

To cater for this trend, the English grazier and stall fattener required a younger, earlier-maturing animal. The introduction of Hereford and Shorthorn blood into Welsh herds had enabled the Welsh store producer to meet these requirements to some extent by the last quarter of the century. As Figure IV suggests there were interesting differences between individual counties in the changing age ratio of store cattle. It may be that in those counties with a relatively low ratio of young to older cattle, little expansion in store sales had taken place by the close of the century. This was certainly the case with Glamorgan where the dairying industry was rapidly expanding, and the high proportion of older stock in that county may be explained by the necessity of maintaining animals as replacements for the dairy herd. Moreover, increasing numbers of cattle were being fattened in the lowland regions of Glamorgan to supply the towns of the south Wales coalfield.

In Flintshire, however, a different pattern emerges, suggesting that despite the development of dairying, store cattle sales to Cheshire, Shropshire and the Midland counties were still of considerable significance. In the neighbouring counties of Cardigan, Carmarthen and Pembroke the changes in the proportion of young to older cattle follow a remarkably similar course which indicates the continuing importance of store cattle exports regardless of the increase in dairying on some of the smaller farms. Anglesey had long been a county renowned for its store cattle. In view of this a greater response to the growing demand for younger cattle than the Returns indicate might have been anticipated. This apparent anomaly may be explained, in the first case, by the fact that an increasing number of cattle were being fattened in Anglesey. In addition, there was still a buoyant demand for the 3-4 year old Anglesey "runt" in the Midland counties where this class of animal was prized for its ability to graze down the feeding pastures during the late autumn months.

The Agricultural Returns provide a means of assessing the relative importance of sheep and cattle production in Wales throughout the "depression" period. Taking the Principality as a whole, there was an overall increase in both the sheep and cattle population during the depression, although numbers of both classes fluctuated according to market conditions (Table III).

	CATTLE					SHEEP
	% change 1876/85	% change 1886/95	% change 1896/1900	% change 1876/85	% change 1886/95	% change 1896/1900
Anglesey	+15.6	+0.8	+12.0	-9.6	+29.7	+26.6
Brecon	+ 7.2	-1.2	+ 5.3	-12.5	+23.3	+21.7
Cardigan	+11.1	-5.6	+ 9.4	+2.3	+22.0	+11.6
Carmarthen	+ 13.5	-2.9	+ 5.1	-1.3	+13.9	+ 6.7
Caernarvon	+ 6.1	+0.6	+ 5.1	-6.6	+28.3	+ 5.2
Denbigh	+13.6	+1.6	+ 5.6	+0.6	+30.1	+ 8.3
Flint	+16.1	+6.5	+13.0	+0.5	+26.1	+22.0
Glamorgan	+18.2	-10.5	+ 6.1	+0.8	+ 7.7	+12.3
Merioneth	+ 3.2	-0.6	+ 3.3	+3.6	+20.6	+10.0
Montgomery	+ 6.9	-3.7	+ 4.1	-4.0	+16.0	+14.0
Pembroke	+15.0	-5.1	+ 5.3	-9.3	+20.5	+ 5.8
Radnor	+ 4.4	+0.5	+ 8.7	-8.8	+10.7	+ 2.3

Table III
Percentage changes in sheep and cattle numbers

Between the years 1876 and 1885, all counties with the exception of Cardigan, Glamorgan, Merioneth, Denbigh and Flint, suffered a decline in sheep population accompanied by an expansion in cattle numbers. Since mutton prices remained at an adequate level, it may be confidently asserted that the depression in wool prices occasioned by imports of cheap Australian wool was the prime cause of this reduction in the sheep population, an assertion verified by witnesses before the Welsh Land Commission. In consequence of the depressed wool market, upland farmers who relied upon wool sales for the bulk of their income were most severely affected. Hence the sharp fall in the sheep numbers in Brecknockshire, Caernarvonshire and Radnorshire. Store lamb, mutton and beef prices tended to rise during the period 1876/85. This may explain the small change in sheep numbers in the counties of Denbigh, Flint, Glamorgan and Montgomery, all of which grew a relatively high acreage of root crops by which means they were able to produce fattened animals. The downward trend in sheep numbers was aggravated by the catastrophic outbreaks of liver rot which took place during 1880 and 1881, decimating sheep flocks throughout the United Kingdom. In Wales all counties with the exception of Caernarvon and Glamorgan suffered heavy losses. The effects of the disease were felt most severely in the border counties, Radnorshire alone losing 30,000 animals from liver rot during 1880/81.

The Returns reveal that there was a net decrease in the ratio of sheep to cattle during the period 1876/85. From 1886/95 the trend was reversed, a substantial increase in the sheep population of all the Welsh counties being accompanied, in some cases, by a decline in cattle numbers. Sheep numbers continued to rise throughout the remainder of the century, the pre-1875 population level being exceeded by the mid 1890s. The expansion in sheep numbers may be attributed to several factors. The overhead costs incurred by a farmer in expanding his sheep flock to utilise land converted to permanent pasture would have been substantially less than those incurred by increasing cattle numbers. Furthermore, there are technical grounds to support the assertion that new pasture would have been more efficiently utilised by the expanding sheep population than by cattle. However, there is little doubt that the changing pattern of animal product prices was the major catalyst stimulating the ncreased output of sheep relative to that of cattle. The prices of store lamb and mutton had declined proportionately less than those of store cattle and beef, a situation reflected in an expansion in the output of store lambs relative to a decline in store cattle production. Moreover, some fattening of lamb may have taken place in those areas suited to the purpose.

The decline in cattle numbers in Glamorgan between 1886/95 is interesting. While the size of the dairy herd in that county remained virtually static, the reduction comprised almost entirely cattle of over two years of age. This suggests that farmers were selling cattle as stores, rather than maintaining dairy replacements, a trend initiated as the price of butter fell in the early 1890s. The returns for Flint and Denbigh, in the lowland areas of which dairying was widely practised, indicate an increase in all categories of cattle. It is possible that in these counties the degree of specialisation was such as to deter farmers from leaving dairying when faced with a decrease in prices. In both counties, the increased stocking density of cattle, together with a substantial expansion in the sheep flock, illustrates the considerable degree of intensification which had taken place by the closing years of the century.

From the late 1890s, prices of butter and wool began to move in an upward, albeit fluctuating, direction. The price of prime beef had remained reasonably static at around 83 per cent of the 1867/77 average while that of mutton had hovered at between 85 and 90 per cent of the "pre-depression" price. Subsequent to 1895, prices of these commodities followed a sporadically upward trend, and thus, in spite of a high level of foreign imports, the last five years of the nineteenth century witnessed expansion of both the sheep and cattle enterprises of Wales.

Livestock and the personal wealth of farmers c.1800–1850

Apart from occasional comments in the contemporary literature, there appears to be little information concerning the changing prosperity of the Welsh farmer throughout the nineteenth century. The extant farm account books are, with few exceptions, quite inadequate for this purpose, while statistical information is totally lacking.

In an attempt to obtain some estimate of the wealth accumulated by Welsh farmers as a result of their trading activities, I have analysed rather more than twelve hundred wills and administrations of farmers from the Welsh dioceses.[137] The enormous volume of wills for the fifty years deterred any attempt comprehensively to analyse every will. Instead, it was decided to take a given year (e.g.1800) and to inspect all wills of *bona fide* farmers. A similar procedure was followed for each decade up to 1850 after which few wills with annexed probate inventories were available. It could, of course, be argued that the sworn statement of an executor and executrix annexed to the will or administration would tend to underestimate total personal wealth, as the fees for proving the will were based upon the magnitude of the wealth of the deceased. If, however, such underestimates were common to all wills, then from a comparative point of view, the wills provide a reasonable method of assessment of personal wealth among the farming community. Certainly, the inspection of a random sample of wills from a given year did not suggest any significant divergence between dioceses in the valuation of most items of the available probate inventories. A further criticism may be levelled at the use of probate material, in that the inventories generally fail to value real estate and thus only include personal and moveable goods. However, of the 1,215 farmers' wills studied, some 93 percent contained no reference to real estate. The percentage distribution of wills for each year is set out on the next page in Table IV.

The Table clearly shows that the overall distribution of personal wealth did not change significantly over the first fifty years of the century, so that between 1800 and 1810 approximately 90 per cent of wills were below £500 while in 1820/30 and 1840/50 the proportion declined only marginally to 87 per cent. Although there is some suggestion that the percentage of wills of over £1,000 had increased by 1850, there was no positive trend in this direction. As a means of establishing any differences in

£	1-50	51-100	101-200	201-300	301-400	401-500	501-600	601-800	801-1000	1001-2000	Total
	%	%	%	%	%	%	%	%	%	%	
1800	12.1	39.7	10.0	21.9	2.1	0.9	7.3	0.8	4.4	0.8	240
1810	13.9	22.2	20.4	14.7	3.3	11.4	4.5	5.2	1.3	3.1	158
1820	13.9	27.7	23.2	12.2	1.2	7.0	3.6	5.7	1.2	4.3	166
1830	14.2	28.9	23.4	11.4	2.8	7.7	3.9	3.5	3.0	1.2	184
1840	14.2	29.7	24.0	10.0	2.5	6.2	3.0	3.5	3.8	3.1	258
1850	11.8	25.9	24.2	10.8	1.0	6.3	3.9	8.4	1.5	6.2	209

Table IV
Overall distribution of farmers' wills by total value of personal estate

personal estate between farmers occupying holdings at different elevations, the wills in Figure V are distributed according to whether the deceased lived in an upland, lowland or hill parish. For this purpose, lowland parishes were defined as those in which more than half of the land lay below one thousand feet, while upland and hill parishes contained half and three quarters respectively of their land above the one thousand foot contour.

In the absence of any information on farm size, it might reasonably have been assumed that those farmers occupying holdings in the more fertile lowland parishes would have enjoyed a greater income than those on upland and hill holdings. This would presumably have been reflected in the magnitude of their personal estate. On the other hand, Figure V reveals no consistent differences between the three environments either within a given time period or between the three periods. Nor were there any overall differences between the 1800/10, 1820/ 30 and 1840/50 periods in the general distribution of the various categories of wills. Between 1800 and 1810, for example, the proportion of wills of below £300 varied between 76 per cent on the lowland and 81 per cent on the upland, while in 1840/50 the proportions were 74 per cent and 80 per cent respectively. At the other end of the scale, it appeared that the number of wills from lowland and hill environments in excess of £1,000 had increased by 1840/50. Hence 2.5 per cent of the lowland wills and 2.1 per cent of hill wills exceeded £1,000 in 1800/10, the proportion advancing to 5.9 per cent and 5.4 per cent by 1840/50.

The availability of probate inventories for many of the wills provides an informative picture of the composition of the personal wealth of Welsh farmers in the first half of the nineteenth century. In particular, the inventories emphasize the relative significance of cattle and sheep as components of personal estate.

Table V highlights a definite downward trend in the contribution of cattle towards total personal estate between 1800 and 1850. This decline is common to lowland, upland and hill environments Sheep also appear to have declined in importance, although the trend is less clearly defined. More-over, these figures show that sheep were a rather more important element in the hills and the uplands by comparison with lowland farms – a finding supported by contemporary literary evidence. Among other components of the inventories cash and securities were only represented in approximately 10 per cent of wills between 1800 and 1830, these elements comprising 24 per cent of the personal estate of lowland farmers and 53 per cent of that of farmers on upland and hill holdings. "Corn and hay" accounted for 10 per cent of the personal estate of lowland and 7 per cent of that of upland and hill farmers, these proportions not changing materially throughout the period 1800/1850.

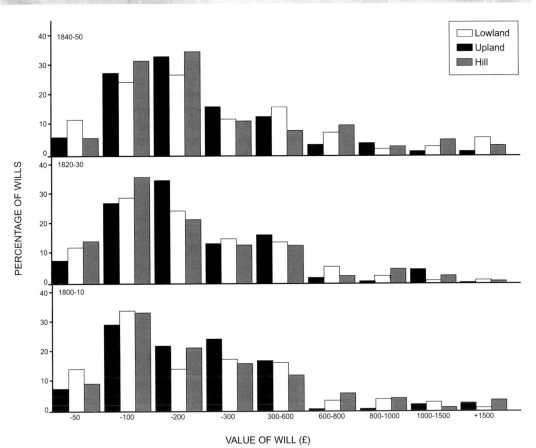

Figure V. Value of farmers wills according to situation of farm

Table V						
Percentages of cattle and sheep in the probate inventories						
Period	Elevation	No. of Inven- tories	Mean Value	% cattle	% sheep	% cattle and sheep
1800-10	Lowland	41	£241	39.1	6.6	45.7
	Upland	27	£224	36.5	14.4	50.9
	Hill	45	£288	33.4	14.9	48.3
1820-30	Lowland	38	£269	30.3	3.9	34.2
	Upland	14	£269	21.2	7.7	28.9
	Hill	15	£265	30.8	18.9	49.7
1840-50	Lowland	48	£228	28.0	6.3	34.3
	Upland	26	£205	22.0	12.8	34.8
	Hill	16	£308	14.1	7.1	21.2

In Anglesey and the coastal parishes of Caernarvonshire and Merionethshire it seems that numerous farmers were partially involved in marine trading activities, for the inventories frequently refer to "shares in a vessel." That ship ownership was relatively common among the farmers of the North Wales coastal counties is clear from the Beaumaris Shipping Registers which reveal that 20 per cent of owners of vessels with definite Anglesey associations were farmers. The proportion of total personal wealth absorbed by shares in shipping in the examples given below gives the impression that coastal trading was probably an important source of income for these farmers.

1810	Owen Jones, Llandegfan, Anglesey (Total £120)	$^1/_4$ share of the sloop *Success* ... £26
1820	Edward Davies, Penmorfa, Caernarvonshire (Total £394)	$^1/_2$ share of the brig *Endeavour* ... £20 $^1/_2$ share of the brig *Ester* ... £22 $^1/_4$ share of the brig *Robert* ... £24
1830	William Watkins, Criccieth, Caernarvonshire (Total £1,038)	$^5/_{32}$ share of the brig *Marquess* £62 10s 0d
1840	William Jones, Llanfacraeth, Anglesey (Total £294)	Share of vessel ... £72
	Ellis Richard, Llaneddwyne, Merionethshire (Total £99)	Share of vessel *Glyndwr* ... £15

The five representative probate inventories set out below give some indication of the range of personal wealth among Welsh farmers in the early nineteenth century, and further examples are given in Appendix II.

Robert Williams, Llandyfriog, Anglesey (Lowland 1820):

	£	s	d
His apparel	3.	3.	9
5 horses and furniture	30.	0.	0
6 cows, 8 three year old oxen, 7 two year old oxen and 8 yearlings	174.	0.	0
16 sheep	16.	0.	0
3 swine	3.	0.	0
Poultry	2.	6	0
Growing wheat	5.	0.	0
Corn and hay in barns	85.	10.	0
Carts and other implements of husbandry	16.	2.	0
Household furniture	40.	3.	6
Books	1.	5.	6
	374.	7.	3
Deduct one third for W. Williams	124.	15.	9
	£249.	11.	6

John Pritchard, Beddgelert, Caernarvonshire (Hill 1830):

	£	s	d
Wearing apparel	£ 1.	10.	0
Saddle and bridle	1.	10.	0
14 cows and a bull	75.	0.	0
6 three year old runts	30.	0.	0
8 two year old runts	32.	0.	0
10 yearlings	20.	0.	0
3 mares	18.	0.	0
400 sheep	160.	0.	0
Implements of husbandry	3.	0.	0
Household furniture	20.	0.	0
	361.	0.	0
Deduct funeral expenses	11.	0.	0
	£ 350.	0.	0

William Norbert, Llanhader, Pembrokeshire (Lowland 1830):

	£	s	d
5 cows	£ 12.	10.	0
1 bull	2.	2.	0
5 yearlings	5.	5.	0
6 calves	3.	0.	0
1 old horse	1.	0.	0
1 old mare and colt	2.	0.	0
12 sheep	3.	0.	0
8 lambs	1.	0.	0
2 pigs		5.	0
2 acres of wheat	9.	0.	0
12 acres of oats	15.	0.	0
Potatoes	1.	0.	0
Cart and plough	3.	0.	0
Household furniture	6.	0.	0
	£ 64.	2.	0
Rates, rents, tithes and funeral expenses	29.	14.	4$^1/_2$
	£ 34.	7.	7$^1/_2$

Richard Blunt, Llanidloes, Montgomeryshire (Upland 1840):

	£	s	d
4 milch cows	£ 26.	0.	0
1 heifer	3.	0.	0
3 eighteen month olds	6.	15.	0
3 calves	4.	10.	0
Mare and saddle	8.	0.	0
Mare and saddle	6.	0.	0
2 pairs of gearings	2.	0.	0
Pony	3.	10.	0
Grain	16.	8.	0
Implements of husbandry	5.	2.	0
2 store pigs	3.	5.	0

Poultry		13.	0
Wearing apparel	2.	10.	0
Kitchen	3.	0.	0
Back Kitchen	2.	10.	0
Chamber	4.	0.	0
Chamber	1.	5.	0
	£98.	8.	0

David Jenkins, Laugharne, Carmarthenshire (Lowland 1840):

11 cows	£ 71.	10.	0
9 calves	11.	5.	0
4 horses	28.	0.	0
Suckling colt	2.	0.	0
14 pigs	7.	8.	0
18 geese and poultry	1.	0.	0
2 carts and harnesses	6.	0.	0
2 ploughs	3.	0.	0
Planks		5.	0
Furniture	80.	0.	0
Hay	30.	0.	0
Corn	60.	0.	0
Potatoes	2.	0.	0
4 two year olds	20.	0.	0
9 yearlings	27.	0.	0
2 year old fillies	9.	0.	0
Barley	16.	0.	0
Money at interest	360.	0.	0
	£ 734.	8.	0

It was these farmers, great and small, whose labour and husbandry provided the countless cattle traded by the drovers and dealers whose doings are chronicled in the remaining chapters of this book.

FOOTNOTES FOR CHAPTER 2

1   N.L.W. Glansevern MS. 271.
2   N.L.W. MS. 2719C.
3   *J.R.A.S.E.* Ser. i, 14, 1853, p. 457.
4   *J.R.A.S.E.* Ser. ii, 11,1866, p. 17.
5   H.W. Keary, *J.R.A.S.E.*, Ser. i, 14, 1848, p. 424.
6   J. Coleman, *The Cattle, Sheep and Pigs of Britain*, London, 1857, pp. 210-11.
7   N.L.W. MS. 13147A.
8   U.C.N.W. Bangor MS. 18607.
9   T. Rees, *A Topographical and Historical Description of the County of Cardigan.* London, 1894, p. 140.
10   C. Hassall, *A General View of the Agriculture of Pembrokeshire*, London, 1815, p. 41.
11   T. Lloyd & D Turnor, *A General View of the Agriculture of the county of Cardigan*, London, 1794, p. 22.
12   J. Kay, *A General View of the Agriculture of the county of Carnarvon*, London, 1794, p. 19.
13   *Farmers Magazine*, Jan. 1859, p. 71.
14   Kay. *op. cit.*, p. 19.
15   John Lawrence, *A General Treatise on Cattle*, London, 1805, p. 56.
16   Discussing the basic conservatism of the late 19th century Welsh farmer, D. Parry-Jones relates a case where a farmer had been appalled by the fact that his sons had borrowed a cart to haul manure rather than use the time-honoured sledge. The farmer could not conceive of how his sons could usefully fill the time saved by using the cart. "The notion of time-saving threw his mind into a state of confusion; it meant the re-planning of the whole year's work and he was not equal to it" (*My Own Folk*, Gwasg Gomer, 1972, p. 70).
17   C. S. Read, "On the Agriculture of South Wales", *J.R.A.S.E.*, Ser., 10, 1849, p. 140.
18   J. Gibson, *Agriculture in Wales*, London, 1879, p. 72.
19   T. Rowlandson, "On the Agriculture of North Wales", *J.R.A.S.E.* Ser i, 10, 1846, p. 582.
20   J. Clark, *A General View of the Agriculture of Brecknockshire*, London, 1794, passim.
21   Hassall, (Pembs.) *op. cit.*, p. 41.
22   J. Bannister. *A Synopsis of Husbandry*, London, 1799, p. 47.
23   In Coleman, *op. cit.*, p. 212.
24   Read, *op. cit.*, p. 139.
25   W. Youatt. *Cattle, their breeds, management and diseases*, London, 1834, p. 54.
26   C. Hassall, *A General View of the Agriculture of the county of Carmarthenshire*, London, 1793, p. 35.
27   Lawrence, *op. cit.*, p. 54.
28   Coleman, *op. cit.*, pp. 212-213.
29   W. Barrow Wall, "On the Farming of Pembrokeshire", *J.R.A.S.E.*, Ser., ii, 23, 1887, p. 78.
30   *Carmarthen News*, May 16th, 1879, p. 14.
31   Carm. R.O. Castell Gorford MS. B. 178.
32   Barrow Wall, *op. cit.*, p. 78.
33   Clark. *op. cit.*, p. 70. As early as 1800, Thomas Johnes of Hafod was crossing local stock with Hereford bulls, the progeny being fattened in the 'beast house' at Hafod. *A Cardiganshire Landlord's advice to his Tenants*, Hafod, 1800, pp. 78-79.
34   J Evans, *Letters written during tours through South Wales*, London, 1804, p. 32.
35   N.L.W. MS. 1659.
36   *Victoria County History of Berkshire*, II, p. 324.
37   N.L.W. MS. 13147A.
38   N.L.W. MS. 1659.

39   Read, *op. cit.*, p. 140.

40   S Lewis, *A Topographical Dictionary of Wales*, London, 1833, sub. nom.

41   C. Hassall. *General View of the Agriculture of the County of Monmouth*, London, 1812, p. 14.

42   *Farmer's Journal*, January 26th 1824, p. 73.

43   S. Lewis, *op. cit.*, sub. nom.

44   N.L.W. (Tredegar) 57/336, Bradley's letter provides further support for Lewis' contentions: "I certainly have had a struggle to redeem the merit of the breed which had almost become extinct through the neglect of our county farmers who, during the period of our last protracted warfare were reduced to break up most of our rich and valuable pastures for the purpose of cultivating corn which bore such an enormous price during those times."

45   Davies, (South Wales), *op. cit.*, p. 219.

46   J Clark, *General View of the Agriculture of the County of Radnorshire*, London, 1797, p. 13.

47   H. Keary. *op. cit.*, p. 440.

48   T. Rees, *op. cit.*, p. 406.

49   W. Davies, *General View of the Agriculture of South Wales*, London, 1815, p. 219.

50   Read, *op. cit.*, p. 140.

51   J. Morgan, *Powysland Club*, XIX, 1889, p. 113.

52   Davies, (North Wales), *op. cit.*, p. 313.

53   *Ibid.*, p. 313.

54   R.C.L.W.M, *Report*, B. P. P. XXXVI. p. 748.

55   Davies, (North Wales), *op. cit.*, p. 311.

56   Lewis, *op. cit.*, sub. nom. As early as 1707 it was observed that, "A good sort for fattening on barren or middling land are your Angleseys or Welsh." (J. Mortimer, *The Whole Art of Husbandry*, London, 1707).

57   In Coleman, *op. cit.*, p. 209.

58   W. H. Beever, "Notes on fields and cattle", London, 1870, p. 21.

59   Davies, (North Wales), op, cit., p. 312.

60   Lawrence, *op. cit.*, p. 56.

61   Youatt, *op. cit.*, p. 4.

62   Lewis, *op. cit.*, sub. nom.

63   Davies, (North Wales), *op. cit.*, p. 312.

64   Davies, (North Wales), op, cit., p. 315.

65   *Ibid.*, p. 315.

66   Rowlandson, *op. cit.*, p. 582.

67   Davies, (North Wales), *op. cit.*, p. 319.

68   G.E. Fussell, "The size of cattle in the Eighteenth Century", *Agricultural History*, 3, 1929, p. 160-81.

69   Charles Gordon Grey, *Letters to the Bath Society*, X, 1805.

70   R. Parkinson, *Treatise on the breeding and management of Livestock*, London, 1810, Vol.1, p. 53.

71   *Gentleman's Magazine,* Aug. 1801, See also *Gentleman's Mag.*, May 1801 and July 1802, and *Farmer's Mag.*, Jan. 1800.

72   J.B. McDonald, *J.R.A.S.E.*, Ser. ii, 18, 1881, p. 339.

74   18 Car. II, cap. 2, 1666.

75   Kay, *op, cit.*, p.14. For an admirable account of life on the *hafod* and *hendre,* see R. U. Sayce, *Montgomeryshire Collections*, LIII-LIV (1953-56) & LV (1957-58). To some extent, the system might be said to have survived in the contemporary practice of "tacking" sheep on the lowlands during the winter months.

76   B.P.P. XXXIII. Appendix D.

77   For an extended treatment of this subject see D. Williams, *The Rebecca Riots*, Cardiff, 1971, p. 79 et seq.

78   Leland, *Itinerary in Wales*, Pt. VI, L.T. Smith (ed), London, 1906, pp. l22-3.

79   Lewis, *op. cit.*, (Brecknockshire entry).

80   *Select Committee on Commons Inclosure*, 1844, B. P. P. VII. pp. 335-8.

81   *Ibid.*, p. l05.

82   Kay, *op. cit.*, p. 7.

83   Lloyd and Turnor, *op. cit.*, p. 21. While references to clover, sainfoin and trefoil occur regularly in early nineteenth century correspondence and demesne farm material, they appear to have been infrequently used by the hill farming tenantry in the first thirty years of the century. Fussell has indicated that they were introduced in Glamorgan in 1796 with very little success. (*Morgannwg I*, 1957 pp. 31-34). Unfortunately, the probate inventories studied for this book fail to clarify the situation, as they do not specify the nature of the hay stores belonging to the deceased farmer.

84   University College of North Wales (Penrhyn) MS 1740 (3).

85   Lloyd & Turnor, *op. cit.*, p. 14.

86   Lewis, *op. cit.*, (Brecknockshire entry).

87   Davies (North Wales), *op. cit.*, p. 141.

88   S Meyrick, *The History and Antiquities of Cardigan*, London, 1805, p. 249.

89   W. Barrow Wall, *op. cit.*, p. 89.

90   In South Cardiganshire at the turn of the present century virtually no use was made of either artificial fertilisers or artificial feeds. (D.Jenkins, *The Agricultural Community in South Wales*, Cardiff, 1971, p. 59.)

91   Rowlandson, *op. cit.*, p. 566.

92   W.H. Keary, *op. cit.*, p. 441. Walter Davies in 1815 drew attention to the complaints voiced by the compilers of the quarto "*General Views*" to the effect that the farm buildings throughout Wales were totally inadequate. He maintained, however, that since the turn of the century more buildings had been erected than throughout the previous 40 years, and, "many instances of the cases of complaint which then existed are now removed." He observed, significantly, that Brecknockshire landlords had taken more interest in building improvement than other landed proprietors, attributing the probable cause to the early establishment of an Agricultural Society in that county. (Davies (S. Wales) I, *op. cit.*, p. 128).

93   Evans, *op. cit.*, p. 326. In his "*beast-house*" at Hafod, Thomas Johnes had constructed an internal conduit into which dung and urine were thrown through two-foot apertures between each pair of feeding stalls. (Davies (South Wales) II, *op. cit.*, p. 117.)

94   A similar practice was pursued in Ireland (R. H. Pringle. *J.R.A.S.E.*, Ser. ii. 8, 1872, p. 58.)

95   UC.N.W. Mostyn MS. 6607.

96   However, in the valuation report of the Vaynol Estate, Caernarvonshire, of 1799, it was suggested that the tenants "be restrained from the incouragement (sic) of gorot (sic) unless on some rockey (sic) parts." (Vaynol MS 4019, quoted by R. 0. Roberts, *Farming in Caernarvonshire around 1800*, Denbigh, 1973.)

97   N.L.W. (Aberpergwm) MS. 1258.

98   Thomas Johnes in 1800, was using powdered oilcake as a fertiliser for turnips, while Colonel Brooks of Noyadd near Lampeter was informed by one of his correspondents that rape dust was "by far the best artificial manure." (N.L.W. 11727 D; N.L.W. Lucas, 643). Further correspondence between Brooks and a Liverpool merchant reveals the latter purchasing both oilcake and rape dust (N.L.W. Lucas, 631-2).

99   The Carmarthen *Welshman* of 10th December 1841 published a breakdown of weather conditions from 1816-41. This is reproduced *verbatim* as Appendix I.

100   *Farmers Magazine*, September 1800, p. 485.

101   *Ibid.*, March 1801, p. 235.

102   *Ibid.*, October, 1801, p. 487.

103   *Ibid.*, January 1802, p. 124.

104 E. H. Whetham, "Livestock Prices in Britain 1851-93", In *Essays in Agrarian History*, W. E. Minchinton ed., Newton Abbot, 1968, Vol. II, p. 203.

105 D. Howell, *Welsh Agriculture 1815-1914*, unpublished Ph.D. Thesis, University of London, 1969.

106 *Farmers Magazine*, July 1816, p. 356.

107 The Board of Agriculture, *The Agricultural State of the Kingdom in February, March and April 1816*, B.P.P. 1, p. 93.

108 *Ibid.*, p. 90. From a meeting of gentlemen, freeholders and clergy held at Aberaeron in March 1816 under the chairmanship of John Lloyd of Mabws a petition concerning the plight of the country was sent to Parliament. A similar petition was despatched by Caernarvonshire Agriculture Society in April (*The Cambrian*, March 30th, 1816; *North Wales Gazette*, 11th April, 1816).

109 *Farmers Magazine*, January 1817, p. 126. The appalling weather of 1816 resulted in virtual famine on many farms. Moreover, the collapse of some country banks caused widespread suffering, particularly among the smaller hill farmers, many of whom emigrated to the New World.

110 N.L.W. Harcourt Powell MSS. (unnumbered).

111 D. Williams, *A History of Modern Wales*, (1969 edn.) p. 168. John Miller, agent on Lord Kensington's Pembrokeshire estates explained to his master in March 1818, "The weather is now more like December than March, the ground is so wet that it is impossible to sow any corn and it is unfavourable for the lambing. Immense numbers of sheep have died of the rot. Lord Milford's flock are almost all dead." (N.L.W.Lucas, MS 3101). By mid August, "Almost every one of your tenants in the district of Llanfrynach has been under the necessity of buying their bread corn since seed time... butter brings a good price, wool sells well but cattle are almost unsaleable from the excessive drought in England." (N.L.W. Lucas, MS 3102.)

112 B.P.P. II. 1821, p. 703. Herbert Evans, Highmead to Col. Lloyd, Noyadd, May 12th 1821, "Newcastle(Emlyn) fair two days ago went off smartly. Every head sold and as I was told by one of my own tenants, at a very fair price." (N.L.W. Lucas, 625).

113 N.L.W. Tredegar MS. 106/677.

114 N.L.W. Lucas. 3240.

115 D. Lleufer Thomas, *Digest of the Report of the Welsh Land Commission*, London, 1896, p. 53.

116 *Farmers Magazine*, July 1837, p. 16.

117 R. Davies, A defence of the Agricultural Interest, quoted by E. L. Jones, *Seasons and Prices*, London, 1964.

118 N.L.W. 9600-9614. Writing to her agent in Wales in July 1846, Mrs. Sophia Paynter, keen to increase the rent roll from her Welsh estate in order to maintain her household in Bath and to finance her frequent European tours, pointed out that, "Times seem so good that farmers must be making well and I hope rents will rise for here the prices of everything have risen in a most alarming manner." (N.L.W. Behrens, MS 510.)

119 N.L.W. Gwredog, MS 35.

120 Merioneth R.O. D/O/543/6.

121 Haverfordwest R.O. DX/ 130/7. In his Journal for 1849, George Bowen of Ffynone, Pembrokeshire drew attention to the low prices prevailing at the July and September fairs in that county. At Haverfordwest on September 24th he sold twelve cattle for £4.5s., "it was the cheapest fair that ever was." (N.L.W. 6641 B.)

122 *Farmers Magazine*, May 1859, p. 550.

123 *Ibid.*, September 1862, p. 362.

124 R.C.L.W.M. 1894, B.P.P. XXXVII, p. 393.

125 Lleufer Thomas, *op. cit.*, p. 349.

126 *Ibid.*, p. 349.

127   Caernarvon RO. Vaynol 3110.

128   Caernarvon R.O. Vaynol 3074.

129   Caernarvon R.O. Vaynol 3075.

130   N.L.W. (Ellis) 2068.

131   J.H. Clapham, *An Economic History of Modern Britain 1850-1886*, Cambridge, 1952, p. 282. In his study of bankruptcies in Victorian Britain, P. J. Perry has highlighted the pronounced differences between the arable and livestock rearing areas in respect of agricultural bankruptcies during the Depression. In Wales, failures were rare throughout the whole depression period. In 1881/3, for example, a relatively significant level of bankruptcy was recorded only in the counties of Glamorgan and Denbigh, both of which grew a substantial acreage of cereals by comparison with other Welsh counties. Moreover, rent abatements and reductions rarely exceeded 10 per cent in western Britain. (P.J. Perry, (ed.) *British Agriculture 1875-1914*, London, 1973, p. xxx & xxvi.)

132   D. G. Davies, "Welsh Agriculture during the "Great Depression 1873-96", Unpublished M.Sc (Econ) thesis, University of Wales, 1973, pp. 92-3.

133   Whetham, *op. cit.*, p. 29.

134   R.C.L.W.M., 1894, B.P.P. XXXVII, p. 678.

135   *Ibid.*, 1895, B.P.P. XL. p. 161.

136   Davies D. G., *op. cit.*, p. 83. Over the same period store cattle prices fell by a modest 13 per cent. (*Ibid.*, p. 93).

137   These wills, deposited in the National Library of Wales, were proven in the Archdeacon's Court of one of the following dioceses; Llandaff, St. Davids (which included most of the present-day diocese of Brecon and Swansea). St. Asaph and Bangor. While approximately a fifth of the wills included probate inventories, the majority merely have attached to them a statement of the personal estate of the deceased as sworn by his executor or executrix. For adiscussion of marine trading off Anglesey. see A. Eames, *Ships and Seamen of Anglesey 1558-1918,* Denbigh, 1973.

THE CATTLE DROVERS IN WELSH SOCIETY

3

The physical environment of much of Wales has always imposed severe limitations upon the evolution of farming systems. A comparative absence of good quality pasture together with a climate unsuited to the conserving of adequate forage for the winter maintenance of cattle has, until relatively recent years, prevented the development of large scale fat cattle production except on the lowland fringes. Moreover, soil type and elevation are such that in many parts of Wales the growing of cereal crops is extremely difficult.

Historically, the small acreage of cereals grown on the individual farm, particularly in upland Wales, was used for the subsistence of the family and perhaps for feeding the household pig which often represented the principal source of animal protein available to the family over the winter months. Only on the larger lowland farms was a surplus of cereal grains available for cattle fattening. It might also be argued that even if widespread cattle fattening had been feasible, the thinly distributed population of Wales, many of whom lived close to subsistence level, would not have created sufficient demand for meat and meat products. This would certainly have been the case in the period prior to the Industrial Revolution.

In England, however, not only was the environment more amenable to corn growing, but also rich pastures were available in abundance for the conversion of lean animals into beef. Thus, there developed, over the centuries, a flourishing export trade in store cattle between Wales and the rich pasturelands of the midland and southern counties. Evidence for the significance of this export trade to the domestic economy of both England and Wales is provided by the extensive illicit trading which took place during the Glyndŵr rebellion when all transactions between the English and Welsh were prohibited. Even so, despite the preventative measures taken by the bailiffs, cattle from Wales were still brought into the western hundreds of Cheshire.[1] The importance of cattle sales to the economy of Wales is apparent also from the frequent and ever growing number of law suits relating to cattle from the fifteenth century onwards. In particular, among cases heard before the Court of Star Chamber in Wales, offences relating to the stealing of cattle feature prominently.[2,3] In 1525, when the people of the lordship of Brecon petitioned the King concerning their extreme poverty, they complained that they: "... had but little sale or utterance of beasts or cattle, which is the chief commodity in these parts."[4]

By the mid-seventeenth century, cattle sales had become the mainstay of the economy, as evidenced by the much-quoted letter written by Bishop John Williams of Bangor to Prince Rupert, in which the Bishop implored the Prince to permit the passage of the Welsh drovers into England: "... for they are the Spanish fleet of Wales which brings in what little gold and silver we have." [5] At the same time Williams wrote to an anonymous official requesting that the bearer, David Lloyd: "a very substantial drover of these parts", be allowed to ply his trade and "to move quietly through your parts."[6]

Following the seizure of nine hundred cattle from eighteen Welsh drovers in March 1645, the House of Commons ordered:

"... that Mr. Speaker shall have Power to grant Passes to such Persons as he shall think fit, that shall desire to trade for the Buying of cattle in Wales and to drive and bring them to London." [7]

It is unlikely, in view of widespread Welsh support for the Royalist cause, that such an order would have been made unless the cattle trade had been essential to the economy of Wales, and for that matter, the economy of England.[8]

Undoubtedly there were sporadic movements of cattle from Wales into England since the very earliest times, and the possible existence of a regular traffic in cattle between the two countries during the pre-Norman period is particularly intriguing. Although Sir Cyril Fox noted the presence of several recognisable traffic gaps in the great dyke constructed by the Mercian King Offa in c.780, he tended to give a rather low assessment of their importance.[9] It is a fact, nevertheless, that at least one of these gaps, that on Spoad Hill on the Radnorshire-Herefordshire border, lies on a drove road in use during the last quarter of the nineteenth century. In addition to the gaps noted by Fox, there must almost certainly have been other openings in the dyke, particularly in the vales and lowlands, which have subsequently become obscured by more recent agricultural practices. It is tempting, although perhaps a little contentious, to suggest that where these openings coincide with an established drove track, the track may be of considerable antiquity.

The tenth century *"Ordinance concerning the Dunsaetae"* was an agreement drawn up by the English Witan and the borderland tribe of the Dunsaetae in c.926 and was concerned with border arrangements across the lower reaches of the River Wye.[10] The Ordinance sets out provisions for the control of cattle stealing, and also strongly indicates the existence of a legitimate cattle trade between the Dunsaetae and the English. In particular, the Ordinance refers to established cattle "tracks" on both sides of the river bank, and reference is made to the consequences of a track being wrongly followed. It is clear from the context that a track being wrongly followed implied that the track was being used for the trafficking of stolen cattle. The converse would seem to suggest that the normal use of the tracks was for the legitimate movement of cattle across the river, which at this time delineated the border of the lands of the Dunsaetae.

If this Ordinance, drawn up by King Athelstan and his advisers, was based upon either texts or oral traditions arising from the regulations for Offa's Dyke, there would seem to be some justification for the assertion that a legitimate cattle trade was in existence from the late eighth century. This apart, the earliest indication of the Welsh cattle trade relates to the granting, at Newent, of an annual fair and weekly market to the Norman abbot of Cormeilles in 1253. In consequence, "... the Welshmen who come from the parts of Wales to sell their cattle" deviated from their normal route in order to trade in Newent.[11, 12]

From the beginning of the fourteenth century frequent references occur to cattle being taken from Wales into England for a variety of purposes. In 1312, for instance, the Chamberlains of Carmarthen and North Wales were ordered to supply between them some nine hundred oxen for use in the King's household at Windsor, while several years later, in 1317, the Bishop of Winchester sent John de Radynges into North Wales to purchase cattle for the household of the Chancery. [13] Among the Minister's accounts of the Earldom of Chester, reference is made to oxen being purchased at Ruthin and Abergele in 1347/48, while the Earl of Chester's stock keeper accounted for seventy-five cattle from Rhys ap Iowerth ap Ithel and Iowerth ap Madoc in 1356/57.[14] The export trade in cattle from Anglesey, which was to achieve such prominence in the eighteenth and nineteenth centuries, appears to have been in existence in the early fifteenth century. Thus the Minister's accounts for 1407 refer to a sum of 34s. over three years "... for the passage of beasts at Porthaitho by divers persons."[15]

The presence of Welsh cattle drovers in the midlands by the mid-fifteenth century is apparent from the accounts of John Broome of Baddesley Clinton, who purchased at Birmingham Fair in 1445, twelve oxen from Gruff Hope Wallace.[16] Later in the same century, Henry Tudor, on his long march to Bosworth Field, was joined near Welshpool by William ap Griffiths of Penrhyn and Richard ap Howell of Mostyn, both of whom brought with them large herds of black cattle for the sustenance of the army.[17] In the diary of Dr. John Dee, the Elizabethan philosopher and mystic, there occur several interesting comments relating to cattle being driven from Wales. In 1596 Dee was appointed to the Wardenship of Manchester. On August 10th of that year:

"Mr. Thomas Jones of Tregaron came to me at Manchester and rode towards Wales bak agayin the

This building in Llandovery was formerly the Black Ox Bank, but perhaps not where it first opened for business. See page 62

13th day to mete the cattail coming."
By September 5th Dee had received:
"... seventeen head of cattail from my kinsfolk in Wales by the courteous Griffith David, nephew of Mr. Thomas Griffiths bought."
Thomas Griffiths was Dee's cousin from Lampeter, while his nephew Griffith David was a drover. Not only did Dee receive beasts via his Welsh kinsmen, but he also sent his servant Roger Kay on several occasions to Vandyles (Llanidloes?) in order to procure cattle.[18]

Notwithstanding the uncharitable criticisms levelled at them by eighteenth and nineteenth century observers, the drovers played a vital part in the forging of an economic and cultural link between England and Wales beneficial to both countries. Prior to the extensive exploitation of the mineral resources of South Wales, the "export" of store cattle, and to a lesser extent, pigs, sheep, wool and leather, provided the major inflow of wealth to much of rural Wales. Moreover, as the trade proliferated and expanded, links were forged between the less accessible areas of Wales and the towns of central and southern England, by which news of political, social, cultural and religious development was transmitted from east to west and west to east by the drovers and dealers involved in the trade. In addition to their straightforward trading function the drovers had often been responsible for the execution of financial transactions and the conveyance of mail and other goods. This was particularly so in the sixteenth and seventeenth centuries when communications between Wales and the remainder of Britain were extremely limited. On April 19th 1585, Sir George Chaworth explained to the Countess of Rutland that:
"... I have done my best to procure you some money to be paid in London, but I could not do so as most of the drovers who were likely to have served you had already gone to London." [19]
Material preserved among the Wynn papers sheds interesting light on this aspect of the droving

saga. David Lloyd, a tenant of the Wynn estates, frequently combined his activities as a drover with the transmission of correspondence and money between various members of the Wynn family. In 1624, Henry Wynn wrote to his father, Sir John, complaining of the small sum sent him in London by David Lloyd.[20] Almost forty years later, Lloyd was still actively involved in the cattle trade. Writing to Sir Richard Wynn in 1661, Robin Hughes explained that the £65 which Sir Richard had ordered the writer to send to London had been paid to "old David Lloyd, the drover", who was bound by his bill of exchange to pay this sum through Henry Maurice of the King's Head tavern in Fleet Street.[21]

By 1671, however, Lloyd had disappeared from the scene. Nevertheless, the Wynns continued to employ the services of drovers for the execution of financial transactions, the name of Thomas Hewes featuring frequently in this context.[22] By the mid-eighteenth century improved transport had reduced the importance of the drovers as a means of communication, yet William Bulkeley was still trusting to their services in order to forward money to his sons in the Metropolis. In the mid-seventeen thirties, for example, he is recorded as having sent sums of £15 and £20 to his son by way of the drover Thomas Lewis of Trefeibion Meyrig, while in 1741 he employed the services of another drover, Hugh Lloyd, for the delivery of £60 to London.[23]

The exchange of correspondence between the Rev. Thomas Jones of Creaton in Northamptonshire and the Rev. Thomas Charles of Bala reveals the former requesting Thomas Charles to send him books and pamphlets by way of the Welsh drovers.[24] As a subsequent chapter will show, the drovers generally avoided travelling during the winter months. In this respect, a letter received in 1637 by Richard Bulkeley from his cousin in Newborough, Anglesey is of interest:

> "... we pray you endeavour that our money (i.e. the Ship Money) be paid by November 1st yearly as we cannot return our money (to London) otherwise than by drovers."

More than a century later, the delivery of the North Wales taxes to London was to some extent determined by the seasonal activities of the drovers. In 1743, the Receiver General of Taxes for North Wales, one Mr. Bull, was threatened with prosecution by the Treasury for failing to send the tax to the capital. Bull, however, contended:

> "that he had very few opportunities of remitting the moneys but by the drovers, and desires indulgence from Candlemas to the beginning of May, in which time the drovers transact all their affairs." [25]

The involvement of the drovers in the collection of the Denbighshire Ship Money is well known and well documented in the Domestic Series of the Calendar of State Papers. The collection and delivery of the Ship Money did not always proceed smoothly. Hugh Lloyd, Sheriff of Denbigh, was informed in 1636 that although the money had been delivered, "by sufficient men who are drovers of that county", it had not been paid in, owing to the presence of the plague in the City of London. Occasionally, it would seem, the drovers defaulted on their commission safely to deliver the Ship Money. Writing to Kenrick Endisbury in 1637, Richard Lloyd explained that:

> "... My nephew Wynne, the new sheriff of Co. Denbigh, having been entrusted with the collection of the Ship Money, entrusted a drover with the return of £400, in payment whereof the drover has disappointed him, whereby he is in danger of being committed before the Lords." [26]

The temptation to abscond with large sums of money must have been very great indeed, although cases of default were almost certainly rare for had they been of more frequent occurrence the authorities would doubtless have had recourse to some alternative means of sending the money to the capital. The legal material of the eighteenth and nineteenth centuries highlights individual cases of dishonesty and betrayal of trust, while contemporary observers often drew attention to the drovers' lack of integrity and scruples. Such cases, however, would tend to attract the attention of commentators and occasion vituperative accusations levelled at the droving fraternity in general. It should not be overlooked that for every drover convicted of fraudulent activities there must have been many others who plied their trade honestly and diligently, enjoying the implicit trust of the farmers with whom they dealt and the landowners by whom they were employed. These were the men whose contributions to the promotion of Welsh literature, both secular and religious, to the development of banking and to lay preaching within the nonconformist fold, played such a fundamental role in Welsh life.

This building may have been where the Black Ox Bank first opened for business in Llandovery in 1799

A great deal has been written about the contribution of the drovers to the cultural and social life of Wales. This is rightly so, especially before the nineteenth century when mobility was restricted and a relatively small proportion of the working population had the opportunity of travelling far beyond their home villages. The drovers enjoyed the advantages of extensive contact with English culture, social life, farming systems and financial matters, besides representing an essential communications link with England. Thus, Edmund Hyde Hall's observation that "the drovers are distinguished persons in the history of this country's economy" was by no means an overstatement.[27]

Moreover, throughout many parts of Wales there remains a rich tradition of "drovers' tales." If it is accepted that stories, sometimes apocryphal, of "characters" become enshrined in folk memory, then the drovers must have been persons of considerable local importance. While the bulk of the drovers doubtless made little contribution to life outside their own communities, there are numerous examples to illustrate the profound influence of individuals on the cultural, spiritual and financial life of Wales.

One of the finest of seventeenth century Welsh poets, Edward Morus of Perthi Llwydion, regularly plied his trade as a drover between North Wales and Essex, where he was regarded by local farmers as being of unimpeachable character.[28] More than once did drovers lend financial support to the publication of Welsh literature, both sacred and profane, as indicated by the following list of subscribers to various literary enterprises.[29]

Drover Subscribers to Welsh Publications

Rhys Jones: Gorchestion Beirdd Cymru (1773)
Hugh Jones of Bala, Drover
Mr. Hugh Jones, Drover
Thomas Jones, Ty-Isaf, Drover
Mr. Hugh Parry of Penmorfa, Drover
John Thomas of Bala, Drover
The Holy Bible: Carmarthen (1779)
John Watkins, Drover, Narberth
John Bunyan: Dull priodas mab y Brenin Alpha (1758)
Robert Jones, Drover, Llangwm
Timothy Thomas: Traethiad am y wisg-wen ddisglair (1759)
Mr. David Jones, Dderi, Drover
Mr. William Jones, Nant-henfol, Drover
Thomas Edwards: Gardd o gerddi (1790)
Mr. Robert Evans, Eglwysfach, Drover
David Jones: Udgorn Sion (1859)
Mr. Evan Evans, Cattle dealer, Anglesey
Dafydd Jones: Blodeu-gerdd Cymry (1759)
Mr. Thomas Jones, Pengwern, Drover

The establishment of an efficient system of banking in west Wales was made possible by the pioneering efforts of certain drovers, while others became deeply involved in the business life of the country.[30,31] The cause of Nonconformity was also well served by several members of the droving fraternity. The Pembrokeshire drover, Benjamin Evans, became pastor of Llanuwchllyn in 1769, and among the many ministers of Yr Hen Gapel he was perhaps the best known and most loved.[32] Another drover, William Jones of Trawsfynydd (1770 –1837), having been converted by the preaching of William Romaine, began his own preaching career in 1802.[33] The celebrated Dafydd Jones of Caeo (1711–77), the great hymnologist, achieved a mastery of the English language as a result of his activities as a drover. After his "conversion" he put his fluency in English to good purpose by translating the hymns of Isaac Watts in addition to writing his own Welsh hymns often using imagery reflecting his earlier calling. There is a picturesque local story in the Beulah-Llanwrtyd area relating to Jones' renunciation of his former life style and his embracing of the Christian ethic. Seemingly Jones was returning from one of his droving enterprises when he was attracted by singing from the old chapel at Troed-rhiw-dalar. On entering the chapel, it is said, he was so deeply moved by the preacher that he was dramatically converted. It is equally likely, however, that Jones' conversion took place in Brecon where he is known to have listened to the open air sermons of John Wesley.[34]

It will be seen subsequently that the cattle dealer and drover in the eighteenth and nineteenth centuries was regarded with mistrust and suspicion by many of his contemporaries. It is true, nevertheless, that from among the ranks of the drovers arose many men of the highest integrity and cultural attainment, whose contribution to the economic and social life of their times was of the greatest importance.

Legislation concerning the cattle trade

In Tudor and Elizabethan Britain travelling was both difficult and dangerous. Footpads lurked by the roadside, vagrancy was widespread and life was relatively cheap. Consequently, a long journey by a merchant, tradesman or any other citizen was not undertaken without a certain degree of trepidation. Until the passing of two statutes which carefully set out the conditions under which they could ply their trade, the Welsh drovers had been liable for arrest under the vagrancy laws. Hence the cryptic observation that "Most of these that walke about be Welchemen."[35] However, an attempt was made to reduce the extent of vagrancy by the statutes of 5 & 6 Ed. VI, cap 14, 21 and 39 Eliz. I, cap 12. It was necessary, under the terms of these statutes, for a drover or dealer to be a married householder of above 30 years of age, and not a hired servant. If he could fulfil these conditions, the drover was free to apply to the local Quarter Sessions for a licence, which, if granted, cost him the sum of 12d. At the cost of a further 8d. the drover was bound to register the licence with the Clerk of the Peace who recorded his name and dwelling place, together with details of the type of licence granted.

An Order in the Council of the Marches of Wales at Ludlow in 1617 noted that many drovers were disregarding the statutory requirement for a licence. The Lord President had apparently been in-formed of the numerous wrongs perpetrated by unlicensed drovers, most of whom were:

"... suspicious and base persons of evil name and of little or no worth... who under cover of driving their droves... not only receive cattle stolen by thieves, but themselves do steal by the way other men's cattle or sheep."

It was ordered, therefore, that drovers might only follow their calling if they were: "known to be honest men of good sufficiency according to the statutes." Furthermore, any drover found without a licence was to be apprehended and brought before the Council.[36] Transgression generally resulted in a fine of £5 together with a prison sentence under a charge of vagrancy. Details of licences were frequently set down in Quarter Sessions Order Books, which accordingly represent a useful means of establishing the identity of drovers who may have been active in a particular area. In April 1709, it was ordered in the Shrewsbury Quarter Sessions:

"... that all badgers and drovers appear at next sessions to take licences, and such as refuse be prosecuted according to the law."

No doubt pressure was applied in some cases, for in July of the same year, the Order Book records that the justices instructed the high constable:

"... to take care that all badgers, drovers, etc. be presented at the next Sessions."[37]

The Order Books contain numerous references to personnel involved in the droving trade. Thus, in 1719, Joseph Harryman of Much Wenlock was licensed to be a buyer and seller of cattle, while in 1765 and subsequently in 1770:

"... Thomas Hinton of Whitchurch, butcher, was licensed by three of his Majesty's justices to be a common drover of cattle for one next year ensuing."[38]

Although the Order Book does not record the fact, it is highly likely that Hinton, being a butcher would have provided:

> *"recogniscances not to sell any cattell by him brought within the distance of sixty miles where he brought the same."*

Such recogniscances were required by both graziers and butchers under 22 and 23 Chas. II, cap 19 (1670) before droving licences were granted. It was believed that this measure would reduce local price inflation.

Substantial penalties were levied on unlicensed drovers for forestalling and regrating, while those in possession of licences were theoretically protected against charges concerned with forestalling. Essentially, the various ancient statutes relating to forestalling and regrating aimed to reduce the disrupting effect of these practices on the normal processes of supply and demand and thus of fair competition in local markets and fairs. Clearly, if cattle were sold en route for the fair, supply would be reduced, and thus the selling price inflated. Moreover, tollowners would suffer loss of revenue as a result of cattle not passing through the fair.[39] During the reign of Edward III, a series of statutes had emphasised the illegality of pre-fair trading, while under 3 & 4 Ed. VI, cap 18, 19 (1551-2) it was enacted that:

> *"... no person shall buy or commune and conclude to buy, any manner of oxen, steers, Runts, Kine, Heyfers and Calves, but only in the open fair or market, where the same shall happen to be bought or put to sale, and shall not sell the same again alive in that market or fair... upon pain of the forfeiture of the double value of such cattle."*

The second part of this statute was extended by 5 & 6 Ed. VI, cap 14 (1552) which forbade speculative traders from re-selling cattle within five weeks of the initial purchase. The burgesses of Carmarthen condemned the "fraudulent and illegal practices of drovers and jobbers" at a meeting in 1764, resolving that the stipulations of 3 & 4 Ed.VI be "strictly put into execution", and that those drovers buying and re-selling cattle at the same fairs be suppressed.[40] The tolls from the fair held at Newport, Monmouthshire, had been granted to the town burgesses by Edward VI. In 1843, the burgesses petitioned the Lords Commissioners of the Treasury with the complaint that the annual toll had been severely reduced:

> *"... owing in great degree to the drovers of cattle selling their stock at home and elsewhere, where better prices may be obtained."* [41]

While the statute of 5 & 6 Ed. VI, cap 14 was repealed in 1772, the final repeal of the remaining offences of forestalling, regrating and engrossing was not effected until 1844.[42,43] Even so, the authorities in some areas attempted to limit the extent of forestalling by means of local statutes and by-laws. Thus in 1852, the Portreeve of Usk issued a proclamation which declared that:

> *"... persons repeating the offence of forestalling the market after this notice will be punished with the utmost rigour."* [44]

An interesting glimpse of the cattle trade in Tudor Wales is provided by two statutes enacted during the reign of Henry VIII. It appears that during the sixteenth century, cattle straying from droves had frequently been seized by local people and subsequently claimed as their own property. Under the terms of 27 Hen. VIII, cap 7 (1535/6), however, this practice was deemed illegal. Thus, if cattle straying from a drove into the possession of another party were claimed by their original owner, the person finding the cattle was bound to return them within a year and a day.[45] Contravention of this statute rendered the offender liable to a fine of twice the value of the cattle concerned. By way of further reducing the incidence of cattle stealing, 34 and 35 Hen. VIII, cap 26 (1542) stipulated that no person could buy or sell cattle in Wales:

> *"... unless he can bring forth sufficient and credible witness of the name of the person (and) what place he bought the same."*

Infringement of this statute resulted in the offender being subject to an unspecified punishment as determined by the President of the Council. In spite of Ellis Wynne's reference to the drovers as "The very worst kind of highwaymen", and subsequently of the uncharitable comments of Twm o'r Nant, only occasional early references to the conviction of a Welsh drover for stealing have been found.[46] Thus, in 1634, Humphrey Davies, a drover of Guilsfield, Montgomeryshire, was committed to gaol in Northampton for stealing two heifers, the property of Edward Taylor of Stretton-upon-Dunsmore in Warwickshire.[47] There are, however, frequent cases in Quarter Sessions and Great Sessions records which would tend to support the view, widely held by contemporaries, that in spite of their valuable role in the economy of rural Wales, some of the drovers were not overburdened with an excess of scruples and honesty.

Before the late eighteenth century when the country banks began to finance much of the cattle trade, it had been the practice of drovers to borrow cash or, more frequently, to obtain credit from affluent local farmers and tradesmen in order to purchase cattle. It seems that a great deal of the distrust of the drovers arose from this habit of buying on credit. The practice was by no means universal, but many smaller drovers and dealers would arrange to pay for cattle purchased from the Welsh farmers on their return from the English fairs. If, as was often the case, shortage of keep reduced the demand for Welsh cattle in England, the drover was forced to sell at a loss and was accordingly unable to meet his obligations on his return to Wales. Thus as Hyde Hall pointed out:

"The speculation does not always succeed and the bankruptcy of the drover leaves his creditors with but a very small dividend." [48,49]

The statute of 6 Anne, cap 22 (1706), which forbade drovers from declaring themselves bankrupt, was apparently rarely enforced.[50] One writer, discussing livestock improvement in Caernarvonshire in the late eighteenth century, felt that the introduction of English bulls would so improve native stock that:

"... this would be a great inducement to many drovers to come into the country with ready cash instead of credit, which is at present the practice whereby many an honest farmer is duped out of his property in whole or in part." [51]

As mentioned previously, merchants or others wishing to remit money to creditors in London, often entrusted this money to drovers. In order to avoid the possibility of being robbed en route for England many drovers would leave this cash in safe keeping, either in their own homes or in private banks, subsequently paying the merchants' creditors from the proceeds of cattle sales in England.[52]

A reference in the Depositions by Commission out of the Exchequer of the 1730s suggests that on at least one occasion a mutually advantageous pact was forged between a member of the tax administration and a drover. Thus, one Robert Clayton, Receiver General of His Majesties Taxes for Hereford, was arraigned for his practice of lending tax money at the rate of 5 per cent to drovers for the purchase of cattle. Upon selling their cattle the drovers would then pay the sum (plus interest) owing to Clayton into the Bank of England before returning to Wales. The benefits of such an arrangement to the drovers were made clear by one David Williams who contended that the availability of cash permitted him to buy cattle at a cheaper rate than would have been possible had he been forced to obtain credit.[53]

Early in 1775 John Johnes of Dolaucothi wrote to his brother Thomas of Croft Castle in Herefordshire with the common complaint that he was having difficulty in extracting rent from his Cardiganshire tenants. The letter hints at the problems inherent in credit trading and in so doing reveals the drover and (eventually) landowner David Jones of Derry Ormond as rather less of a shining example of moral rectitude than his staunch Methodist credentials would lead one to expect:

"tis really a most dreadfull thing upon the Country to suffer so exceedingly by these villains that call themselves Drovers 'tis very wonderfull considering the losses that they every year sustain that they (the farmers) will give one day's Credit, I am in hopes most of my Tenants sold all their cattle to David Jones, but this year they seem very cautious and probably they may have had some dealings with this Rogue, which they may thank themselves for, as I desired them all in the summer not to sell their cattle upon any account but for ready money and then they cou'd go to Market again immediately – but I am afraid nothing will ease them of their folly and credulity!" [54]

The common use of the promissory note or bill could also yield problems for those placing too much trust in the abilities of the drovers to sell their animals at a profit to English buyers and to gather

The Llandovery RFC has this painting of a drover on its stand. The club are known as "The Drovers"

Exhibits in the Museum at Llandovery (above the Tourist Information Centre)

the proceeds of the transaction in hard cash. Robert Myddleton of Chirk was doubtless mortified when informed by his agent in 1732 that promissory notes from drovers totalling £450 would not be discharged because the latter had received "nothing but paper" upon selling their cattle in England.[55] Some years later the London solicitors, Kirton and Grey, enquired of Edward Jones, the Llandovery attorney, as to the circumstances of one William Thomas, farmer and drover, explaining that since one of their clients held Thomas's bill for £220 they proposed bringing a court action to secure payment, "... if there is anything to be got from him." [56]

Common though defaulters may have been, gentlemen were still prepared to rely upon drovers for the conveyance of goods and cash to England and to employ their services in the conduct of all manner of financial transactions. Presumably a landed family like the Myddletons would over the course of time build up a working relationship and forge a bond of understanding with a drover or group of drovers whose integrity they could totally trust.[57] In like manner Henry Jones of Talgarth was quite happy to entrust the return of a horse loaned to his brother, the Rev. Jones of Darrington, Yorkshire, "... by some of the drovers." This little episode, in October 1756, indicates that on occasions the Welsh drovers travelled rather further north than usual to conduct their business.[58]

Edward Jones of Llandovery seems to have spent a disproportionate amount of his time dealing with complaints as to the alleged skullduggery of drovers. In August 1775 he became embroiled in a dispute between Daniel Jones of Sunnyhill, Tregaron (?) and two drover brothers, John and William Jones of Nantyrhenfoel. The brothers, it appears, had purchased cattle (on credit) from Daniel to the value of £28 and had failed to discharge their debt. Daniel, a canny operator in the honourable Cardiganshire tradition, having discovered that William was under-age, and thereby contravening the Elizabethan statute precluding a man from dealing in cattle unless he were over 30, had persuaded the brothers to sign a partnership agreement which was clearly of questionable legality. In so doing he had hoped to bring the law to bear and thereby receive his money. However, he had clearly underestimated the cunning of the elder brother John who, in order to circumvent the law of 6 Anne, cap. 22, 1706 which forbade drovers from bankruptcy, had entered into a partnership with another 'rascally' drover, one Davies of Radnorshire, to commence a legitimate non-droving trade which would enable him to go bankrupt and defraud his creditors. Daniel was less than amused, and though expecting little from the bankruptcy gave notice that he intended to strain every sinew to force, "... the villain to give a true account of his efforts". [59]

Some years later Edward Jones received a frenzied letter from one David Jones of Nant-y-ci who, having bought certain sheep from the drover Rees Pryce, had received, in change for a £100 note, ten counterfeit guineas. Pryce, it seems, made a habit of using counterfeit coinage and though he was usually prepared to compensate his victims once they had discovered the fraud, David Jones had not been so privileged and had unwittingly passed on some of the coins to a Rhayader man who now proposed to take action against him! [60]

Other cases, held before local Quarter Sessions and elsewhere, provide a less than flattering view of the droving fraternity. Thus we find Isaac Morris of Llanddewi'r-cwm, being indicted for stealing a bay gelding in 1743 and William Jones of Llanfrothen languishing in prison after being found guilty of assaulting the widow Lowry Jones of Beddgelert in 1806.[61] Again, in 1804, William Price of Maentwrog, drover, was bound over in a recognisance of £40 to: "... hereafter demean himself as a good and loyal subject ... and be of good behaviour."[62] However much this concentrated Williams' mind it did little for his business acumen since, ten years later, he found himself in Dolgellau Gaol at the suit of John Lloyd for a debt of £16 17 0d.[63]

An interesting case, held before the Cardiganshire Great Sessions of 1793, illustrates the considerable pecuniary risks taken by persons advancing capital to those drovers who were either unable or unwilling to exploit the country banks.[64] This case was extremely complex. In essence, however, Charles Jones of Llanddewibrefi was attempting to recover debts of £1,300 from his stepfather, David Rowlands, drover of the same parish. It had been necessary for Jones to provide his stepfather with this money for the purchase of cattle:

"... otherwise he could not have gone on with the purchase for the bankers would never enable him to buy cattle."[65]

In his deposition, Jones stated that he had been forced to provide continual financial support for Rowlands in the forlorn hope that he might eventually recover the earlier loans. It also transpired during the course of the case that Rowlands, in addition to not repaying his debts, had also wilfully sold some of his stepson's cattle and appropriated the proceeds. This became clear following the evidence of Edward Abel, drover, who appeared as a witness on behalf of Jones. Seemingly Abel had been commissioned by Jones to conduct a drove of the latter's cattle to Steyning Fair in Sussex. Abel maintained that Rowlands, who was also present at Steyning, had been heard to offer one guinea to any person who might be prepared to assist him in removing a number of Jones's cattle from the drove. Assistance was apparently forthcoming, for the case records that Rowlands removed and sold twenty-seven of Jones's cattle on the evening before the fair.

A further example, involving a clear cut case of bankruptcy, is provided by the confrontation of Edward and Ellis Jones, drovers, with Thomas Owen, farmer, held at the Caernarvonshire Great Sessions of 1806.[66] The Joneses had managed to persuade Owen to give them:

"... credit and countenance in the island of Anglesea by endorsing their drafts and joining them in some notes for cattle."

Having eventually purchased their cattle, the Joneses had failed to make profitable sales in England. Accordingly they had been unable to meet the demands of their creditors, who had turned to the unfortunate Owen for settlement of the drovers' outstanding debts. Other legal documents and newspaper reports provide further information as to the doubtful integrity of some of the Welsh drovers and dealers. In the Caernarvonshire Great Sessions of 1809, we find Hugh Owen suing the drover Richard Cadwallader for debt. Apparently Owen had advanced Cadwallader money for the purchase of cattle:

"... which he hath hitherto altogether refused and still doth refuse to pay, wherefore the said Hugh said he is injured and hath sustained damage to the value of £200."

Again, in 1814, Cardiganshire Quarter Sessions dealt with the case of Thomas Lloyd versus David Evans and David Davies. Evans and Davies, two drovers, had been commissioned by Lloyd, a farmer, to purchase cattle on his behalf. For this purpose Lloyd had advanced a sum of money. However, the two drovers had 'craftily and subtly' deceived Lloyd by not delivering the purchased cattle which they disposed of on their own account.[67]

Notwithstanding the cases quoted above, evidence laid before the Committee on the Bank of England Charter suggests that many country bankers had sufficient confidence in the drovers to lend substantial sums of money on little or no security. John Wilkins of the Old Bank at Brecon, for example, was prepared to advance large amounts of cash to drovers provided their promissory notes were underwritten by 'responsible persons'. Other banks, however, such as the "Black Ox" of Llandovery, and Waters, Jones and Co., of Carmarthen had lent between £5,000 and £7,000 to drovers unable to offer any security.[68,69]

If the cases cited earlier give some credence to the 19th century adage 'Not only a drover, but a 'rogue', other evidence hints that from time to time drovers could justifiably claim to be more sinned against than sinning. The death at the hands of a highwayman of John ap Howel of Llanfihangel, drover and 17th century ancestor of the artist Thomas Jones of Pencerrig, was probably one of many cases in which drovers returning with cash from England were subject to the unwelcome attentions of highwaymen and footpads.[70] More commonly, though, business misfortunes (often beyond their control) were the drovers' undoing. Englishmen dealing with the Welsh drovers tended to assume that the latter would swindle them if they could and accordingly themselves resorted to all manner of stratagems to ensure that the boot was on the other foot. In 1768 for example, a Welsh drover at Brentwood Fair in Essex sold a group of cattle to the steward of Lord Halifax, agreeing, so he alleged, a price of 6 guineas per head. However, when he called on Halifax's man to collect his money, the drover was firmly told that the agreed price had been 5 guineas! The upshot of this unsatisfactory

Cilgerran Fair, late in the 19th Century

saga is taken up by Edward Price in a letter to Robert Myddleton at Chirk Castle:

"As luck would have it the Poor Drover had 2 of his countrymen with him when the Bargen was made and they call'd the Stuart a Rogue and told him he bt. the cattle for 6 guineas and if so I fear it makes good the old proverb; Trim Tram, like Master, like Man. The poor Drover is come up to London in order to have Mr. Wilkes' Council how to proceed to come to his money."[71]

One suspects that the drovers in the Halifax case were of a rather more pacific disposition than some of their fellows. In 1850 a drover at Barnet Fair was robbed of a sum of money by a group of pickpockets. Having succeeded in capturing one of the thieves with the help of his countrymen, he fastened the unfortunate man across the back of an unbroken colt and galloped the animal some four or five miles after which a bruised, battered and doubtless chastened pickpocket was only too ready to purchase his freedom by repaying the stolen money. Again, evidence given before the Somerset Quarter Sessions in 1657 indicates that the drover could be easily provoked into violence when he thought his interests were being threatened:

"William Jenkins with many other Welshmen treated at Thomas Hoddinot's house with Mr. William Knoyle of Sandford to buy a close of grass to put their cattle in and not agreeing they drew their swords and assaulted Mr. Knoyle, Hoddinot, the tythingman's deputy, his wife and many of them who came to part them using violent language, cudgells and stones."[72]

The account books of David Jonathan of Dehiwyd in Cardiganshire reveal that this dealer encountered great difficulty in exacting payment from some of the English graziers with whom he dealt. In January 1860, a Surrey farmer, George Hawkins, wrote to Jonathan, explaining that he was:

"... exceedingly sorry but I shall not be able to meet your last bill... I will pay the £55 in the course of a fortnight."

As things turned out, a great deal more than a fortnight elapsed before the debt was discharged. A year before, John Read of Middlesex explained to Jonathan:

"... that I have not been able to spare the money for the last lot, nor can I say exactly when I can..." [73]

Where a drover or dealer met with such unwillingness or inability to pay up, it is not surprising that he found difficulty in discharging his debts on returning to Wales.

Severe limitations on the activities of the drovers were imposed by the statute of 3 Chas. I, cap 22 (1627) and subsequently by 39 Chas. II, cap 7 (1676). The latter stipulated that:

"... noe Drover, Horsecourser, Waggoner, Butcher, Higler, their or any of their servants shall travell or come into...an Inne or lodgeing upon the Lord's Day or any part thereof...upon pain that each and every such offender shall forfeit twenty shillings for every such offence."

No doubt this statute was frequently contravened. In 1817, for example, two Welsh drovers were convicted for: "... profanation of the Sabbath in driving cattle through the village of Mordiford in Herefordshire."

It was hoped that:

"... such legal interference will tend to check a practice which has of late been too general and must have proved truly painful to the Christian observer." [74]

As late as 1886, the Anglesey dealer, John Evans, was deeply concerned about starting his journey by rail to London on a Sunday in order to be at Smithfield Market by Monday morning. As he wrote to his wife:

" I could not tell (my children) that I was going to London on the Sabbath Day, it would have grieved their hearts. It will do no good to tell your mother. It will only fret her to think how unfortunate you have been in being yoked to such an ungodly husband." [75]

It is somehow difficult to conceive of such expressions of troubled conscience flowing from the pens of the bibulous old drovers who caroused with Captain Johnes of Dolaucothi in the late eighteenth century.[76,77] Even so, John Evans' dilemma was perhaps shared by many dealers and drovers in Victorian Wales, whose account books often contain not only details of financial transactions, but also references to hymns, prayers and other manifestations of a fear of God.

FOOTNOTES FOR CHAPTER 3

1   H.J. Hewitt, *Medieval Cheshire, A Social and Economic History of Cheshire in the reigns of the three Edwards*, Manchester, 1929, p. 84.

2   I. Edwards, *Star Chamber Proceedings in Wales*, Cardiff, 1929, passim.

3   The annual tribute of 25,000 oxen imposed by Athelstan upon the Welsh suggests that cattle were also vital components of the rural economy of Wales during the tenth century. (G. Price, in *The Agrarian History of England and Wales*, Cambridge, 1972, p. 318.)

4   H. Thomas, *A History of Wales, 1415-1660*, Cardiff, 1972, p. 127.

5   A.H. Dodd, *A History of Caernarvonshire, 1284-1900*, Denbigh, 1968, p. 92.

6   *Calendar of Wynn Papers*, National Library of Wales, 1926, p. 302.

7   C. Skeel, "The Cattle Trade between Wales and England from the Fifteenth to the Nineteenth Centuries", *Trans. Royal Hist. Soc.*, ix, 1926, p. 140.

8   The Parliamentary army included at least one cattle drover among its officers; Captain Edward Taylor of Pickhill, Denbighshire, who was buried at Marchwiel in 1679, and who led a troop of horse. This stalwart was voted a reward of £200 by Parliament for personally capturing Sir John Owen, leader of the Royalist uprising in Bangor in 1648. (N. Tucker, *Denbighshire Officers in the Civil War*, Denbigh, nd., p. 131-2).

9   C. Fox, *Offa's Dyke*, 1955 edn., pp. 34-5, 112-3, 156-7.

10   I am indebted to Mr. F. Noble for kindly drawing my attention to this Ordinance.

11   H.P.R. Finberg, "An Early Reference to the Welsh Cattle Trade", *Agric. Hist. Rev.*, 2, 1954, pp. 12-14.

12   The settlement of Welsh estates on the younger sons of Norman magnates may possibly have resulted in supplies of cattle from Wales being sent to the family estates in England.

13   Calendar of Close Rolls, Ed. 11, 1309-13, p. 292.

14   Hewitt, *op. cit.*, pp. 53-4.

15   H.R. Davies, *The Conway and Menai Ferries*, B.C.S. No.8. p. 45.

16   C. Dyer, "A Small Landowner in the fifteenth century", *Midland History*, 1(3), 1972, p. 7.

17   D. Williams, (Mod. Hist.), *op. cit.*, pp. 19-20.

18   J.O. Halliwell, ed. *The Diary of Dr. John Dee*, Camden Society, 1842, passim.

19   H.M.C. Duke of Rutland MSS. Vol. I, p. 246.

20   *Calendar of Wynn Papers, op. cit.*, p. 201.

21   *Ibid.*, p. 365.

22   *Ibid.*, p. 404.

23   G Nesta Evans, *Social Life in mid Eighteenth Century Anglesey*, Cardiff, 1935, p. 122-3.

24   D.E. Jenkins, *The Rev. Thomas Charles of Bala*, II, Denbigh, 1908, p. 138.

25   *Calendar of Treasury Books*, LVIII, 1743, p. 225.

26   J.E. Lloyd, *Arch. Camb.* Ser 4, III, 1870, p. 47.

27   Edmund Hyde Hall, *A Description of Caernarvonshire, 1809-11*, (ed. E. Gwynne Jones, Caernarvon, 1952).

28   H. Ellis Hughes, *Eminent Men of Denbighshire*, Liverpool. 1946, p. 111.

29   I am indebted to Miss E. Rees of the National Library of Wales for providing me with most of the names of the subscribers on this list.

30   R.T. Jenkins, *Y Ffordd yng Nghymru*, Wrexham, 1933, p. 75.

31   F. Green, "Early Banks in West Wales", *Trans. Hist. Soc. West Wales*, 1916, pp. 129-164.

32   P.G. Hughes, *Wales and the Drovers*, London, 1943, p. 32.

33   *Dictionary of Welsh Biography*, London, 1959, p. 524.

34   Personal Communication: Professor E.G. Bowen.

35   Tawney and Porter, *Tudor Economic Documents*, London, 1924, III, p. 142.

36   "Calendar of the Records of the Borough of Haverfordwest, 1539-1660", B.C.S. No.24.

37 Salop Q.S. Order Book, April 1709.

38 Salop Q.S. Order Book, July 1770.

39 The considerable tolls demanded of drovers at local fairs were highly unpopular and only reluctantly paid. The burgesses of Dinas Mawddwy explained to the Lord of the Manor that the drovers had refused to pay toll at the Easter fair of 1843. They had drawn his attention to the fact: "... *in order that he may enforce payment there of and uphold our ancient privileges.*" (N.L.W. Schedule of Dinas Mawddwy Records 1940).

40 N.L.W. Dynevor Deeds and Documents, Parcel 4.

41 Monmouthshire R.O. TM/ B27. However, despite such complaints, "pre-fair " trading was still widely practised and the tradition of dealers purchasing cattle directly from farmers persists in Wales to this day.

42 12 Geo., III, cap 71(1772).

43 7-8 Vict., cap 24 (1844).

44 Monmouthshire R.O. D15632.

45 The necessity of impounding these animals may explain the widespread distribution of "cae pound" and "cae ffald" field names throughout Wales.

46 Ellis Wynne, *Gweledigaethau y Bardd Cwsg*, 1864 edn., pp. 19, 102.

47 Northants R.O., I.L. 1961.

48 Hyde Hall, *op. cit.*, p. 19.

49 Kay also was vehement in his condemnation of the credit system suggesting that it should be abolished. (*General View of the Agriculture of Anglesey*, London, 1794, p. 25).

50 Repealed by Statutory Law Revision, 1876.

51 Kay, (Caernarvonshire), *op. cit.*, p. 19.

52 F. Green, *op. cit.*, p. 131.

53 P. R.O. E134/8, Geo. II, Easter 8, quoted by 0. Parry, B.B.C.S. 8, (1935-7).

54 T Baynes, "Derry Ormond; sone new evidence," *NLW Journal* 22, 1981-2, pp. 218-20.

55 N.L.W. D.T.M. Jones MS. E1098.

56 N.L.W. D.T.M. Jones MS. 9100.

57 For examples see N.L.W. Chirk Castle MS. E2812; E3367; E62977.

58 N.L.W. D.T.M. Jones MS. 1187.

59 N.L.W. D.T.M. Jones MS. 7808.

60 N.L.W. D.T.M. Jones MS. 8820.

61 Merioneth Q.S. Trinity,1806 (14).

62 Merioneth Q.S.Trinity, 1814 (31).

63 Merioneth Q.S. Hilary, 1614 (31).

64 N.L.W. G.E. Owen MSS. 7266-7.

65 Clearly Rowlands was a bad risk, for see Wilkins's evidence to Bank of England Charter committee discussed on p. 69.

66 U.C.N.W. Porth yr Aur MS. 33281.

67 N.W.L. Evans (Aberglasney) MS. 18/741.

68 *Report of the Committee on the Bank of England Charter*, B. P. P. VI, 1831-2, pp. 115-8. Wilkins observed that banks often lent cash to drovers on the understanding that the sum would be collected by their agents after the cattle sales at Barnet Fair.

69 In addition to financing local drovers, the Brecon Old Bank extended its facilities to drovers from the midland counties. These people arrived at the bank with notes for denominations between £5 and £30 from local Midland banks which they changed for Brecon notes, these being "well known" in Cardiganshire, Pembrokeshire and Glamorgan, where the Midland drov ers purchased the bulk of their cattle. (R.O. Roberts, *Brycheiniog*, VII, 1961, p. 65.)

70 D.S. Davies "Extracts from the Diaries and Account books of the artist Thomas Jones of Penncerrig", *Radnorshire Society Transactions*, XII, 942, p. 6.

71 N.L.W. Chirk Castle MS. E223.

72 M. Williams, "Glamorgan Farming in Preindustrial Times", *Glamorgan Historian*, ii, 1965, pp. 178-9

73 N.L.W. MSS. 9600-9614.

74 *Gloucester Journal*, August 4th 1817.

75 N.L.W. Broadhead Evans MS. 102.

76 Vicar Pritchard, in his delightful *Cyngor i'r Porthmon*, warned drovers of the potential danger of alcoholic indulgence:

Gochel feddwi wrth Borthmonna,

Owin hel borthmon i gardotta;

Os y porthmon a fydd meddw,

F'ar holl stoc i brynu cwrw.

(See Appendix III for translation).

77 Elizabeth Inglis-Jones, *Peacocks in Paradise*, Faber and Faber, 1971, p. 60.

THE WELSH CATTLE TRADE IN THE NINETEENTH CENTURY

The Pre-Railway Era

In the previous chapter, attention was drawn to the variety of "social services" provided by the drovers and dealers, particularly in terms of the transmission of money and correspondence to London and other parts of England. It is the purpose of the present chapter to discuss the basic "mechanics" and some aspects of the costs and returns of the cattle trade.

The majority of cattle were purchased by dealers at the local fairs, the abundance of which in so many Welsh towns and villages may be attributed to the inadequacy and difficulty of communications. The bulk of the fairs were held between May and November in order to cater for the demand by English farmers for store cattle, particularly in the spring and autumn months. Contemporary eyewitness accounts reveal that many of these local fairs were on a very large scale. When the Reverend Evans visited Cilgerran Fair in 1804, he noted that all the fields within three miles of the village were full of cattle and that: "the number of cattle, though this was considered a small fair, we were informed, exceeded twenty thousand." [1] That this was undoubtedly a substantial exaggeration may be gauged from the returns of several fairs in South Wales, which provide some indication of the scale of business which the local fair attracted. In 1833, for example, four fairs were held at Narberth. On the 21st January, 281 cattle changed hands, the number of transactions increasing to 478 on July 5th, while visitors to the fair of September 20th witnessed the sale of 532 beasts. On December 11th, however, only 216 animals were sold, indicating the reduced supplies following the large autumn fairs of Carmarthenshire and Pembrokeshire.[2] Table VI opposite sets out the numbers of beasts sold at the September and November fairs of Talsarn in Cardiganshire between 1802 and 1837.[3]

Although the trend is not altogether clear, this return suggests that more beasts were marketed at the autumn fairs held on November 7th. This was one of the later fairs of the area, and the increased volume of beasts by comparison to that of the September fair may reflect a desire, on the part of local farmers, to dispose of surplus beasts before the early winter when demand for stock tended to fall.[4] With the advent of the railways, many of the more isolated local fairs declined in importance, while those in close proximity to the railroad such as Aberystwyth, Lampeter and Machynlleth continued to thrive.

Notwithstanding the importance of the local fair, it appears that a significant proportion of dealers' purchases were made outside the confines of the fair. Richard Bulkeley, the Anglesey squire, noted in his diary as early as 1737 that the drovers preferred to buy cattle from local farms rather than at the fair. At Newborough Fair, for example:

"an abundance of cattle went from parts to it, but the Drovers, having bought the best cattle up and down the countrey (sic) they'll not be many at the fair." [5]

By travelling the locality and purchasing cattle directly from farmers, the dealer would avoid the pressures of competitive buying at the fair.

This practice, which was subject to a great deal of criticism, would effectively reduce the supply of animals to a given fair and thereby disturb the normal market forces. Moreover, it is not difficult to

Table VI Cattle Sales at Talsarn Fair		
	September 9th	November 7th
1802	16	66
1808	n.a.	43
1809	65	87
1810	67	na.
1813	60	36
1816	28	na.
1817	51	21
1819	121	56
1820	48	28
1821	56	85
1822	79	12
1823	39	138
1824	56	79
1825	47	60
1830	53	188
1831	57	101
1832	48	115
1833	94	n.a.
1835	na.	182
1836	55	122
1837	82	na.

imagine the ease with which a persuasive dealer or drover could purchase cattle from a farmer at prices considerably below those which would have prevailed in a normal market situation. It is for this reason, among others, that cattle prices returned for fairs and markets of the early and mid-nineteenth century may not entirely reflect true market forces. Some indication of the effects of private transactions on the trade at local fairs is provided by the comments of Edmund Hyde Hall, who visited Beddgelert Fair in Caernarvonshire in 1809 and found that:

> *"The show of animals was in general but trifling as the drovers have for many years been accustomed to go about from house to house in order to make their private bargains with the farmers."*[6]

Furthermore, supplies of animals to a given fair would often be reduced by intending purchasers procuring cattle from drovers before the fair began. In the Llanfair Caereinion area of Montgomeryshire, for example, it was common practice for a farmer to ride as far west as Dolymaen in order to secure bargains with the Cardiganshire drovers before the start of the fair at Llanfair.[7]

In the absence of suitable documentary material it is virtually impossible to determine the extent to which the cattle trade was carried out by capitalist entrepreneurs with a large business turn-over, as opposed to small time operators such as failed farmers and their workers. It is clear, however, that many farmers were extensively involved in the trade at times of the year when the labour requirement of their farms was low, and when they could leave the holding in the charge of family members or farm servants. Nevertheless it is unlikely that these small "seasonal" dealers or drovers with severely limited financial resources and lack of expertise in the art of buying cattle would have had much influence on the volume of the trade. While there is no direct evidence on this point, it is possible that by the late eighteenth century, when the credit system of financing the cattle trade had been largely replaced by the facilities provided by the country banks, the trade became concentrated in the hands

The Jonathans would have known this pub in Carno, established in 1632

of the larger dealers whose credit-worthiness in most cases would have been greater than their smaller counterparts. Within the former category fall the Jonathan family of Dihewyd in Cardiganshire whose books of account provide a basis for much of the remainder of this chapter.

Judging from the account books of the Jonathans and others, the more substantial drovers and dealers were eminently capable of accurately recording details of transactions and also of bargaining with their clients in the English language. A century and a half previously Sir Richard Myddleton of Chirk's drover, languishing in Kettering, Northamptonshire, was quite capable of writing a progress letter to his employer as quoted below:

"*Hond Sr'*

This is to aquaint yr worhsip that I have sould ye beast alredy 2 runts that I did value at £6 4s which I had £7; 4 steers which cost £7 14s for £19 5s, one ould cow for £1-10-0 and wee cam so fer verey well but gras is verey scarce I faine to go out of the road a mile or to sumtimes. Thanke god wee had very good weathar and the beast is in verye good ordr nor nevar a one lame but ye cow yt I sould. There is but few beast going towards this faire, I cannot have an acct of but 800 and that is not above half what use to be an othar year. I question not if god please to continue the weathar as it is now that wee shall a good market Good sr I am yr worships humble servant.

   Evan Edwards

To the Honble Sir Richard Myddleton"

Although it has been maintained that two hundred words of English were sufficient for the dealer to ply his trade, the capacity to speak good English with some degree of fluency was no doubt a major asset.[8] Indeed, there are at least two recorded cases of drovers capitalising upon their fluency in English by establishing themselves as schoolmasters. Thus in 1845 a school was opened in Pumsaint Carmarthenshire by a young man who had been previously employed as a London drover, while William Harris, schoolmaster of Ffaldybrenin in the same county from 1871-78, had spent his early years driving cattle to the Metropolis.[9,10] That many of these drovers and dealers not only spoke the English language, but were also men of some cultural attainment has been previously implied. Referring to the hundred of Caeo in Carmarthenshire in his evidence to the notorious Commission of Inquiry of 1847, John Johnes of Dolaucothi explained that:

"the majority of the small farmers can read and write very imperfectly; the writing seldom extends beyond signing the name."

But:

"There are a great many cattle dealers in this parish who travel to England and practically learn the value of education."[11]

To visit London was regarded by the drover as the high watermark of his career. Hyde Hall writes:

"I have frequently been accosted by them with an enquiry whether I was from London. My answer in the affirmative has been followed by the information of their not only having been there themselves, but that they know Smithfield and all about it. This important fact is always accompanied with divers significant leers and winks, such as the politesse of that well-bred quarter might easily supply."[12]

Estimation of the total number of cattle purchased in the fairs of Wales and driven to the central and southern counties of England is not possible. A few extant turnpike returns provide a fleeting glimpse of cattle movements during the pre-railway period, but these, of course, do not record the movements of the many drovers who eschewed the use of the turnpike roads in favour of the tracks across open mountain and unmade road. An attempt was made, during the preparation of this book, to locate individual gate returns as a means of determining the rate of flow of cattle along turnpike roads traversing the Welsh border. Extensive search and enquiry, however, revealed that among collections of turnpike material hardly any such returns have survived. It is necessary, therefore, to resort in the main to the few literary accounts to obtain some suggestions as to the volume of the trade. In 1638, it was recorded that some 3,000 cattle were annually driven from Anglesey, while Kay maintained that by the close of the eighteenth century, the number of cattle exported each year from the island approached 10,000.[13,14] Writing several years later, Walter Davies ventured to suggest that Kay's estimate was somewhat exaggerated and that:

"it may be asserted, from a good source of information that the average annual export is not above 8,000 head from one to four years old."[15]

Fortunately, there exists a detailed monthly account of the cattle numbers passing over Menai Bridge between 1829 and 1846.[16] From this account it can be shown that 6,452 cattle left Anglesey between May 21st 1829 and April 20th 1830. Subsequently, between the years 1830 and 1846, the annual traffic varied from 5,095-8,651 cattle, dependent, to some extent perhaps, upon the demand from graziers in the eastern counties of Wales and the English midlands. These figures do not, however, represent an absolute indication of the volume of exports. As the compiler of the manuscript accounts pointed out, of the annual traffic in cattle across the bridge some five to six hundred head would be depastured on the mainland throughout the summer, eventually returning to Anglesey in the autumn. This would tend to reduce the yearly export figure to around 6,000 head.

During the first decade of the nineteenth century, Edmund Hyde Hall attempted: "by comparing the opinions of as many dealers as I could" to arrive at an estimate of the total cattle exports from Caernarvonshire. This enquiry led him to conclude that some 12,000 head left the county each year, although many of these animals may have originated in Anglesey.[17] Exports from Caernarvonshire itself were doubtless extensive, for Walter Davies, usually a reliable witness, contended that 6,000 cattle from Llŷn alone arrived each year at the English fairs.[18]

Isolated references occur to cattle being exported from south Wales into England, although these fail to give any indication of changes in the volume of the trade.

By the mid-eighteenth century, upwards of 30,000 cattle from the summer and autumn fairs of Wales travelled annually through Herefordshire towards the south-east, while in 1887 it was asserted that Pembrokeshire alone supplied, each year, 25,000 beasts for the feeding pastures of Northamptonshire and the neighbouring counties.[19,20] Although these sporadic references provide some measure of the importance of the cattle trade, meaningful discussion of the scope and volume of this trade during the pre-railway period is precluded by an almost total absence of statistical data.

The Mechanics of Droving

It was the objective of a dealer or drover to assemble an evenly-matched drove of animals which would cater for the requirements of his grazier clients attending the English fairs. This would require substantial cash expenditure, loans from the country banks, or extensive credit from local farmers. The credit system, whereby farmers were paid by the dealers on the latters' return from England, was frequently abused. Several legal cases illustrating this point were quoted in the previous chapter. John Evans, in 1804, mentions the credit system, while Hyde Hall, having commented upon the abuses of this system, pointed out nevertheless that:

> *"... as the necessity of selling seems to be greater than that of buying, these very bankrupt dealers are again employed and again trusted."*[21]

In other words the fact that cattle sales formed the mainstay of the net farm income meant that the dealers were generally favoured with a buyer's market. It is clear, nevertheless, that many of the more substantial dealers or drovers, having established their businesses, eventually accumulated the capital resources necessary to deal in cash. It was suggested earlier that cattle purchased with cash could generally be secured at a rather cheaper rate than beasts bought on credit.

Among the larger "capitalist" dealers who dealt strictly in cash transactions were the Jonathan family of Dihewyd, whose finely written accounts embrace the period 1839-1882.[22] Figure VI illustrates the evolution of the business activity of this group of dealers both in terms of cattle numbers purchased and annual cash outlay. The Figure reveals that in spite of annual fluctuations occasioned by variations in supply and demand, there was a steady increase in the number of purchases and thus cash expenditure until the late eighteen seventies. Subsequently there was a steep decline in business activity, related perhaps to the influence of the depression which was by now beginning to affect English livestock farmers.

In addition to buying and selling on their own account, various entries in the notebooks and several letters among the material show the Jonathans acting from time to time as buyers on commission. Thus a letter to David Jonathan from William Grey of Leatherhead requested the former to advise him as to the cost of buying Welsh cattle and delivering them to Leatherhead. The Jonathans adopted the practice of commission buying regularly after the mid 1860s, perhaps on account of the saving in fair tolls and charges which arose from direct selling on a "contract" basis.

The Reverend Evans noted that commission buying was practised during the first decade of the century.[23] The Anglesey dealer, John Evans, active in the eighteen eighties, not only purchased cattle on commission, but acted as salesman for a prominent local farmer, William Williams. He received for his services £150 per year, together with a rent-free house, summer grass and winter keep for two cows, ten quarters of oats and three tons of hay for the upkeep of his horse. The conditions of the contract drawn up by Williams stipulated that:

> *"... all cattle going from my farms in Anglesey to England for sale go up with Mr. Evans and only expenses charged upon them."*[24]

The wide-ranging activities of the Jonathans and their drovers is clear from Map 1 which sets out the geographical distribution of the fairs and markets recorded in the account books. With the exception of Welshpool all these fairs lay to the west of the central mountain mass, where the economy was largely based upon store cattle sales. In an attempt to establish the relative importance of each of these centres, the accounts have been analysed to show the percentage of the total purchases at different centres throughout four periods for which the material is particularly detailed. The results of this analysis are shown in Table VII.

During the first period purchases were almost exclusively from south Cardiganshire, Carmarthenshire and Pembrokeshire, with only the occasional visit to Montgomeryshire. However, as the scale of business increased in the late forties, so did the "catchment area" for cattle expand, the Jonathans and their buyer-drovers travelling as far afield as Dolgellau and across the mountains to Welshpool. Although a large number of cattle were still being purchased in the southern fairs, particularly those of Newcastle Emlyn, Abergwili and Haverfordwest, the dominant feature of this second period was the

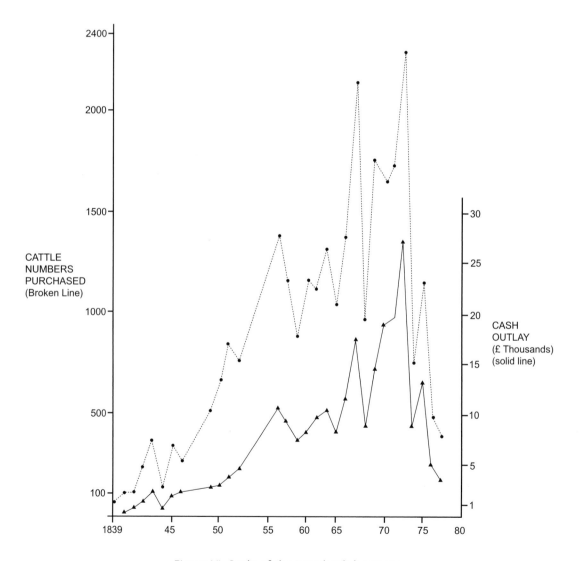

Figure VI. Scale of the Jonathan's business

		Table VII			
	Percentage of Purchases from Different Centres (Jonathan Accounts)				

Centre	Total Purchases	% of total purchases in period 1839/46	% of total purchases in period 1849/62	% of total purchases in period 1863/69	% of toal purchases in period 1876/82
Newcastle Emlyn	2,681	7	3	40	50
Lledrod	387	22	12	41	25
Tregaron	138	100	—	—	—
Aberystwyth	1,134	3	47	7	43
Llanfihangel & Pencarreg	416	28	16	48	8
Abergwili	559	20	55	20	5
Haverfordwest	2,551	10	12	33	45
Narberth	579	22	—	40	38
Maenclochog	129	25	—	56	19
Llandalas	501	19	55	13	12
Cardigan	543	—	—	—	100
Carmarthen	521	—	—	92	8
Llanbrynmair	320	10	86	—	4
Talsarn	416	16	73	6	5
Machynlleth	2,220	—	40	45	15
Dinas Mawddwy	763	—	85	15	—
Aberaeron and "About County"	4,969	—	28	45	27
Dolgellau	452	—	80	3	17
Capel Cynon	525	—	46	28	26
Llanbadarn	713	—	23	67	10
Eglwyswrw	456	—	—	—	100
Llanidloes	81	—	56	44	—
Llanarth	630	—	14	34	52
Pontrhydfendigaid	358	—	49	51	—
Llanrhystud	189	—	100	—	—
Welshpool	134	—	18	82	—
Rhayader	36	—	72	28	—
Lampeter	406	—	14	63	23
Cilgerran	1,056	—	5	35	60
Henfeddau	515	—	15	45	40
Llanybydder	273	—	—	86	14

MAP 1 Drovers' Routes to the English Border (JONATHAN AND RODERICK ACCOUNTS)

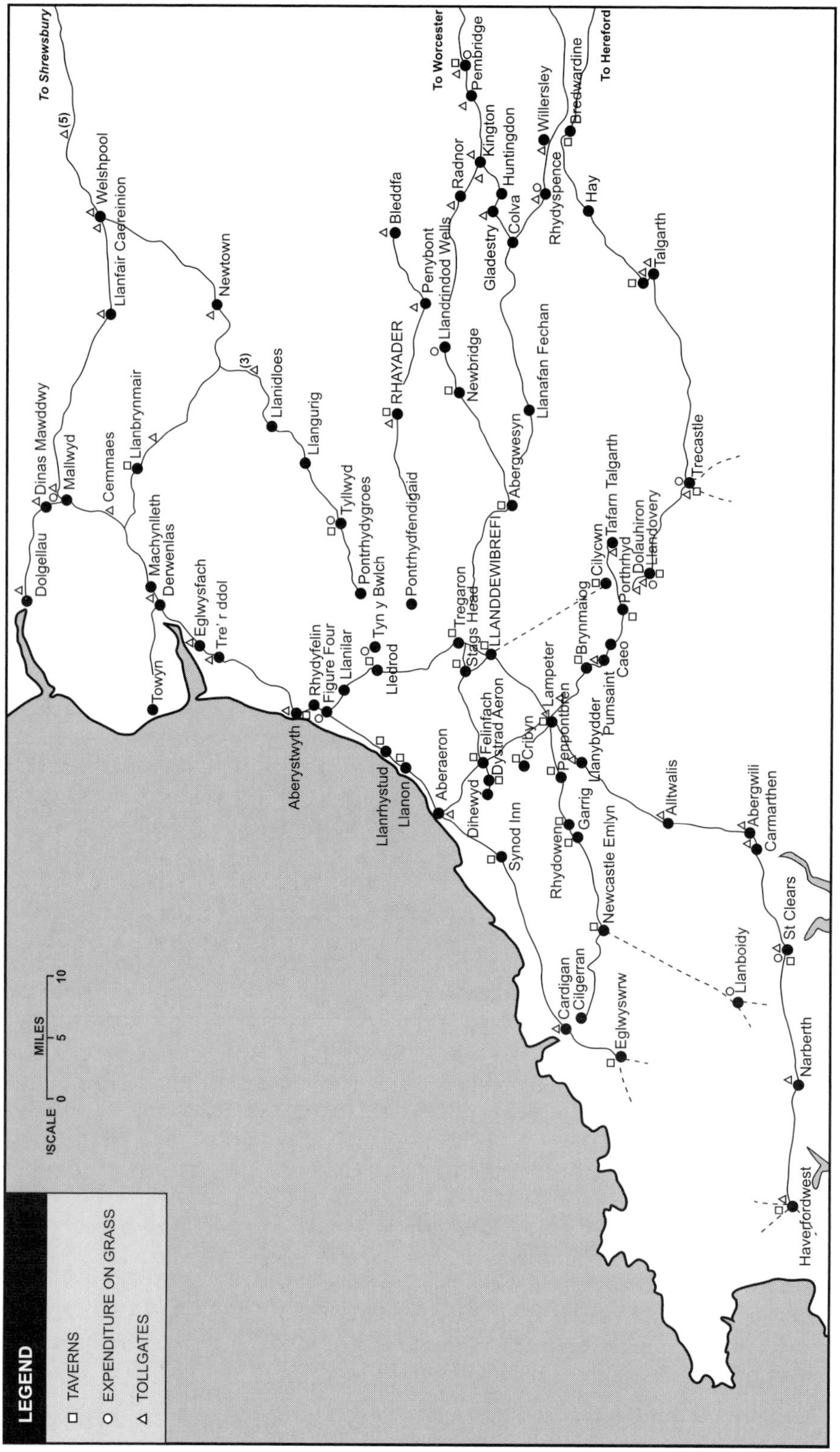

LEGEND

□ TAVERNS
○ EXPENDITURE ON GRASS
△ TOLLGATES

SCALE
MILES
0   5   10

To Shrewsbury

△(5)

Welshpool
Llanfair Caereinion

Dinas Mawddwy
Mallwyd
Cemmaes
Llanbrynmair
Newtown

Dolgellau
Machynlleth
Derwenlas
Llanidloes

Llangurig

Tywyn
Eglwysfach
Tre'r ddol
Tyllwyd
Pontrhydygroes
Llanbrynmair
△(3)

Tyn y Bwlch
Pontrhydfendigaid

Bleddfa
Penybont
Radnor
Llandrindod Wells
Kington
Huntingdon
Gladestry
Colva
Rhydyspence
Hay

To Worcester
Pembridge
Willersley
Breswardine

To Hereford

RHAYADER

Newbridge

Abergwesyn
Llanafan Fechan

Talgarth

Rhydyfelin
Figure Four
Llanilar
Lledrod
Tregaron
Stags Head
LLANDDEWIBREFI

Aberystwyth

Aberaeron
Dihewyd
Ystrad Aeron
Felinfach
Lampeter
Peponthen
Brynmaiog
Cilycwm
Tafarn Talgarth
Porthryhd
Dolauhiron
Llandovery

Trecastle

Llanrhystud
Llanon
Synod Inn
Cribyn
Garrig
Llanybydder
Pumsaint
Caeo

Alltwalis

Rhydowen
Newcastle Emlyn

Abergwili
Carmarthen

Cardigan
Cilgerran

Eglwyswrw

Llanboidy

St Clears

Narberth

Haverfordwest

- 82 -

growth in importance of Aberystwyth and Machynlleth as centres of purchase. It was during this period that purchases from Aberaeron and "about the county" are first recorded. "About the county" apparently refers to purchases made directly from farmers and from the smaller local fairs of north Cardiganshire. The third and fourth periods witnessed further expansion in the volume of purchases from Newcastle Emlyn, Haverfordwest, Narberth and Aberaeron, together with the southern fairs of Henfeddau and Cilgerran.

The continuing importance of Aberystwyth and Machynlleth was doubtless related to the existence, by this time, of railway facilities at these two centres. In Table VIII the accounts are presented on the basis of the proportion of total purchases from different fairs at various periods of the year. In general there were relatively few purchases during the first quarter of the year, any acquisitions during this period almost invariably being made in March. The low level of purchases at this time was related to the requirement for store cattle by the English graziers and fatteners, which in the late winter months was almost non-existent.

Cattle required for straw and turnip feeding would have been bought during the autumn, while demand for animals to stock the fattening pastures tended to grow only when spring grass became available. Moreover, the long distance driving of cattle at this time of the year presented very real problems, particularly with regard to obtaining forage en route. Roadside grazing would be of little value during the winter months, necessitating the purchase of substantial quantities of hay at a time of the year when supplies were beginning to ebb. Thus would the expenses of the drove be increased and the profit margin narrowed. It is significant that where substantial numbers of cattle were procured during this period, they were purchased from farms in close proximity to the dealers' home farm. It is likely, therefore, that the Jonathans bought cattle relatively cheaply during the late winter months as food was beginning to get scarce, holding them on the home farm until they were eventually sold on the buoyant spring market.

Almost one third of the total purchases were made between April and June at a time when the English grazing pastures were coming into full production and the demand for store cattle was increasing. At this time the Jonathans and their drovers scoured the country between Haverfordwest in the south and Dinas Mawddwy in the north to make their purchases. Over the three months from July to September, however, there was a significant decline in the number of cattle purchases, related once again to a deterioration in the demand for store animals over the summer months when fields would normally be fully stocked. It was not until the later part of September, and thence into October and November, that purchases increased once more in anticipation of the demand for cattle, both from the yard feeders of the home counties and from graziers wishing to clear their pastures of surplus summer grass.

The types of cattle required in the autumn by these two classes of purchaser were rather different. The yard feeder was looking for a store animal which would fatten on roots, hay and straw over the winter months, while the grazier favoured the lighter upland "runts" which were renowned for their ability to process coarse late summer grass. The dealers bought comparatively few cattle at the autumn fairs of Newcastle Emlyn, Haverfordwest and the Aberaeron area, all of which were important sources of supply throughout the earlier periods of the year. This may reflect seasonal changes in the supply of cattle to these markets or alternatively the unsuitability of local cattle types to the purposes of the Jonathans' clients.

The original assembly points for the Jonathans' droves depended upon the area of the country in which the cattle were purchased. Animals bought in south Cardiganshire, Carmarthenshire and Pembrokeshire converged on Tregaron whence they were driven across the mountains to enter England via Herefordshire. Cattle from north Cardiganshire, on the other hand, were generally gathered in Llanbadarn Fawr near Aberystwyth and driven northwards towards Shrewsbury. Prior to commencing the long journey to the Midland and Home Counties, the cattle were shod. This operation was essential, above all, to prevent lameness, which would often result in reduced feed intake and hence loss of body weight. Frequent references to cattle shoeing appear among the printed and manuscript sources, while throughout many parts of Wales, the saga of cattle shoeing is preserved in local folk memory.

The cattle were usually shod at established centres before departing for England, the shoes being forged by blacksmiths during the winter months in readiness for the spring droves. The shoes, varying in length according to the class and size of beast for which they were being made, were generally some

Table VIII

Cattle Purchases from Different Fairs at Different Periods of the Year (Jonathan Accounts)

Fair	% total purchases in Jan/March	% total purchases in April/June	% total purchases in July/Sept	% total purchases in Oct/Dec	Total purchases
Newcastle Emlyn	17	40	29	14	2,681
Lledrod	0	47	0	53	367
Tregaron	0	0	100	0	138
Aberystwyth	7	68	11	14	1,134
Pencarreg	0	0	0	100	416
Abergwili	0	0	7	93	559
Haverfordwest	16	51	28	5	2,551
Narberth	10	22	23	45	579
Maenclochog	0	19	81	0	129
Cardigan	0	39	19	42	543
Llandalas	0	100	0	0	501
Carmarthen	0	16	44	40	521
Llanbrynmair	55	45	0	0	320
Machynlleth	33	18	9	40	2,220
Dinas Mawddwy	4	47	0	49	763
Aberaeron & locality	34	52	4	10	3,072
Dolgellau	0	77	0	23	452
CapelCynon	0	47	0	53	425
Eglwyswrw	0	98	0	2	556
Llanbadarn	7	23	9	61	713
Llanidloes	100	0	0	0	81
Llanarth	5	72	23	0	630
Pontrhydfendigaid	0	0	100	0	358
Llanrhystud	0	0	0	100	189
Welshpool	57	0	0	43	134
Rhayader	0	0	100	0	36
Lampeter	3	55	28	14	406
Cilgerran	0	52	48	0	1,056
Henfeddau	0	0	30	70	515
Llanybydder	0	0	9	91	273
Mean percentage purchases in each period	11	32	22	35	

$^7/_8$ in. wide by $^1/_4$ in. thickness. Unlike the horseshoe, the cattle shoe, or "ciw" as it was known in Wales, comprised two separate plates. Although much of the shoeing was carried out by local black-smiths, in some areas of Wales cattle were shod by "specialists" who moved from fair to fair for the purpose.

In the locality of Ffarmers in Carmarthenshire, during the mid-eighteen sixties, the Ffaldybrenin smith, one Evan Richards, was responsible for shoeing cattle en route for the Herefordshire border. Richards was assisted by a colourful character known locally as Rhys the Nailer of Pant-un-nos.[25] Again, at Llanbadarn Fawr, dealers purchasing cattle ensured that the animals were shod by their own smiths who frequently attended the fair with the dealer.[26] From time to time cattle would lose a shoe en route, smaller drovers relying on the services of a local smith to rectify this problem. A large drove of cattle, however, was often accompanied on horseback by a smith who would carry with him a supply of shoes and nails usually smeared in butter to prevent rusting.[27]

Such was the case with the larger droves of cattle shod at Ffridd Cosyn near Corwen, Merionethshire; they would be followed by John Richards (Jack Ysbytty) carrying an ample sackful of shoes and nails.[28] William Dickenson maintained that drovers in the north of England were frequently tempted to "over-drive" their animals in order to compensate for the delay to the drove occasioned by the re-shoeing of invalid cattle. Thus:

"the drove is either sold at a loss through their jaded condition, or cannot be sold at all " [29]

It was, of course, essential to cast the beasts in order effectively to nail the shoes to the cloven hoof. This required skill in addition to great physical strength and stamina. Casting of cattle was regarded locally as an act of prowess, requiring considerable fortitude, and in consequence each local area had its champion "thrower." In Dinas Mawddwy, Merionethshire, Evan of Hafod Wynn held this exalted position, while in the eighteen sixties cattle were thrown at the "Ffair pedoli gwartheg" on Bala Green by one Siôn Fawr, a giant of six feet three inches. At the end of the day, this stalwart, who was apparently capable of felling an ox with a single twist of its horns, would walk fifteen miles to his house across the Berwyn.[30]

During the same period, cattle at Ffarmers were thrown for shoeing in the field of Llwyncelynbach by one David Morgan, a man noted for his tendency to over-indulge in drink. Methods of throwing varied somewhat according to locality. In mid-nineteenth century Cardiganshire, the thrower seized the muzzle of the beast with his left hand, at the same time gripping the right horn with his other hand. He then placed his heel firmly against the animal's right fore-foot, twisting the muzzle upwards and the horn downwards, thereby causing the beast to fall upon its right side. Animals frequently fell with such force that the right horn became embedded in the earth.[31] A similar technique was followed in Dinas Mawddwy, where having thrown the animal, the feller would lie upon the beast's neck while his assistant secured its feet prior to shoeing.[32]

In his admirable book, *The Gorse Glen,* Hugh Evans has described an interesting method of felling practised in parts of North Wales:

"the cattle feller and his assistant tied a rope to the horns of the steer. The feller then took the animal by the horns while his assistant lifted one of the steer's fore-feet from the ground, bending the leg at the knee. The feller would then give the horns a twist and down went the beast, being kept down by the feller while the assistant made it secure with the rope that had been attached to the horns. An iron rod, about a yard long, pointed at one end and forked at the other, was driven into the ground and the rope with which the beast's feet were bound was passed through the fork. The animal was then ready to be shod." [33]

In Ffarmers, a broadly similar method was adopted, although in this locality, the leg of the felled animal was supported for shoeing by a piece of forked timber.[34] Besides having their cattle shod, some drovers were insistent upon the animals being provided with some form of identification markings. This was particularly the case with cattle from Merionethshire and Llyn, which were identified by having the hair above their left knees cut in a distinctive fashion, usually in the shape of the initials of their owner. [35]

The Drovers Arms, Ffarmers, Carmarthenshire

The drovers' road between Llanddewibrefi and Ffarmers in the attractive setting of the Twrch Valley

That the cattle shoers and their assistants were held in high regard by the rural community has already been implied. The doings of at least one of these people has been enshrined in verse. This was Evan John Williams (Ianto Sion Evans) who shod cattle at Abergwesyn, Brecknockshire, in the 1870s. The following ditty was written about Williams by a travelling bard called Shelby, and recited to the author by the late Mr. John Rees of Abergwesyn one summer evening in 1970:

"Mae Ianto Sion Evans	"*Ianto Sion Evans has a vast shop*
A globen o Siop,	*The earth is its base*
Y ddaear yn waelod	*And the sky is its top*
Ar wybren yn dop,	*It's enormously wide*
Mae'n anferth o led	*And enormously long*
Ac anferth o hyd	*And to it they come*
Maen't yn dod iddi hi	*From the four corners of the world.*"
0 bob chwarter o'r byd."	

The location of "shoeing forges" and shoeing compounds will be mentioned in a subsequent chapter in relation to drove routes throughout Cardiganshire and Carmarthenshire. At Foel, Montgomeryshire, cattle were shod at Glan yr Afon, a demolished inn. It is of interest that close by Glan yr Afon there exist two small fields, "Kent Field", an enclosure of 0.8 acres and "Essex Field" of 0.6 acres. Local tradition asserts that these enclosures were used for drafting shod cattle destined respectively for the grazing lands of Kent and Essex.

No doubt shoeing became less crucial with the advent of railway usage, particularly after the extension of the line to Machynlleth and Aberystwyth in the early sixties. The Jonathans, however, who, made full use of the turnpike roads, were still shoeing their cattle before undertaking the eighty mile journey to the Shrewsbury railhead in the eighteen fifties. Indeed, throughout the eighteen sixties when cattle were being taken by rail directly from Aberystwyth, Machynlleth and Llanidloes, entries such as:

"Paid John for shoeing 192 beast, £9.12.0."; *"Paid David Tregaron for shoeing 44 beast, £2.4.0";* *"Shoeing 100 beast, £5"* ; *"throwing 64 beast, £3. 8.0",* occur regularly. It would seem that shoeing of "trucked" cattle was undertaken primarily to alleviate any loss in condition which might result from the driving of cattle from fair to fair upon disembarking in England.

Size of the drove

The actual size of a drove of cattle varied according to the time of year and the demand for store cattle from the English graziers. However, most accounts suggest that the droves ranged in size from one to four hundred cattle attended by between four and eight drovers and their dogs.[36] However, the huge Rhys Morgan of Tregaron, styled "King of Northampton", who was still trading in cattle and horses at the beginning of the 20th century, normally employed a dozen men to handle droves of up to three hundred beasts.[37] It has often been contended that cattle under eighteen months of age were unable to withstand the rigours of the journey to England and consequently were not to be found among the droves. This was by no means the case. Contemporary sources reveal that although bulls did not leave Wales before they were eighteen months old, heifers of as little as one year of age were frequently to be seen in the droves.[38] However, according to the Jonathan papers, the droves would comprise, in the main, three to four year old store beasts, together with a sprinkling of milch cows and the occasional bull.

Setting off for England

Once the chaos which arose from mixing together and marking several hundred strange cattle had abated, the drove set off for England.[39] It normally took some three or four days for the animals to settle down to a steady two miles per hour, a leisurely pace which would give them plenty of opportunity to graze by the wayside.[40] By travelling at this rate, the drove would cover between fifteen and twenty miles per day. In order to prevent excessive loss of condition and to avoid the loss of "bloom" which would result from the accumulation of sweat upon the skin, it was considered vital not to force the pace of the cattle.

It was important then, to preserve the condition of his beasts, for the experienced drover to plan his journey with great care. A particularly long and strenuous day over rough mountain track would generally be followed by a shorter day's travelling by way of giving the beasts an opportunity to recuperate.[41] Throughout the pre-railway period, these epic journeys necessitated considerable feats of physical endurance on the part of men as well as animals. That the drovers were capable of sustained physical effort is illustrated by an entry in the *Gentleman's Magazine* of 1770, when:

"... a drover that began on Monday last to walk and was to go four hundred miles in six days...for a wager of £300 completed it at fifty minutes after ten this evening."[42]

Moreover, the fact that many drovers survived to very great ages suggests that continued exposure to the elements, together with countless nights of sleeping in the open air had no permanently adverse effects upon their health. Conversations with elderly persons whose forbears were connected with the cattle trade and whose recollections are frequently tinged with a rather nostalgic flavour, tend to give the impression that the drovers were a peculiar breed of supermen who scorned the use of an overcoat and cheerfully faced wind and storm with gay abandon. But the various drovers' and dealers' account books do not support their assertion. Indeed, it seems that some drovers expected their employers to provide them with some form of protective clothing before they embarked upon a journey. In 1822, for example, a Trawsfynydd, Merionethshire, dealer recorded in his accounts that he paid £5.5.0. for clothes and £1.9.6. for "a trunk, accommodation on the way and shoes" for his drover before the latter set off Northampton.[43]

Accommodation on the Way

The provision of overnight accommodation for both drovers and animals was normally arranged by the dealer or master drover who would ride ahead of the drove for this purpose, and who would drop back to re-sell any hay or forage which remained unconsumed by the cattle.[44] Accommodation was provided either at local farms or inns, many of them having adjoining paddocks where cattle could be rested overnight. The location of such farms and inns provide a useful means of tracing the drovers' routes, as a subsequent chapter will show. While the senior drovers would normally spend the night in the farmhouse or tavern, it was the usual practice for the juniors to sleep alongside the cattle and to ensure that their charges were adequately fed and watered.[45]

The cost of overnight accommodation for drovers, to which further attention will be given later in this chapter, appears to have varied little throughout the century, ranging from 4d. per head during the summer to 6d. during the winter months. Drovers passing through Welshpool, for example, were accommodated either at the Dragon Inn or the Common Lodging House, for which they were charged 6d. per night.[46] In London during the 1870s, the Tregaron drovers usually stayed at inns in Shepherd's Bush for the nightly payment of 3d., plus a further 3d. if breakfast was taken.[47] Their colleagues from the Llancrwys/ Ffarmers/ Ffaldybrenin area in Carmarthenshire were accommodated in the "Lock and Key" at Smithfield.[48]

The expenses incurred by drovers both for overnight accommodation and for solid and liquid refreshment taken en route for England were usually met by the master dealer or drover. In some cases the dealer would follow the drove in order to settle his drovers' accounts by cash payments directly to farmers and publicans. Alternatively the drovers would meet the cost of accommodation and refreshment themselves, subsequently claiming these "out of pocket" expenses from the dealer. This latter method was adopted by the drovers in the employment of the Jonathans.[49] The tavern expenses of these individuals formed a significant element in the total costs which had to be set against the dealer's margin. A typical account of the expenses received by David Rees and Charles Jones following a journey to Essex in 1840 is set out below:

October 15th 1840

Account to David	£	s.	d.		*Account to Charles*	£.	s.	d.
Abergwesyn tavern		1	0		Abergwesyn tavern		1	0
Newbridge tavern		1	0		Newbridge tavern		1	0
Bontfraig tavern		1	5		Bontfraig tavern		6	6
Give at Eardisland		5	0		Westinton House			7
Westinton House			7		Bontwillt tavern		2	6
Bontwillt tavern			4		Stanton Inn			4¹/₂
Broadway bread			6		Moreton-in-March		5	6
William Wells		3	8¹/₂		Birmingham Wells			8¹/₂
Elstow			9		Wellingborough		2	0
Walton		1	0		William Wells		6	2
Ongar		3	0		Elstow			9
Chelmsford		3	0		Ongar		2	6
	£1	1	3¹/₂d		Chelmsford		2	6
						£1	12	1d
						+£2	5	0d
						£3	17	1d"

The sum appended to the total expenses refers to the wage of the drover, which at this time was paid on the basis of approximately 2s. per day, supplemented by a lump sum to provide for his needs on the return journey to Wales. In the 1830s the dealer Roderick Roderick of Porthyrhyd was paying his drover John Edwards, a daily wage of 2s. together with a sum for "return." Thus among his accounts are recorded such entries as:

"... work at Narberth Fair for 24 days £2. 8. 0. and return 6s.",

and:

"... John Edwards has been 14 days at 2s. per day and return £1.14.0."[50]

It is difficult to determine the extent of changes in the remuneration received by drovers as the nineteenth century wore on. While Skeel records that drovers taking cattle from Haverfordwest to Ashford at the turn of the eighteenth century received a daily wage of 3s., the Jonathan accounts, covering a period of almost fifty years, suggest that wages remained at 2s. per day throughout the period.[51] Although an anonymous account book in the Merioneth Records Office mentions ls. as being the daily rate of payment for drovers during the 1830s, it is more likely that this was the sum paid to "casual" men who joined the drove for brief periods in order to help the regular drovers over difficult parts of the route. [52]

Cattle Disease and its effects upon the cattle trade

As well as being able to control the animals in his charge, the drover had to be capable of administering rough and ready veterinary treatment from time to time. Several drovers' pocket books contain veterinary 'recipes', often of an extremely bizarre nature, by which common cattle ailments could be treated. As a means of dealing with cases of 'bloat' which regularly occurred when cattle strayed overnight into nearby cornfields, most drovers carried a crude form of trocar and canula, while lactating cows which succumbed to mastitis were treated by the simple expedient of cutting off the affected teat with a sharp knife.

From time to time, however, a dealer was faced with veterinary problems of a rather more serious nature. In Saxon times, references to "murrains and "pestilences" frequently occurred in the saga poetry and the vernacular literature, while the word "murrain" features regularly in medieval stock accounts. By the late sixteenth and early seventeenth centuries, the term "contagion" was in popular use, referring, as did "murrain and pestilence", to any infectious disease capable of producing acute symptoms in livestock. Generally speaking, the "contagion" during the pre-nineteenth century period was the result of outbreaks of Rinderpest known also as Cattle Plague. Foot and Mouth, a debilitating, although by no means fatal, disease, first appeared in 1839, while the earliest recorded out-break of Pleuro-pneumonia in Britain took place in 1840.

The trade in cattle between Wales and England was often seriously disrupted by outbreaks of one or other of the above diseases; in particular by epidemics of Rinderpest. Since the seventeenth century, local justices had been empowered to suspend fairs and forbid the movement of cattle in the event of an epidemic. By so doing it was hoped to isolate the disease to within as small an area as possible. Accordingly, orders for the suspension of fairs occur regularly in Quarter Sessions Records. The celebrated Barnet Fair, venue of thousands of Welsh drovers throughout the centuries, was frequently closed on account of the cattle plague. The Middlesex Quarter Sessions Order Book of 1752 records payments of £1 each to Joseph Walker, John Jones and Thomas Cane for their attendance at Barnet:

"... in order to prevent the holding of any fair for horned cattle on the 23rd-26th days of August last."

The same officials also attended the Bush and Kensington Fairs:

"... so that no horned cattle sold at the said fair were driven into this country without proper certificates (of health)." [53]

Following the 1745 Cattle Plague epidemic, an Act of February 1746 empowered the Privy Council to order the slaughtering of infected beasts and to ban any movement of uninfected animals.[54] Although this Act was often contravened, restriction of cattle movement must undoubtedly have had a debilitating effect upon trade at the local fairs throughout England and Wales. After attending the Anglesey fairs of Porthaethwy and Aberffraw in October 1747, William Bulkeley noted in his diary that:

"... this extraordinary deadness at our cattle fairs is imputed to ye unhappy contagion that has raged in England now above 2 years...the several orders...by the Government in order to prevent the spreading of the contagion, one of which was that the Drover that bought any cattle was required to have a certificate from several Persons he bought them of, attested by a justice of the peace... or the minister of the parish, signifying that such cattle were then sound and had been so for three months before." [55]

The drover and hymnologist, Dafydd Jones of Caeo, had purchased two oxen from John Jones of Llanarthney, Carmarthenshire during the Cattle Plague epidemic of 1768. On completion of the sale, John Jones swore on oath before one of the King's Commissioners of the Land Tax that the cattle had been in his custody for forty days:

"... and are taken from a herd of cattle free from the infectious distemper...neither were the said cattle within one mile of any infected place." [56]

The outbreak of Cattle Plague in 1865, which was to wreak such havoc among herds throughout the length and breadth of the country, prompted Robert Curtis to write to the Plague Commissioners of Tenterden in Kent, suggesting that the droving of cattle be banned for the duration of the epidemic. He considered:

> "... that the case of the Welshmen that lost nearly all their cattle...will be sufficient to prove how hazardous the droving of cattle must be." [57]

The case to which he referred was that of Simon Williams and John Jones, two North Wales drovers who had driven diseased animals to Barnet Fair. A considerable volume of correspondence relating to this case, which sheds interesting light on the pressures imposed upon the conducting of the cattle trade during an epidemic, is preserved among the Privy Council papers.[58]

William Dale, Veterinary Inspector for the Barnet area, had noticed several diseased cattle among Simon Williams's drove which had been grazing in Hillfield Park prior to Barnet Fair. Dale had promptly placed a seven day quarantine order upon these animals, at the same time advising Williams to have the apparently healthy animals slaughtered in order to recover some of their value. Unfortunately Williams had been unable to persuade the butchers to purchase these animals so that by the end of the week only twenty beasts of the original one hundred and twenty four remained uninfected. Eventually one hundred animals died, nine were killed *in extremis*, three were stolen and five recovered, while only twelve remained free from the disease. John Jones had "secretly" driven a number of diseased cattle from Barnet to Elstree, thereby further facilitating the spread of the Plague. As Dale complained to the Privy Council:

> "... this part of my district, (Elstree) was entirely free from the plague, but in consequence of this drove, every herd of cattle belonging to gentlemen and farmers adjoining have been affected by the disease."

Furthermore, according to the *Carmarthen Journal*, Jones and Williams had together sustained losses of between two and three thousand pounds.[59]

The disruptive influence of an epidemic of cattle disease on the nineteenth century Welsh cattle trade was considerable. Prohibition of the movement of cattle by a series of Orders in Council of 1866, and by the *Cattle Diseases Prevention Act* of the same year, substantially reduced the activities of drovers and dealers at the markets and fairs in England.[60,61] The drover Davies of Tregaron, for example, was immobilised in Warwickshire with his cattle for over six weeks during the course of an outbreak of Foot and Mouth disease.[62] A disease outbreak not only decimated the demand for store stock, but also increased the overhead forage and maintenance costs of a drove forced to remain stationary for an extended period of time. The Act of 1866, which introduced a slaughter policy for infected animals, embodied the principle of compensation on the basis of half the value of the healthy beasts. This Act, which was reinforced by subsequent acts between 1873-93 and eventually consolidated in the *Diseases of Animals Acts* of 1894, could have provided little consolation to dealers whose business activities would have been severely curtailed.[63,64]

The Economics of the Cattle Trade

Together with the account books of the Jonathan family, there is abundant evidence indicating the very considerable scale of the business operations of many dealers involved in the Welsh cattle trade. As early as 1806, for example, David Roberts and Griffith Jones were selling cattle annually valued at over £6,000 at the Kentish fairs while later in the century (c. 1860/70), Evan Roberts of Caersws, Montgomeryshire, was expending up to £2,000 per month on cattle for sale in England.[65,66]

Ultimately, profitability was determined by the demand for store stock from the English grazier. Supply and demand considerations, together with the ability on the part of the dealer to assess the productive potential and sale value of livestock, combined to determine the initial price the dealer was prepared to pay for his store animals. Against the dealer's margin, which represented the difference between purchase and sale price, had to be offset the overhead costs incurred by a particular animal on the course of the journey from Wales to England. Essentially the bulk of these overhead costs during the pre-railway era comprised expenditure on wages, toll gates and maintenance, together with the cost of obtaining accommodation and forage for the cattle. Furthermore, if the dealer was operating on a credit basis, or alternatively had borrowed cash in order to effect his purchases, the net margin would be further reduced by the payment of interest charges.

Expenditure on the Droves

Reference has already been made to the dealers' expenditure on wages and also to the cost of meeting the expenses incurred by their drovers at wayside taverns on the road to England. Calculations based upon the Jonathan accounts during the pre-railway era reveal that a combination of these factors accounted for some 26 per cent of the total overhead costs of the drove. Besides the necessity of meeting the expenses of their drovers, the Jonathans themselves accumulated substantial "personal" costs both at the cattle assembly points in Wales and on their travels around the English fairs. These costs arose in the main, from expenditure on travel and from disbursements made in taverns for the purposes of accommodation or refreshment. Details of tavern expenses in particular, occur from time- to-time in the accounts. It was often convenient, for example, to assemble both droves of cattle and pigs at the village of Llanbadarn Fawr outside Aberystwyth prior to departing for England. On such occasions, according to the accounts, the Jonathans frequently had recourse to the good offices of the Black Lion Inn. This hostelry, under the proprietorship of one Evan Killin, clearly provided a variety of useful services for the dealers, as evidenced by the following bill from 1851:

1851
Mr. David Jonathan to Mr. Evan Killin, Black Lion, Llanbadarn.

		£	s.	d.
May 13th	To 2 meals 1/4, Ale 10d. Oats 6d		2	8
	Hay		14	0
	Paid for vetch peas		12	0
Nov 25th	Cash lent to Thomas Jonathan	6	0	0
	Oats for lean pig		2	0
Dec 24th	Cash lent to David Jonathan	5	0	0
Dec 29th	Expenses on 2 pigs	1	0	5
	Cash lent		11	6
	Expenses W. Evans, 6 meals 4/-, Ale 1/10		5	10
		£14	8	5

The dealers' personal expenditure in travelling to the fairs in England tended to increase in parallel with the expansion of trading activities in the 185s. By this time, the cattle were still travelling from fair to fair "on the hoof", yet the dealers had begun to adopt the practice of using the railway services for the purpose of following the droves around the English fairs. In consequence such entries as:

"... *my train from Welford to Harborough and back from Harborough 7/6*", "*my train to Lutterworth 1/-*",

and "*my train to Leicester 2/6*", feature regularly. Rail charges, therefore, together with other minor incidental costs were the primary cause of increased "personal" expenditure.

The components of the cost structure of the cattle trade are perhaps best discussed with reference to the inventories of expenses listed in the account books of several dealer/drovers active during the pre-railway period. The three inventories set out below are taken from the Jonathan accounts of 1839 and from the papers of Roderick Roderick of Porthyrhyd, a dealer whose trading accounts cover the period 1838/39.[67]

Jonathan Accounts (1839)	£.	s.	d.		£.	s.	d.
Cwmdulas House		5	0	Warwick gate		2	6
Abergwesyn Tavern		15	0	Windmill tavern		18	0
Boy drive the beast		2	0	Windmill gate		2	0
Newbridge Tavern			6	Daventry grass		14	6
Llandrindod grass		13	6	Daventry tavern		3	7
Smith, tavern			6	Daventry gate		5	0
Smith, grass		17	0	Northampton tavern		18	0
Maesyfed gate		1	6	Northampton gate		2	6
Pay John for shoeing	1	1	0	Wellingboro' gate		2	6
Kington gate		3	0	Wellingboro' gate		2	6
Kington grass		18	0	Wellingboro' tavern		13	6
Half-the-road gate		3	0	William Wells tavern		8	6
Llanllern gate		2	6	? gate		2	6
Westinton grass	1	0	0	Elstow tavern	1	19	0
Westinton grass		5	9	Elstow tavern	1	10	6
Westinton gate		3	0	Man mind beasts		1	6
Bromyard gate		3	6	Egin tavern		16	6
Bontwillt gate		2	3	Egin gate		1	6
Bontwillt tavern		17	3	Hertford tavern		2	6
Worcester gate		5	0	Hertford gate		2	6
Worcester tavern			6	Stansted tavern		13	3
Worcester tavern		2	6	Ongar grass	1	2	0
Wilbercastle tavern		18	0	Ongar tavern		5	0
Wilbercastle gate		2	9	Chelmsford	1	0	0
Stratford grass		14	6	Other expenses at fair and return home	2	0	4
Stratford tavern		3	0				
Stratford gate		2	6		£26	9	5
Warwick tavern		18	3				
Southam tavern		18	0				

Roderick Accounts (1838)	s.	d.		s.	d.
Lampeter gate		4	Ledbury gate	4	2
Cwmann gate		10	Beer	1	0
Beer at Porthyrhyd	2	0	Allowance at Folly		9
Llanfair-ar-y-bryn gate	5	5	Cash to D. Williams	2	6
Shoes and nails	2	0	Cash to D. Davies		9
Grass at Talgarth	11	6	Hollybush gate	2	10
Beer and lodgings	1	6	Bridge gate	2	10
Allowance	1	0	Tewkesbury gate	2	10
Beer	2	0	Doddington gate	2	10
Grass at Pugh's	16	0	Shoes and nails	1	0
Beer and lodgings	1	6	Lent at Croydon	2	9
Allowance		9	Expense paid	4	0

Keep for mare	4	6	Grass at Staplehurst	4	3
Rhydespence gate	2	9	Staplehurst gate	2	0
Willersley gate	2	9	Cranbrook gate	2	10
Hadmore gate	2	11	Cranbrook grass	8	9
Grass	16	0	Beer and lodgings	2	6
Beer and lodgings	2	9	Hire man	2	9
Shoe the mare	1	0	Beer for man		6
Brockhall gate	2	11	Fair and field	1	4
Shoes and nails	2	0	Fair gate		7
Grass at Hereford	16	0	Grass at Sandway	3	0
Beer and lodgings	2	9	Beer and lodging		10
Hereford gate	2	11	Gate		7
Tarrington gate	4	2			
			£8	**6**	**5**

Roderick Accounts (1838)	s.	d.		s.	d.
Hereford gate	3	8	Allowance (?)		9
Hereford grass	17	6	Grass at Moreton	13	6
Beer and lodgings	2	6	Beer and lodgings	2	9
Gate	3	8	Moreton gate	4	0
Shoeing horse	2	0	Beer at Rollwright		9
?		9	Grass	17	9
Tarrington gate	5	0	Beer and lodgings	2	9
? gate	4	10	Adderbury gate	3	9
Grass at Ledbury	17	6	Beer at 'Barleymow"		9
Beer and lodgings	2	9	Croughton gate	3	8
?		6	Beer at Buckingham	1	9
Nails and shoes	3	0	Beer at Soulbury		9
Beer at "Duke"		9	Grass at Leighton		
Hollybush gate	3	10	Buzzard	6	8
Bridge gate	3	9	Beer and lodgings	1	11
Tewkesbury gate	3	9	Paid Evan Williams 1	12	0
Grass at Tewkesbuty	11	8	Grass at Hitchin	12	0
Beer and lodgings	2	9	Beer at Hitchin	I	6
Doddington gate	3	9	Cash to David	5	0
				£10	**5**	**11**

On the old drovers' road between Tregaron and Abergwesyn

Former roadways converging on the chapel at Soar-y-Mynydd

John Smith, the central character in George Sturt's classic, *A Farmer's Life*, often met the Welsh drovers en route for the Surrey fairs of Blackwater and Farnham, contending that:

"... they'd lose a day goin' round sooner'n they'd pass a gate." [68]

Similarly, the *Hereford Journal* of 1859 refers to:

"... the great abhorrence of the Radnorshire men for a tollgate."

Notwithstanding, it is clear from references to gate charges in the Jonathan and Roderick material that these dealers, both of whom were in a sizeable way of business, were taking their cattle to the English fairs by way of the turnpike roads. In the majority of cases, the turnpike road represented the most direct means of communication between central England and the western and central counties of Wales. However, it was necessary to offset the advantages to be gained from the efficient and relatively rapid movement along the turnpike roads against the overhead costs represented by tollgate charges.

Analysis of the Jonathan accounts shows that between Tregaron, Worcester, Aberystwyth, Shrewsbury and Northampton, toll charges amounted to rather more than one shilling per beast in the 1840s and early 1850s. This figure represented approximately 8 per cent of the total overhead costs at this time, reducing to 5 per cent during the late fifties and early sixties when the Shrewsbury railhead was being exploited. No doubt the use of the turnpike roads by comparison with the tortuous and often treacherous tracks across open mountain reduced the time taken to reach the English fairs. It might be argued then that drovers using the turnpike were able to arrive in good time at the fairs of the midlands – thus to secure more favourable prices for their beasts than their fellows who preferred to follow the less direct routes via the drove and drift ways.

Moreover, shod cattle travelling at a steady two miles per hour along a well maintained turnpike road would almost certainly have lost less body condition than animals driven across the rocky upland tracks where grazing was sparse and where the severe inclines would have been likely to impose considerable stresses. Defoe emphasised the importance and "great value" of road improvement in Wales by which... *"the fat cattle will drive lighter and come to market with less toil."* [69] On the other hand, a petition to Parliament by Sussex agriculturalists in 1710 objected strongly to road improvement:

"because the stones will cripple them (the cattle), before they come to market." [70]

This petition of complaint, however, was perhaps motivated more by concern for the cost of road improvement than by any real anxiety for the well-being of driven cattle. [71]

Along with gate charges, expenditure on grazing is revealed by the inventories as being a major element in the total overhead costs. Since a drove generally moved at a speed rarely exceeding two miles per hour, daily maintenance could be readily obtained by wayside grazing, and thus the disbursements recorded for grass keeping may be assumed to refer to the expense of providing forage for cattle overnight. The magnitude of expenditure on grazing at each centre, together with the distance between centres (averaging 12-14 miles) lends support to this assumption. Moreover, in the Roderick inventories, tavern expenses for "beer and lodgings" regularly occur alongside the outlay on grass.

Several miscellaneous expenses recorded in the inventories shed further interesting light on the conducting of the cattle trade. References to cattle shoeing occur in both the Jonathan and Roderick material. In the former inventory, the payment of £1.1.0. to "John for shoeing" refers to the initial shoeing of the whole drove, while the small sums expended upon "shoes and nails" by Roderick Roderick relate to the necessity of re-shoeing "casualties" at various points along the route. Other entries such as "Hire man", "Boy drive the beasts", and "man drive the beast" indicate that from time-to-time manpower in addition to the regular force of drovers was hired. This would often be necessary where the drove was to be taken across open mountains. Thus the function of the boy hired by the Jonathans at Abergwesyn, Brecknockshire, would be to assist the regular drovers in taking cattle across the open mountain via the Cefn Cardis to Beulah and thence to Newbridge. The "man mind beast" and the "hired man" in the inventories were both employed at points of disposal, and it is possible that these men were taken on to ensure the overnight safety of the drove.

The inventory below illustrates the magnitude of "local costs" once the drove had arrived in the area of sale. This inventory, which is in fact an expense account charged by David Roderick to his brother Roderick Roderick, is concerned with the expenses of a small drove of cattle at the fairs of north Kent.

The account once again emphasises the scale of grazing costs. Thus over half the total recorded expenses arose from the provision of keep for the cattle while selling was in progress. With the exception of some eight shillings, the remainder of the total overhead costs comprised beer and lodgings for the personnel concerned with the drove.

Roderick Accounts (1838)	£	s.	d.
Grass at Croydon		9	0
Beer and Lodgings		1	8
Expenses		1	0
Croydon gate		2	8
Beer Allowance			4
Grass at Duntongreen		1	9
Beer and Lodgings		2	3
Seal gate		1	6
Seal expenses		1	0
Seal grass		5	0
Beer and Lodgings		2	2
Mereworth gate			2
Oats at Mereworth			6
Aylesford gate		1	2
Beer allowance			4
Grass at Maidstone		11	8
Maidstone gate		1	2
Yalding gate			2
Beer and Lodgings		3	6
Beer allowance			4
Grass		8	2
Toll			4
Beer and Lodgings		1	7
Shod the mare			6
Toll			8
Fair Field			8
Beer at Sandway		1	0
Beer at Kings Field		1	6
Maidstone Gate			4
(Beer) allowance			4
	3	2	5
Cash to Roderick		4	0
	£3	6	5

Contemporaneous with the Roderick papers are the accounts of David Davies, a dealer active in the Dolgellau area. The fragments of the Davies accounts in the Merionethshire Records Office are of particular interest in that they provide evidence of a dealer travelling to areas of the eastern counties normally associated with the Scottish, rather than the Welsh cattle trade.[72] The components of the inventory are once again broadly similar to those listed in the Jonathan and Roderick accounts, including payment for wages, re-shoeing, overnight accommodation, grass and ale.

Davis Accounts (1838)	£	s.	d.
Stamford grass	1	1	0
Bed			8
Eating and ale		3	6
Wansford Gate		2	0
Stiltion (?) grass		10	0
Bed, eating and ale		3	6
Gate		2	0
Hillpatrick(?)		12	8
Bed			8
Bread and cheese			9
Eating and ale		3	0
St. Ives gate		2	2
Grass		15	4
Eating			8
Eating, ale and bed		3	4
Evans		1	0
Shoeing horse		1	2
Eating		2	9
Bed			8
St. Ives grass		11	9
St. Ives gate		2	2
St. Ives gate		2	3
Eating, ale		1	0
Cambridge gate and toll		3	2

	£	s.	d.
Sawston gate		2	6
Sawston grass		9	0
Sawston bed			9
Eating and ale		4	4
Langley, grazing		6	0
Evans crus (?)		4	0
Coulhill eating and ale		2	0
Toll		3	5
Eating and ale		2	6
Bed		2	6
Cattle feed			5
Eating and ale		1	6
Harlow			8
Oil			6
Gate			9
Shoes for bullock			9
Epping, feed			5
Hay		3	0
Eating and ale		2	0
Bed and stable		1	3
Black Horse			4
High Ongar		3	1
Paid old Tom	1	3	0
	£9	1	10

It is interesting to compare these mid-nineteenth century inventories with two similar inventories from the late eighteenth century. The first of these relates to the cash expenditure incurred by a Merionethshire drover, John Williams, in taking a drove of 113 cattle from Bala to eastern Essex.[73]

Williams Accounts (late eighteenth century)	£.	s.	d.
The expense of the whole drove from Bala to Billerkey (Billericay)	26	10	0
Their expenses till Brentwood fair	7	4	0
Beds for five of us at the two fairs		8	0
The whole expense of Owen Richard		19	6
For a standing place for the two fairs		10	0
The expense of the cattle from Brentwood fair till Epping fair was over	7	0	0
The expense of myself, the mare, and cattle from Epping till Coldhill fair was over		15	0
For hands to keep the cattle together at Epping and Coldhill		6	0
For myself and the mare upon the road from Coldhill to London		2	6
For hay and oats at London for the mare: 3 days and 3 nights		5	3
My own expenses there for meat and drink		4	0
My own expenses coming home from London with the mare		16	0
My own expenses for meat and drink from Brentwood till Epping Fair	1	16	0
For my bed after Brentwood Fair at London and elsewhere		10	6
Paid for a shoe for the black horse at Brentwood			6
Paid out in treating the several buyers, in the whole the sum of		10	0
	£47	17	3

Although it does not itemise the expenses involved in driving the herd from North Wales to Essex, the Williams account further illustrates the substantial cost of merely maintaining a large drove of cattle at the English fairs until all the animals were sold. The entry "Beds for five of us at the two fairs" suggests that in addition to Williams and Owen Richard, three other drovers were employed. As there is no reference in the account to "casual" wage payments as in the Jonathan and Roderick material, it would seem that these people were regular drovers. Why then is no payment for wages included, as, for example, in the David Davies papers and many of the Jonathan inventories? The explanation is a simple one. Williams himself was a hired servant of a Mr. Garnons, and the inventory represents a personal expense account which he handed to his employer on his return to Wales. Upon receipt of the account Garnons would reimburse Williams' expenses and pay his wage while the junior drovers would collect their wages directly from Garnons on their return. During the course of his business John Williams spent a period of time in London. Like so many drovers, he may have visited the city in order to deposit cash in one of the merchant banks either on behalf of his employer or on behalf of other Merioneth gentlemen. Among the accounts of a Trawsfynydd dealer operating in 1822, there appear entries such as "left with Sir John Perrun, Bankers of London on account of Dolgellau Bank £100", which illustrate this point.[74] The hazards and potential dangers of highway travel in the nineteenth century prompted many dealers and drovers to leave the proceeds of their sales under lock and key in the care of an obliging and no doubt trustworthy landlord. This may partially explain the frequent occurrence of "Lock and Key" Inns along established drove routes in southern Wales, many of which may have been named after the "Lock and Key" at Smithfield, the venue of so many Cardiganshire and Carmarthenshire drovers.

The second late eighteenth century inventory has been transcribed from the accounts of an English dealer, one John Jackson of Easington in Oxfordshire.[75] These accounts refer to purchases of cattle in Northamptonshire and subsequent sales at fairs in Oxfordshire, Berkshire and Wiltshire in 1796/99. As with the Williams inventory discussed above, this account refers not to the expenses of the dealer himself, but to those of his chief drover, Richard Weston.

Jackson Accounts (1799)		*£.*	*s.*	*d.*
April 12th	*Hay to 23 beast*	*1*	*1*	*0*
	Corn		*1*	*10*
	Eating to the man		*3*	*0*
	Ale		*3*	*1¹/₂*
	Liquor to Mr. White			*2¹/₂*
	Give a lad to go a little way with the beast			*3*
	Chambermaid			*6*
April 19th	*8 cwt of hay for 42 beast*	*1*	*12*	*0*
	Eating to the man		*2*	*8*
	Me		*2*	*6*
	Corn			*10*
	Chambermaid			*6*
April 22nd	*Eating to the man as he came back with the cart and beast*			*8*
	Me			*5*
	Corn			*6*

April 25th	Man ('s) dinner			8
	Me			7$^1/_2$
	Paid for 2 calves	1	8	0
	Hay for 25 beast		18	0
	Eating to the man		2	0
	Me		1	10
	Corn			5
	Chambermaid			3
May 4th	Hay and keep for 22 beast, one night		14	8
	Eating to the man		3	8
	Ale		2	6$^1/_2$
	Corn			9
	Chambermaid			3
May 9th	Man breakfast			8
	Corn			4
	Hay to keep 20 beast one night		13	4
	Eating to the man		2	8
	Me		1	7
	Corn			4
	Chambermaid			3
		£8	2	10

Here, once again, are the familiar droving expenses of accommodation, food and forage. Significantly, however, tollgate charges do not appear, suggesting that Weston was able to drive his cattle from south Northamptonshire along a route which avoided the expense of using the turnpike road. The payments for the services of a chambermaid are interesting in that they show Weston to have been a substantial "master drover" with the privilege of passing the night in a tavern. In a similar fashion to the Williams inventory, this account reveals that although Weston covered the expenses of his junior drover ("the man") he did not pay out this man's wages which would have been met directly by Jackson. At first sight the considerable expenditure upon hay at a time when abundant supplies of wayside grazing might reasonably have been expected is rather surprising. The winter of 1798-9, however, was particularly severe and had resulted in a deficiency of fodder in the spring months.[76]

That little had changed over the course of nearly a hundred years is clear from the early eighteenth century expense account of Evan Edwards which sets out the familiar expenses for grass, tolls, and accommodation.

Evan Edwards, charges to Blackmor Fair, 1701 (N.L.W. Chirk Castle MS F7174)

	£	s	d
Att Redbrooke	00	10	00
Att Newport	00	11	08
Att Norton	00	12	04
Att Smockinaton(?)	00	13	00
Att Kelmarch	01	05	00
Att Partunhall	00	12	06
Att Cummington	00	13	06
Att Langley Green	00	15	04
Att Bishop Starford	00	16	00
Att Woodbarnes	04	00	00
Att Blackmore	01	00	00
Pd to Daniel Jones for 20 days	01	00	00
Pd ye same to Richd Price	01	00	00
Pd to kepars	00	06	06
Pd for standing	00	03	06
Toule and hewards(?)	00	09	00
Chargis to London			
Att Chickwell	00	05	00
For Gras at London	00	18	00
For keepars and standing	00	07	00
Paid to Richard Roberts for 30 days	01	10	00
In all	17	09	00

Profitability of the trade

How profitable was the Welsh cattle trade? The paucity of adequate manuscript material once again bedevils any detailed statistical discussion of this aspect of the trade. With the exception of the Jonathan papers, only two manuscript sources have been found which permit a glimpse of overall profitability at a given point in time. The Jonathan material, although frustratingly incomplete in parts, is at least sufficiently detailed to allow the calculation of net profitability over a series of several years.

The annual purchase and sale prices of Welsh "runts" as revealed by the Jonathan papers are plotted in Figure VII. Over the period as a whole there was an upward trend in prices, subject to considerable fluctuations between years according to the supply and demand situation. It is important to approach the interpretation of Figure VII with some caution, for the annual prices plotted represent the mean of purchases and sales in the spring and autumn months. In Figure VIII however, the monthly pattern of purchase prices has been plotted over three periods for which the accounts are particularly detailed. Between these three periods, the trend in price movements is surprisingly consistent.

The upward movement in purchase prices between April and May reflects the demand for store cattle by dealers hoping to sell to graziers for the production of beef from summer grass. The absence of any advance in prices during this period between the years 1863 and 1869 may be related to the persistent run of dry seasons characteristic of the mid and late sixties. During such years, graziers were hesitant to invest in large numbers of cattle in anticipation of enforced sales of half-fat stock

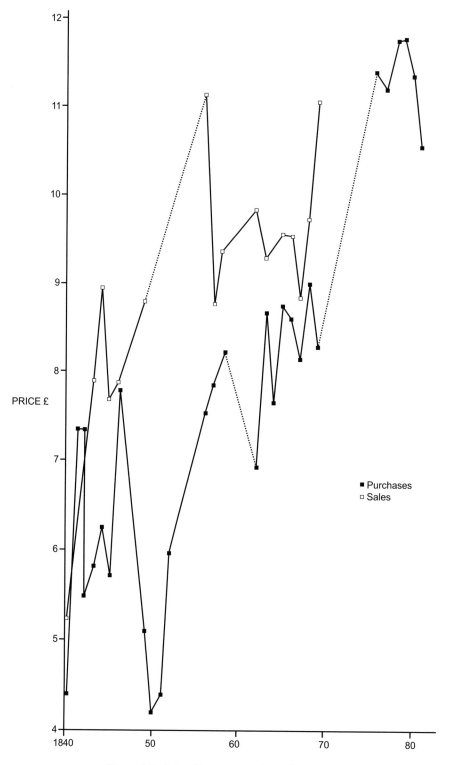

Figure VII. Price Movements (Jonathan Accounts)

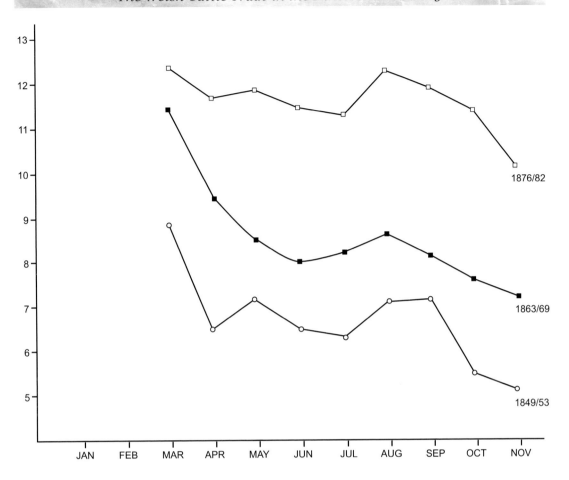

Figure VIII. Monthly Price Variation (Jonathan Accounts)

later in the season when supplies of forage were exhausted. Thus did the fall in prices continue unrelieved until the late summer recovery. With the coming of autumn, English farmers and graziers would be seeking cattle for autumn depasturing and for fattening over the winter months on roots and oilcake, although any tendency for prices to advance would be checked by increased supply. This being so the late autumn price decline reflects a seasonal increase in the supply of cattle to the markets and fairs of Wales, in an attempt on the part of the farmers to avoid the heavy cost of overwintering such beasts. The fact that dealers were selling cattle on to entirely different production systems during the spring and autumn months, suggests that their demand for Welsh store cattle of differing types, sizes and ages, varied according to the time of the year. Thus graziers would require a better quality beast for summer feeding than for autumn grazing. They insisted upon a large animal capable of fattening entirely on grass (or supplemented, perhaps, with a little oilcake) and of leaving the fattening pastures before the autumn decline in fatstock prices. Conversely, the Essex yard feeders, whose prime objective in fattening cattle was to obtain manure for cereal production, would often fatten a rather inferior animal, provided it could be purchased cheaply.

The achievement of an adequate margin to offset overhead expenses was a fundamental factor affecting the profitability of a given drove. Unfortunately, the Jonathan accounts are not sufficiently accurate to enable a profit and loss account for each season to be set down and thus trends in profitability established. Frequently details of cattle purchases were entered without reference to sales, while the mixing together of different lots of cattle before sale makes it particularly difficult to follow through complete transactions. Nevertheless, some assessment of the net profitability of the business for individual years may be obtained, as indicated in the table below:

Table IX Profitability of sample transactions								
	No. of Purchases	Mean Purchase Price		Mean Sale Price		Recorded Expenses		Net Profit per head	
		£	s.	£	s.	£	s.	£	s.
1840	95	4	8	5	4	0	15	0	1
1846	137	7	8	8	17	0	12	0	17
1849	278	6	16	7	10	0	9	0	5
1856	476	8	5	9	5	0	9	0	11
1858	190	9	16	10	11	0	10	0	5

The accounts are particularly detailed between 1862 and 1865, and in an attempt to establish possible within year variations in profitability, a monthly analysis was undertaken as set out in Table X.

Neither the margin between purchase and sale price nor the recorded expenses show any consistent trend within a given year. Both fluctuations in the margin (about a mean of 19s.) and the recorded expenses(about a mean of almost 10s.) resulted in a wide spectrum of profitabilities around the average of 10s. per head, so that over the four year period the dealer enjoyed a maximum gain of almost £2 to a loss of 11s. per beast. The wide variation in the dealer's margin may be ascribed largely to variations in demand. Hence there was a tendency for the margin to be relatively high during the spring and early autumn months when graziers were anxious to purchase cattle.

Table X
Monthly Profit and Loss 1862-1865

Period	No. of Purchases	Average Purchase Price		Average Sale Price		Margin		Average Recorded Expenses per head		Average Profit or Loss per head	
		£	s.	£	s.	£	s.	£	s.	£	s.
1862											
March	107	9	0	10	1	1	1	0	17	+0	4
April	130	7	6	8	8	1	2	0	8	+0	14
May	228	7	6	8	5	0	18	0	9	+0	9
June	80	6	16	7	5	0	9	0	12	-0	3
July	28	6	12	7	3	0	11	0	12	-0	1
August	82	7	15	8	9	0	14	0	4	+0	10
September	80	6	9	7	5	0	16	0	6	+0	10
October	257	6	8	7	6	0	18	0	6	+0	12
November	219	5	19	6	12	0	13	0	6	+0	7
1863											
March	244	10	2	10	16	0	14	0	13	+0	1
April	66	7	14	8	9	0	15	0	9	+0	6
June-September	(Records incomplete)										
October	98	8	18	9	18	1	0	0	8	+0	12
November	266	6	15	7	4	0	9	0	15	-0	6
1864											
March	268	10	0	10	12	0	12	0	15	-0	3
April	146	8	12	9	12	1	0	0	13	+0	7
May	318	8	12	9	5	0	13	0	12	+0	1
June	82	8	13	8	16	0	3	0	14	-0	11
July	(No sales or purchases)										
August	42	5	18	6	13	0	15	0	6	+0	9
September	(No sales or purchases)										
October	95	7	19	9	3	1	4	0	7	+0	17
November	100	7	8	8	8	1	0	0	17	+0	3
1865											
March	98	12	4	13	4	1	0	0	9	+0	11
April	189	10	2	11	15	1	13	0	11	+1	2
May	274	8	8	11	1	2	13	0	15	+1	18
August	30	7	9	8	12	1	3	0	2	+1	1
September	38	6	18	8	12	1	14	0	4	+1	10
October	(Records incomplete)										
November	149	9	7	10	4	0	17	0	6	+0	11

Other dealers' Accounts

The other dealers' account books are of limited value as a means of indicating the profitability of the cattle trade. The Trawsfynydd account book, however, does record details of two transactions effected in March and April of 1822. The dealer's margin on 37 cattle sold in March was £17. 3. 6. (9s. per head), against which were charged overhead costs as below:

Trawsfynydd Account, March 1822	£	s.	d.
Charges at Penmorfa		4	0
Charges at Maentwrog		1	0
Paid Blacksmith	1	8	6
Paid postage of letters		6	6
My charges up	1	6	0
At Lutterworth	2	16	0
Paid by W. Lewis	6	3	4
By John Newbut (?)	7	15	6
At Lubenham	1	14	6
Gate to Harborough		1	8
Me		3	6
My charges at Harborough		2	0
Old William's wages	2	2	0
John (?) wages	2	16	0
My charges home	1	4	6
	£28	5	6

Trawsfynydd Account, April 1822	£.	s.	d.
By W. Lewis	1	16	6
At Voelas (?)		2	6
My charges	1	1	0
At 4 crosses	2	1	0
Unpaid at Widmarsh	2	6	6
At Lutterworth	2	11	6
John Newbut (wages)	2	2	0
John Rowlatt	12	16	0
Will	2	10	0
Gate to Harborough		2	6
Fair Field		12	0
Men		10	6
Paid old will	2	5	0
Charges at Harborough		2	6
At Lubenham	5	8	0
Shoeing mare		2	6
To meet beast		8	0
Paid Will	2	12	0
	£39	10	0

Having met his overhead costs, the dealer was faced with a loss of £11.2.0. (6s. per head). By April, his fortunes had changed, and a margin of £67.14.6. (21s. per head) was set against expenses of £39.10.0. to yield a net profit of £28.4.6. (8s. 6d. per head).

The profit and loss incurred in these transactions falls well within the range of the figures calculated from the Jonathan papers. A similar range of variation in profit margins occurs in the accounts of John Jackson of Easington which cover the Spring months of 1796 (Table XI).

	Numbers	Purchase price/head		Sale price/head		Charges/head		Profit/head	
		£	s.	£	s.	£	s.	£	s.
March	38	14	12	15	14	0	8	0	14
	21	13	12	15	0	0	10	0	18
	30	12	10	14	0	0	8	1	2
	21	9	14	10	16	0	8	0	14
	54	10	18	11	18	0	4	0	16
	38	9	8	10	6	0	6	0	12
April	59	13	2	14	4	0	8	0	14
May	34	12	12	13	18	0	8	0	18
	38	13	2	14	6	0	4	1	0

Table XI
Trading Account of John Jackson, 1796

It is interesting to compare the prices paid and received by Jackson with the purchase and sale prices recorded in the Jonathan accounts. The substantially higher prices in the 1790s may be explained by a combination of wartime inflation and the fact that Jackson was dealing in the highly sought-after Devon, Shorthorn and Longhorn cattle types, all of which realised greater prices than the Jonathans' Welsh "runts."

David Jonathan, senior member of the Jonathan family, began his trading activities with extremely limited capital resources. The dramatic expansion of the business throughout the forties and fifties was financed by capital generated out of profit. This in itself would suggest that the trade was sufficiently profitable to provide for the needs of Jonathan and his family and also to lend financial support to the developing business. Indeed, some measure of his success may be grasped from the fact that at the time of his death in the mid-eighties, Jonathan was the owner of a small estate and the occupier of three substantial farms.[77] Richard Jarrett, drover for the Trawsfynydd dealer whose accounts are discussed above, himself became a dealer in the 1830s, having accumulated a capital sum of £13. Jarrett, who operated in the Corwen area in partnership with his cousin Richard Roberts, eventually retired in 1860 and purchased the considerable mansion of Plas-y-Faeder in Corwen.[78]

It is, of course, dangerous to rely too heavily upon the accounts of one dealer in forming an assessment of the profitability (or otherwise) of the nineteenth century Welsh cattle trade. David Jonathan, having eventually established his business was in a position to create capital from profits and thus to increase business turnover and generate further profit. There were, however, many smaller dealers who operated either upon credit or borrowed capital. Although these people unfortunately left few records of their trading activities, the several legal cases quoted earlier would tend to the conclusion that a man whose business was based upon credit was highly susceptible to a series of "bad deals." Hence a run of dry summers and reduced demand for store stock, combined perhaps with high mortality occasioned by an outbreak of cattle disease, might easily result in severe financial loss. A capitalist dealer of the Jonathan class would be in a position to weather such a storm of adversity by virtue of his capital reserves. On the other hand, the smaller dealer, continually pressurised by his creditors, would find extreme difficulty in withstanding the financial stresses resulting from a series of unprofitable years.

Taking the mean profit of 10s. per head calculated from the Jonathan accounts, a mid-nineteenth century dealer would require to sell some six hundred beasts to earn a reasonable income of £300. To maintain this average profitability would necessitate keen buying, selling on a rising market and the avoidance of mortality. While an outbreak of Cattle Plague or Pleuropneumonia would decimate his drove, a dry summer in the English Midlands might readily reverse his profit of 10s. per head to a loss of similar magnitude. The experiences of Richard Roberts, a tanner from Bala who also dealt in cattle throughout the eighteen sixties and seventies, underline the speculative nature of the trade. Thus Roberts's financial returns varied over the years from an annual loss of £800 to a profit of £700. Varying market conditions were largely responsible for this financial fluctuation.[79] Edmund Hyde Hall drew attention to the risk involved in the pursuance of the trade. Mentioning a dealer who purchased cattle to the value of £1,200 in 1809, he pointed out:

> *"that a capital so great and so frequently turned ought to afford great profits, but the instability of the markets occasions but too frequently a repetition of loss."* [80]

Hyde Hall's summary lays emphasis on the condition of the market which was undoubtedly the principal factor affecting the profitability of the trade. If, however, he had attempted to summarise the other salient factors involved, he would have mentioned also the importance of "keen" buying, and the minimisation of overhead costs.

The Coming of the Railways

This section examines some aspects of the functioning of the cattle trade during the so-called "railway era." It is important at the outset, to attach some qualification to the use of the term "railway era", since the railway network in Wales developed in a piecemeal fashion and its effects upon livestock and, indeed, grain and mineral flows differed between localities. Moreover, it has been held that long distance droving from Wales came to an abrupt halt with the development of railway systems in the Principality. Bonser, for example, contended that little droving took place after the mid-nineteenth century and that droving "ceased with the coming of the railway in 1838." [81]

However, the opening of the Llanelli railway in 1839 and its extension to Pontardulais and Cwmann in 1840 had little or no influence on the cattle trade with England. In common with the other early lines in the metalliferous and quarrying regions of Wales, the Llanelli line was used almost exclusively for the transport of minerals, particularly of coal and limestone.[82] However, as the railway system began to proliferate in the fourth, fifth and sixth decades of the century, many dealers and drovers were beginning to exploit the facilities provided by rail transit, and by 1865 the railway had captured the majority of the livestock flows.[83] Even so, long distance droving did not "cease." Edward Egerton provided evidence for this in his testimony to the Select Committee of 1866, when he pointed out that despite the extension of the South Wales railway to link Carmarthen and Haverfordwest in 1853/4, the majority of the cattle from South Wales still arrived in England by road.[84] Again, many cattle were sent by rail from the Hereford Great Fair of 1868 yet:

> *"the high road to the Midland pastures by Worcester and Stratford-upon-Avon is still vocal for many days later with the drover's cry."* [85]

The minute books of the many Select Committees concerned with the development of the Welsh railways reveal a widespread realisation of the advantages, both to the cattle trade and to other elements of the Welsh rural economy, to be gained from an efficient railway system. Lord Cawdor, for example, submitting evidence to the Select Committee deliberating upon the establishment of the Pembroke and Tenby Railway, highlighted the need for a link with the Great Western Line to assist with the cattle trade, pointing out that at that time, cattle had to be driven from south Pembrokeshire to Narberth before reaching the railhead. [86] Furthermore, one of the arguments advanced in support of the establishment of the Vale of Llangollen Railway, concerned the conveyance of:

> *"great quantities of cattle sent from Merionethshire ... (which) must pass through Llangollen to get to England."*

Again, in the discussions held before the Select Committee on the Aberystwyth and Welsh Coast Railway, the cattle and sheep trade was mentioned and it was implied that the coastal railway would be beneficial to this trade.[87,88] Another witness, Thomas Jones of Newcastle Emlyn, testified to the advantages which would accrue to the townships in the Teifi valley on the Cardiganshire – Carmarthenshire border, given an efficient rail link. This would be particularly beneficial to Newcastle Emlyn with its weekly market and eleven fairs.[89]

The potential advantages to the cattle trade tended to increase in parallel with the expansion of the Welsh railway system which, by comparison to that in England, occurred in a seemingly *ad hoc* and unplanned fashion. Apart from local mineral lines in the South Wales coalfield, the first main lines in Wales represented a continuation of the English network to ensure rapid communications with Ireland. Thus the rail link between Chester and Holyhead was completed in 1852 following the opening of the Menai Bridge, thereby facilitating the speedy and efficient movement of Irish cattle through North Wales to the English grazing counties. Similarly, by the mid 1850s the Great Western Railway had extended from Newport to Milford Haven via Carmarthen and Haverfordwest. The late 1850s and the 1860s witnessed the tapping of the Welsh heartland by ramifications of these main lines to the north and south, and also by branch lines from the Chester-Shrewsbury-Newport railway which had been completed in the 1840s. In 1858, for example, the Tywi Valley was provided with a railroad linking Llandeilo with Llandovery.

This line eventually met the branch route from the Newport-Chester railway which had been extended from Craven Arms to Knighton in 1861 and thence through Llandrindod and Builth Wells (1866), Llanwrtyd Wells (1867), to Llandovery in 1868. In consequence a direct rail link now existed between south-west Wales and Craven Arms by way of Carmarthen. Rail communications with the mid-western and central counties of the Principality arose from the construction of the Newtown-Llanidloes railway (1859), and the Oswestry-Welshpool and Welshpool-Newtown lines in 1860 and 1861 respectively. The latter was subsequently continued to Machynlleth in 1863, reaching Borth and Aberystwyth the following year. The line from Machynlleth, which had been extended in 1863 around the Merionethshire coast to Llwyngwril, had passed through Barmouth and reached Pwllheli by 1867, thus affording an opportunity for dealers from the Llŷn Peninsula to "truck" their cattle to Caernarfon and thence directly to Chester. Another valuable east-west rail link was provided in 1869 by the completion of the line linking Ruabon, Corwen and Bala with the important market centre of Dolgellau. By this time also, Aberystwyth was connected with the Great Western line by means of the railroad through Lampeter, Llandysul and Pencader. The Great Western extension from Whitland to Crymych and Cardigan was not, however, competed until 1875.[90]

The establishment of these and other railroads in the Principality precipitated changes not only in the cost structure of the cattle trade, but in the directional movements of cattle droves throughout Wales. It has been suggested above that although some Welsh cattle still arrived in England by road in the mid-sixties, the railways were by that time heavily involved in the cattle trade. Essentially the impact of railway development upon the re-orientation of the cattle trade routes was a two stage process. The first stage involved the extension of the English railway system to Newport in the South and to Chester and Shrewsbury in the north. The connection with Newport and Chester had been established in the 1840s and by 1848 Chester and Bangor were already linked by rail. It was not until 1856, however, that a direct link between Shrewsbury and the Midland grazing counties was forged by the extension of the railroad from Nuneaton. The establishment of the Shrewsbury rail head at a point close to the centre of the Welsh border provided dealers from mid-Wales direct and relatively rapid access to the Midland markets. Documentary evidence is scant, but it might be assumed that this opportunity would not have been lost to the larger cattle dealers, men whose shrewdness and business acumen rendered them amenable to any change which would reduce the overhead costs of their trading activities. The Jonathans were just such dealers, for their accounts reveal that after 1856 they abandoned the old Tregaron-Abergwesyn route to England through Herefordshire in favour of the turnpike from Aberystwyth to Mallwyd or Newtown and thence to Welshpool and the railhead at Shrewsbury. This is illustrated in the two inventories of expenses set out below:

Jonathan Accounts (1861)	£.	s.	d.
About the county		5	0
Llanbadarn	1	0	0
Machynlleth	3	10	0
do. 2 gates		5	6
Cemmaes and Dinas gates		5	0
Train to Llanidloes and (Welsh) Pool		7	0
Pool gate		6	9
5 gates from Pool to Salop	1	0	6
Salop tavern	2	14	6
Train beast to Tamworth	16	16	6
Gate to Fazeley and Tavern	2	2	6
Daniel Jones' wages	1	1	0
Harborough tavern	1	19	0
Men and ale		6	6
Train to Lutterworth		1	0
Lutterworth hay	7	10	0
do. tavern		12	6
Two men at fair		18	0
Ale at fair		7	6
My train to Leicester		2	6
J. Chapman at Lutterworth		10	0
2 gates to Leicester		3	4
Edward Pantglo	1	6	0
Issac driver		12	0
Leicester tavern	1	8	0
Ale		1	6
Train to Spratton		2	0
Spratton tavern		2	9
Spratton hay	6	10	0
Kingsthorpe tavern		4	0
Men and ale at Northampton		7	6
Train to Harborough		1	6
Men at Harborough		11	6
Driver		12	6
Harborough hay	9	1	0
Harborough tavern		10	0
	£63	14	10

Jonathan Accounts (1862)	£	s.	d.
Aberystwyth gate + Machynlleth tavern	3	6	6
Machynlleth gate 6-6 and boy to mind beast		8	0
Cemmaes gate 3-6 and Dinas gate 2-0		5	6
Mallwyd gate 3-9 and Cann Office gate 3-9			
Cann Office tavern	2	3	6
Llanfair tavern	2	7	0
Llanfair and Welshpool gates		14	0
Welshpool tavern	2	8	0
3 gates from Welshpool to Shrewsbury		12	0
Halfway House	1	17	6
Shrewsbury Tavern	3	15	0
Shrewsbury Train	6	12	6
Man to drive from W. Pool to Shrewsbury		7	0
Feazley tavern and gate	4	2	6
3 gates to Three Potes	1	12	6
Three Potes Tavern	3	5	6
2 gates to Rugby	1	1	0
Rugby Tavern	6	11	0
Men at Rugby Fair		3	6
2 gates to Northampton		16	6
Northampton tavern	1	8	0
2 gates to Turvey		16	6
Turvey Tavern	2	10	0
2 gates to Clophill		13	6
Clophill Tavern	3	6	0
Starneck (?) Tavern	4	3	0
2 gates at Stanstead	5	6	
Stanstead hay for one lot	5	15	0
Harlow Fair			
Norton Inn grass	1	12	6
Ongar hay	4	1	0
Daniel Evans	3	0	0
Ingatestone Fair	1	5	0
Men at Fair		6	9
Myself		8	6
Romford toll		2	0
My expenses and train fare from Chelmsford to London and back			
to Romford.	1	3	6
Chelmsford hay	3	19	0
Men at Chelmsford		8	6
Romford hay	1	1	0
David Lewis' son	4	8	0
David Capel	3	16	0
John?		12	0
Thos. Ellis	4	11	0
John Smith, Driver	3	10	0
John Evans	1	7	0
My expenses in London		9	6
Romford toll		2	0
Myself		13	0
Brentwood gate			10
Chelmsford, hay and myself	1	10	0
Men to keep the beast		3	0
My expense back home	1	10	0
	£101	6	7

Carno on the Machynlleth to Newtown road, now A470, saw many drovers heading for England

The Talbot Hotel, Tregaron where drovers assembled their cattle before heading across the mountains for Abergwesyn. Cattle were shod behind the hotel

The extension of the railway to the western seaboard of Wales heralded the second stage in the impact on the cattle trade of the proliferating railway network. The Great Western Railway had reached Milford Haven by 1856, while Machynlleth and Aberystwyth were linked by rail to Shrewsbury by 1864. Thus, cattle from Pembrokeshire which normally passed up the Tywi valley to Llandovery and over the Epynt to the Wye crossing for Hereford, could now be taken from Haverfordwest, Narberth or Carmarthen directly by rail to Newport and Chepstow and thence to England. Moreover, the completion of the Carmarthen-Shrewsbury line via Craven Arms in 1868 provided a direct link with the Midland pastures. Such was the effect of these developments as far as the Jonathans were concerned that droving within Wales became merely a matter of conveying the animals to the nearest railhead where they were unceremoniously loaded into trucks for the remainder of the journey. The inventory below illustrates this second stage resulting from the extension of the railhead to Machynlleth:

Jonathan Accounts 1864	£.	s.	d
Newcastle (Emlyn) tavern	2	0	0
Stephen Davies, Capel		8	0
Drive beast to Ffyrneithin		5	0
Aberystwyth gate		4	6
Llanbadarn tavern		7	6
Trerddol tavern	2	12	6
Carreg gate		1	2
Machynlleth tavern	2	2	0
Machynlleth gate		3	6
Train beast Machynlleth to Welshpool	11	3	0
Train myself		3	1
Welshpool tavern		8	6
Two gates Pool to Salop		12	8
Harborough tavern and grass		16	0
Harborough tavern myself		7	6
Stand and ale at fair		10	6
Lutterworth tavern		7	6
Meal		1	0
Lutterworth gate		4	0
Spratton grass (3 nights)	6	0	0
Spratton tavern		12	6
Brixworth gate		3	6
Northampton ale		2	6
Myself to Harborough		1	0
Thomas Lewis (drover)	2	7	0
Richard Richards	1	17	0
Timothy Evans	2	0	0
Harborough grass (3 nights)	2	19	0
Harborough tavern		11	0
Ale and stand		5	0
	£39	16	5

Operating and Cost Structure Changes

In addition to influencing the directional movements of dealers and drovers, the impact of the railways brought about significant changes in both the basic operation and the cost structure of the trade. Orwin and Whetham have observed that the railways provided not so much an advantage in terms of comparative money costs, but more by way of a saving in indirect costs such as weight loss and the problem of obtaining forage for cattle en route.[91] Certainly it was increasingly more difficult, as the nineteenth century progressed, both to obtain forage and to secure accommodation for cattle on the established drove routes to England. This became a particularly acute problem following the Cattle Plague epidemic of 1865-6 when farmers became aware of the dangers of disease transmission via droves of cattle assembled by dealers from many different sources. In consequence they were less willing to provide accommodation fields, this effectively inflating the forage costs incurred by the drove.[92]

As far as fat cattle were concerned, the problem of weight loss and reduced carcase quality resulting from long-distance droving was particularly acute. Exhaustion of muscle glycogen reserves would have lowered the carcase quality of driven animals by adversely affecting post-slaughter characteristics of the meat, while even on the relatively short distance from Norfolk to Smithfield, weight losses varying from 28 to 64 pounds were recorded by contemporaries.[93] Clare Sewell Read pointed out that cattle destined for the Smithfield market on a Monday morning normally left Norfolk on the previous Wednesday. By exploiting the rail-link, however, (at an admittedly higher cost) cattle could leave Norfolk on Saturday to arrive at Smithfield on the same evening. The net effect conditional upon reduced weight loss and improved carcase characteristics, was a £1 price advantage in favour of "trucked" as opposed to driven cattle. It is arguable that loss of condition would have been markedly less with the lean store cattle from the Welsh hills, most of which would have built up a sound muscular frame but would be carrying little surplus fat. While fat is an extremely labile tissue readily mobilised in the event of nutritional deprivation or physical stress, it is only under conditions of extreme privation that an animal begins to metabolise muscle tissue. Given the extreme care taken by the Welsh drover to preserve the condition of his animals and to minimise the stress upon them, it is unlikely that weight losses reached the magnitude of those suggested by Hawke.[95]

The Cost of Shipping by Rail

Of perhaps greater significance was the effect of the railways on the basic cost structure of the cattle trade, discussed previously in terms of the drovers' account books. Hawke has estimated that by the mid-nineteenth century, in the absence of railways, droving costs would have amounted to not less than 0.6d. per mile. He rightly pointed out that costs would tend to be higher in the spring and autumn months due to the problem of obtaining adequate supplies of forage at these times and accordingly imposed an upper limit of 1½d. per mile on his estimate.[96]

In the Jonathan accounts, the average recorded expenses of droves not using the railway facilities amounted to approximately ten shillings per head over the years 1862/1865. It is difficult to compute the expense on a per mile basis, owing to the fact that within a given drove some animals would be sold in Northampton and Leicester while others would be taken to Market Harborough, Rugby, Daventry and other local fairs. In general, however, distances varied between 150 and 200 miles, representing a per mile cost of 0.6d. and 0.8d, figures which fall well within the range of Hawke's estimates. In an attempt to assess the rail mileage rate for cattle transit, Hawke analysed the 1865 returns of ten railway companies, ranging from the Northern and South Western Railway carrying a mere 658 beasts to the London and North Western Railway which transported in excess of 400,000 cattle. This analysis revealed that with the exception of the high rates of the local North London

Railway, the rate per mile for the remaining companies lay within the range 0.61d.–0.88d. per head.[97] The Jonathan manuscripts provide isolated examples which enable a comparison with Hawke's assessment. Some such examples are set out below:

Table XII				
Jonathan Accounts – Railway transit costs				
Date	No. of beasts	Journey	Cost	Cost/head/mile
1856	197	Shrewsbury - Tamworth	£ 6	0.13d.
1856	146	Shrewsbury - Nuneaton	£ 7	0.12d.
1856	161	Shrewsbury-Nuneaton	£ 6	0.11d
1862	118	Welshpool - Nuneaton	£16	0.32d.
1863	116	Shrewsbury -Tamworth	£17	0.45d.
1864	189	Welshpool - Tamworth	£27	0.45d.
1866	38	Aberystwyth - Rugby	£11	0.30d.
1867	170	Machynlleth - Rugby	£40	0.33d.

Not only are these rates substantially lower than those calculated by Hawke, but they are also below the rate of 0.8d. per head per mile charged by the L.N.W.R. as early as 1847.[98] Hawke's calculations are based on the returns to a questionnaire circulated by the Royal Commission on Railways in 1865 and he admits that:

"This data does not give an unequivocal figure of cost per mile for livestock transport because charges were quoted per truck load and the number of beasts in a truck varied... because of the differences between store and fat cattle..."

A further complication arose from the fact that some companies quoted their rates in terms of per "truck-mile", and thus rates per head could not be discerned without reference to the number of beasts in each truck.[99] In 1847, for instance, the L.N.W. R. calculated charges on the basis of six fat beasts or seven to eight lean beasts per wagon.[100] On the other hand, the Great Western Railway considered seven fat or ten store cattle to be a "fair average small truck-load" while the Great Northern Railway charged at the rate of 5d-6d. per mile for a "small" wagon, 6½d.-7d. for a "medium" wagon and 7d.-8d. for a "large" wagon of store cattle, this rate also varying according to distance.[101]

This highly confused situation renders virtually meaningless any generalised statement on cattle transit rates per mile, unless it is specified whether these rates refer to fat or store cattle. Herein may lie the explanation for the considerable disparity between the estimates of Hawke and those calculated from the Jonathan accounts, for while Hawke was no doubt dealing with varying ratios of fat and store cattle, the Jonathans were concerned almost exclusively with store beasts, the rates per head for which were lower due to the greater number of animals which could be accommodated in each wagon. However, despite Robert Moseley's testimony to the Select Committee on the Trade in Animals, that in terms of cost, droving competed favourably with "trucking" over a 40-50 mile journey, it appears from the figures of Hawke and from the Jonathan accounts (in which the railway charge component comprised 30 per cent of total costs between 1862 and 1865) that over long journeys at least, rail usage tended to reduce the cost of cattle transit.[102]

The Jonathan papers reveal a reduction in average overhead costs from 12s per head in 1840/49 to 9s.9d in 1862/65. Indeed, it has been argued that the advent of the railway system effected a halving in the real transport costs of livestock flows, resulting in an overall social saving of £0.04-£0.24 million. [103] Moreover, use of the railway network had the effect of reducing the impact of unfavourable weather conditions on droving costs. This was particularly the case during periods of drought when the drover, unable to obtain sufficient cheap overnight grazing, would be forced to purchase hay to maintain his beasts. The opposite situation no doubt occurred during the spring and autumn months when heavy rains, or even snow, would severely impede the progress of the drove, and it could never be guaranteed with complete certainty that the cattle would arrive before the end of a given market or fair. It might be said, therefore, that in addition to reducing overall costs, exploitation of the railways permitted more efficient timeliness of marketing.

The Impact of Railways on Local Fairs

The influence of the evolving railway network on the geographical distribution and frequency of the old periodic local fairs is an important one and has been briefly referred to in the earlier pages of this chapter. Although the coming of the railway sounded the death knell for many local cattle fairs in the midland and eastern counties of England, this was not altogether the case in Wales. Indeed, there was a marginal rise in the number of fairs held in Cardiganshire in 1888 by comparison with 1792, while in Carmarthenshire and Pembrokeshire the numbers increased dramatically.

Principal Fairs in South West Wales in 1792 and 1888

Cardiganshire	1792	1888
Cardigan	4	5
Capel St. Silin	1	0
Capel Cynon	3	0
Dihewyd	1	2
Lampeter	6	12
Llechryd	0	1
Llanarth	1	4
Llandysul	2	0
Llanwnen	1	0
Llanwenog	1	0
Ffair Rhos	3	0
Pontrhydfendigaid	0	5
Talsarn	2	0
Tregaron	2	1
Ystrad Meurig	1	0
Total	28	30

Carmarthenshire	1792	1888
Abergwili	2	3
Carmarthen	6	12
Caeo	2	0
Dryslwyn	2	0
Ffair Fach	1	0
Kidwelly	3	3
Llanllawddog	0	1
Llanedi	1	0

Llanelli	2	2
Llandybie	1	3
Llandeilo Fawr	0	10
Llandovery	6	11
Llangadog	5	6
Llangendeirne	1	0
Llanon	1	2
Llansadwrn	1	0
Llansawel	3	0
Llanfihangel	2	0
Llanwinio	1	0
Llanybydder	3	5
Myddfai	0	2
Meidrim	1	0
Newcastle Emlyn	3	13
Pembrey	0	1
Pentre	2	0
Penybont	1	0
Talley	0	1
Three Lords	2	0
Total	**52**	**75**

Pembrokeshire

Camross	2	0
Carew	0	4
Cilgerran	2	2
Crymych	0	12
Eglwyswrw	2	4
Fishguard	0	5
Haverfordwest	8	12
Henfeddau	0	2
Herbertston	0	1
Laugharne	2	0
Letterston	0	11
Little Newcastle	0	3
Llandeloy	0	4
Maenclochog	1	9
Mathry	1	1
Narberth	4	13
Newport	1	2
Pembroke	4	7
Puncheston	0	1
St. Davids	0	5
Templeton	0	1
Tenby	4	0
Waterston	0	1
Whiston	1	1
Total	**32**	**101**

Several significant points emerge from this list.[104] Firstly, it appears that in the majority of cases the increased frequency of fairs occurred alongside the principal rail routes, particularly in the vales of the Tywi and Teifi. Thus the number of fairs held at Carmarthen, Llandovery, Newcastle Emlyn and Lampeter doubled between 1792 and 1888, while at Llandeilo Fawr, where there were no fairs in 1792, ten fairs were held in 1888. Similarly the fairs of Haverfordwest increased in frequency with the extension of the railway to Milford Haven, while the branch line from Whitland to Cardigan was largely responsible for the establishment of twelve important fairs at Crymych by 1888.

The advent of the railways also precipitated local shifts in the siting of fairs. Ffair Rhos, for example, declined in favour of nearby Pontrhydfendigaid (Bont) which lay in proximity to the railroad, while the fair at Llanbadarn Fawr was moved to the railhead at Aberystwyth. Ultimately Aberystwyth Fair, along with that of Tregaron and many other towns connected by the railway, were replaced by weekly auction markets. However, as Howell has pointed out, many of the old-established fairs survived until well into the twentieth century, owing to the unwillingness of farmers to pay commission to auctioneers and also to the fact that in store rearing areas, the local fair was still the most efficient means of assembling willing buyers and sellers to trade in a free market situation.[105] Besides, the local

fair permitted the farmer some degree of personal control over the price he received for his store animals while also enabling him to indulge in the traditional time-honoured haggling over prices with the dealers and drovers to whom he was selling.

The demand for the services of the long distance drover declined as dealers began to rely progressively more upon railway transit, yet the "local" drover was still very much a part of the Welsh rural scene. Drovers were required to assist with the movement of livestock from farms and collecting centres to the local fairs and markets, and it is possible that this became the role of some of those drovers rendered redundant by the coming of the railway.

Other "local" drovers were employed by farmers wishing to send sheep and cattle to fairs, often many miles from the home farm. The drover Dafydd Isaac of Trefenter in Cardiganshire, for example, frequently covered the ninety mile journey from Machynlleth to Brecon fair with 300-400 sheep in the early decades of the twentieth century. Isaac, who

Machynlleth, port of call for many nineteenth century drovers

as a youth had been employed as a farm servant to supplement the income from his parents' small farm, was eventually enabled, largely by virtue of his droving pursuits, to become the successful occupier of a lowland farm.[106]

Whereas the Jonathan accounts indicate that use of the railway system permitted a reduction in the overhead costs of droving during the eighteen fifties and sixties, they do not illustrate the influence of the escalating railway charges of the seventies on the fortunes of the cattle trade. From the late eighteen seventies, however, there were persistent complaints, both to the farming press and to the various committees discussing the course of the agricultural depression, of rapidly increasing railway rates. Thomas Bowstead argued that reduced attendance at livestock shows resulted from high railway rates, while there were frequent complaints, in 1880, that the railway companies were transporting foreign cattle at cheaper rates than home-bred beasts on the same train. [107]

Sixteen years later, in his testimony to the Welsh Land Commission, Walter Evans, a cattle dealer from Haverfordwest, produced figures showing that rates per mile for cattle transported from Milford Haven to Berwick in Sussex exceeded those obtaining for animals conveyed by boat and rail from Cork to Berwick. In consequence, he argued, it was:

> *"... impossible for the farmers of Wales to go to the expense and trouble of breeding stock for the English market at the present low prices, and to pay the extortionate rates."* [108]

Evans's argument was supported by the evidence of the Assistant Commissioners to the Welsh Land Commission, who reported almost universal complaint of the high railway rates for the conveyance of farm produce and of the advantageous differential treatment offered to foreign importers. Cattle dealers from Northumberland lent voice to the general complaint by denouncing the excessive profits which they claimed were being gleaned by the Caledonian Railway from the transport of cattle. They declared that these heavy charges were preventing English graziers from having recourse to the northern and Scottish markets."[109]

It has already been shown, for the mid 1860s at least, that the fundamental change from the droving to the "trucking" of cattle, effected a reduction in marketing costs. Accordingly, it might be argued that theoretically this diminution of overhead costs should have provided a stimulus to the cattle trade. By the late 1850s the railway companies were preparing returns of both their passenger and goods traffic and Table XIII summarises cattle numbers carried by some of the Welsh companies during the early 1860s. The table is compiled from the Railway Returns located in the House of Lords Records Office.

In the absence of any statistics relating to the volume of the cattle trade during the pre-railway period, these figures tell us nothing about any possible expansion of the trade. Furthermore, they do not represent an unequivocal statement of the overall total cattle numbers transported from Wales, as the returns from the London and North Western and Great Western Railways would have included cattle from other parts of Britain. The table nevertheless provides a useful indication of the rapid expansion of the use of the local railways for the purpose of cattle transportation. The later railway returns do not, unfortunately, discriminate between the different classes of livestock transported, so that a comparison of the volume of cattle movements during the period of railway rate inflation in the eighties and nineties with that prevailing in the sixties is not possible. It is unlikely, however, despite the comments of Walter Evans to the Welsh Land Commission, that the increased railway charges significantly affected the volume of the Welsh cattle trade. The demand for Welsh store cattle on the English grazing pastures was maintained throughout the nineteenth century, notwithstanding the growth of the Irish cattle trade. The decline of the old style drover with the coming of the railways meant that the satisfaction of this demand was largely in the hands of the capitalist dealer, an entrepreneur confident of raising credit wherever necessary and an established businessman trusted and respected by his clientèle. Dealers who had built up business goodwill over a number of years would hardly have contracted their trading activities merely on account of inflated transport costs. The smaller dealer may have shivered in the draught of railway cost inflation. The larger operator, however, responsible for the major volume of the cattle trade, would doubtless have absorbed the increased costs in the interests of preserving the integrity of his business.

Table XIII
Cattle numbers carried by various Welsh railway companies 1860–66

Date	Llanelli and Vale of Towy	Monmouth-shire	Vale Of Clwyd Company	Taff Vale	LNWR	Denbigh Ruthin and Corwen	Great Western	Cambrian	Reference
1860	96	725	541	0					B.P.P. LVII p.575 et seq.
1861	23	907	1,193	0					B.P.P. LIII p.752 et seq.
1862	119	1,065	1,814	323		288			B.P.P.LXII p.1 et seq.
1863	289	1,462	2,143	344	524,585	758	166,139	76	B.P.P.XLIX p.19 et seq.
1864	400	1,539	3,100	327	491,978	1,005	156,363	12,750	B.P.P.XLIX p.173 et seq.
1865	1,288	1,265	2,805	571	402,042	1,229	144,465	19,172	B.P.P LXIII p.25 et seq.
1866	940	1,96	4,840	318	388,005	5,800	147,730	22,598	B.P.P. LXII p.23 et seq.

FOOTNOTES FOR CHAPTER 4

1   Evans, *op. cit.*, p. 320.
2   Narberth Fair Transactions, Haverfordwest RO. D/ RTP.
3   N.L.W. Llanllyr MSS. l12-125.
4   By the close of the nineteenth century the summer and autumn fairs of Cilgerran were inun dated with drovers intent upon purchasing cattle for the English market. One of my correspondents vividly remembers cattle lining the streets from the rectory to the station. She recollects also the inconvenience of having to vacate her room in her parents' public house in order that the drovers be accommodated for the duration of the fair. (Personal Communication: Miss E. Bowen, Shrewsbury).
5   G. Nesta Evans, *op. cit.*, p. 120.
6   Hyde Hall, *op. cit.*, p. 227.
7   Personal communication: Mr. Thomas Bebb, Llanfair Caereinion.
8   H.Evans, "The Welsh Drovers", *Wales and Monmouthshire*, No. 8, 1937, p. 19.
9   N.L.W. Brigstocke MS. 18.
10 Timothy Richards, *Reminiscences of Ffaldybrenin*. (From 1931 programme of Esgairlas St. David's Day concert).
11 *Commission of Inquiry into the State of Education in Wales*, 1847, Vol. I, B. P. P. XXVII, p. 217. Johnes' comment on the literacy of the small farmers is supported by an inspection of contemporary wills, a majority of which are signed with a mark. Giving evidence to the Commission, the Rev. Price Lewis attributed the anxiety for learning on the part of the villagers of Llancrwys in Carmarthenshire to the fact that so many drovers from that parish visited England (*Ibid.*, p. 218).
12 Hyde Hall, *op. cit.*, p. 19.
13 H.R. Davies, *op. cit.*, p. 193.
14 Kay (Anglesey), *op. cit.*, p. 24. He maintained, moreover, that between November 1791 and November 1792 two drovers alone purchased 4,786 cattle from Anglesey.
15 W. Davies, (North Wales), *op. cit.*, p. 310.
16 U.C.N.W. MS. 6938.
17 Hyde Hall, *op. cit.*, p. 167.
18 Davies, (North Wales), *op. cit.*, p. 312.
19 S. and B. Webb, English Local Government, *The Story of the King's Highway*, London, 1913, p. 412.
20 W. Barrow Wall, "The Agriculture of Penbrokeshire" *J.R.A.S.E.*, Ser. ii, XXIII, 1887, p. 78.
21 Hyde Hall, *op. cit.*, p. 279.
22 N.L.W. MSS. 9600-9614.
23 Evans, *op. cit.*, p. 320.
24 N.L.W. Broadhead Evans MSS. 32 and 33.
25 I am indebted for this information to Mr. Ben Morgan of Farmers.
26 J.E. Jones, *op. cit.*, p. 94.
27 N.L.W. MS. 6733.
28 *Bye Gones*, April 13th 1904. In Corwen, six of the strongest men in the village were employed to assist with shoeing.
29 "Prize Essay on the Farming of Cumberland", *J.R.A.S.E.*, Ser. i, XIII, 852, p. 261.
30 Thomas Davies, Dinas Mawddwy, 1893. I am indebted to Mr. D. Wyn Jones of Machynlleth for forwarding translations of relevant sections of this work.
31 J.E.Jones, *op. cit.*, p. 99.
32 T. Davies, *op. cit.*, (Trans).
33 Hugh Evans, *The Gorse Glen*, Brython Press, 1948, passim.

34 I am indebted for this information to Mr. Daniel Morgan, retired blacksmith. Mr. Morgan contends that in Carmarthenshire many of the personnel involved in cattle shoeing were paid in kind rather than in cash.

35 NLW. MS. 6733.

36 John Bannister, *A synopsis of husbandry*, London, 1799, p. 327; N.L. W. MS.6733; Personal Communication: Mr. J. Dobson, Audlem.

37 Personal Communication: Mr. B. Jones, Tregaron.

38 Particularly Bannister, *op. cit.*, p. 328.

39 Marking was normally effected by cutting the hair above the left knee in the monogram of the dealer; (N.L.W. 6733).

40 Personal Communication: Mr. B. Jones, Tregaron.

41 Mrs. Jane Davies, Tregaron, recalls that her father, who died in 1950 at the age of 96, began his droving life at 12 years of age, making four journeys from Tregaron to Warwickshire each spring. With a drove of cattle, he and his associates took 16-17 days to complete this journey.

42 *Gentleman's Magazine*, 10th September 1770, p. 34.

43 NLW. 17927A.

44 K. Bonser, *The Drovers*, London, 1970, p.40. Having once established the farms and inns willing to accommodate his drovers, it would subsequently be unnecessary for the dealer to precede the drove. (Personal Communication: Mr. D. Jones, Bronnant.)

45 The ready availability of water on the drove routes was of paramount importance. Mr. Edward Roberts of Clatter relates a story of his great grandfather, John Roberts, who frequently took cattle from Montgomeryshire to Kent. During a particularly dry Summer in the mid 1850s Roberts paid a Gloucestershire farmer £5 for the privilege of watering 150 head of cattle in this farmer's pond. Apparently Roberts' cattle succeeded in emptying the pond, much to the annoyance of the farmer who was forced to purchase water for his own stock for the remain der of the Summer.

46 I am indebted to Miss Bowen of Shrewsbury for this information.

47 Personal Communication: Mrs. J. Davies, Tregaron.

48 In 1859, the Llancrwys drover, John Walters, died at Hyde in Middlesex on his return from Barnet fair, leaving a modest fortune of some £1,500. Mr. Robertson of the "Lock and Key" was executor of this will (Personal Communication: Mr. I. Walters, Ffaldybrenin).
The "Lock and Key", in addition to providing accommodation for drovers, was also the venue for harp and singing concerts as early as 1825 (*Byegones* 1, 1889-90, p. 63). John Jones (Jac Glan y Gors), who went to London in the company of drovers, eventually became proprietor of the King's Head, Ludgate Hill, which he established as a social, political and cultural centre for London Welshmen. (H Evans, *op. cit.*, p. 19).

49 By the late 1840s David Rees was employed as head drover, assisted by John and Timothy Lloyd, Charles Jones and Evan Evans, while in the 1860s the names of Thomas Lewis, Robert Richards, Timothy Evans, John Evans and John Williams regularly feature in the accounts.

50 N.L.W. 11706A.

51 Skeel, *op. cit.*, p. 154.

52 By the 1870s many Welsh cattle were arriving by rail in London. The drover Davies of Tregaron was provided with a free railway pass to travel with his cattle, while he received from the dealer Dafydd Griffiths the sum of £1 to cover his expenses his journey home and his wage. (Personal Communication: Mrs. J. Davies, Tregaron).

53 Middlesex RO. MJ/OC/5.

54 19 Geo. II, cap. V, 1746.

55 G. Nesta Evans, *op. cit.*, p. 122.

56 *Carmarthen Antiquary*, 3, 1963.

57 PRO. H.O. 73(1).

58 PRO. P.C. 8/71: 5879.
59 *Carmarthen Journal*, Dec. 31st 1865. p. 19.
60 B.P.P. XVI. App. II.
61 29 & 30 Vict., Cap. 2, 1866.
62 Personal Communication: Mrs. J. Davies, Tregaron.
63 57 & 58 Vict., Cap. 97, 1894.
64 The establishment of a slaughter and compensation policy was essentially a return to the system prevailing in the mid-eighteenth century by which Quarter Sessions were empowered to allocate compensation to both farmers and drovers whose diseased animals were slaughtered. Indeed, the compensation certificates preserved in the Kent Archives Office relating to the autumn and winter of 1753-54, indicate that some three quarters of the total compensation paid to cattle plague victims during that period went to drovers from North Wales who were selling cattle at the Kentish fairs. (D. Baker "An Eighteenth Century Drover; William Williams of Tan y Bwlch", *Jour. Merion Hist. & Rec. Soc.*VI(iv), 1972, p. 369).
65 U.C.N.W. MS. 33281.
66 Personal Communication: Mr. Edward Roberts, Clatter, Caersws.
67 N. L.W. 11706A.
68 Sturt, *op. cit.*, p. 19.
69 D. Defoe, *A Tour through England and Wales*, Everyman ed., Vol. II, p. 127.
70 S&B. Webb, *op. cit.*, pp. 68-9.
71 In medieval England, also, early experiments in artificial road construction had met with considerable protest from drovers who believed this road improvement would deprive their beasts of the casual roadside grazing enjoyed on the drift ways. (F.M. Stenton. "The road system of Medieval England", *Econ. Hist. Rev.* Ser. i, 1936-7, p. 4).
72 Merioneth R.O. D/T 66.
73 Transcribed by K. Williams-Jones in "A Drovers Account", *Merion. Hist. & Rec. Soc. 2*, 1953-6. p. 311.
74 N.L.W. 17927A.
75 Bod. Lib. MSS. Ridley AIII c, 14.
76 Young, (*Annals* XXXIII) quoted by E.L. Jones in *Seasons and Prices*, *op. cit.*, p. 154. John Lown, the 4th Duke of Newcastle's bailiff at Hafod in Cardiganshire explained to his master in December 1837 that to send sheep from Hafod to Newcastle's Clumber estate in Nottinghamshire would be "more expensive at this time than a few weeks ago as they would now require hay on the road" (University of Nottingham library: Ne.C. 8659(a)).
77 J. Llefelys Davies, "The Livestock Trade in West Wales in the Nineteenth Century", *Aberystwyth Studies*, 13, 1934, p. 10.
78 N.L.W. 6733.
79 Personal Communication: Mrs. B. Roberts, Bala.
80 Hyde Hall, op. cit., p. 127.
81 Bonser, *op. cit.*, p. 48.
82 M. Harris. *The Railway Network of Wales*, unpublished M.A. thesis. University of Wales, 1953, p. 23.
83 G.R. Hawke. *Railways and Economic Growth in England 1840-1910*, Oxford, 1970, p. 134.
84 B.P.P. XVI. p. 11-12.
85 H H Dixon, "The Rise and Progress of Shorthorns", *J.R.A.S.E.*, Ser. ii.,3, 1863, p. 286.
86 H.L.R.O.H. of C. 24, 1863, p. 4 (Pembroke and Tenby Railway). It is interesting to note, nevertheless, that the contribution in cash terms of livestock transport to the coffers of the Pembroke and Tenby railway was relatively small during the closing decade of the century.
87 H.L.R.O.H.of L. 8, 1859, p. 6 (Vale of Llangollen Railway).
88 H.L.R.O.H. of C. I, 1861, p. 311 (Aberystwyth & Welsh Coast Railway).

89 H.L.R.O.H. of C. 62, 1872. (Teifiside Railway).

90 Much of the above information is derived from the list of opening dates of Welsh railways given by Harris, *op. cit.*, Appendix II. pp. 158-60.

91 Orwin and Whetham, *op. cit.*, p. 97.

92 An observation to this effect was made by the drover Davies of Tregaron. whose reminiscences have been mentioned in an earlier chapter.

93 CS. Read, "On the Farming of South Wales" *J.R.A.S.E*, ser i, X, 1849,p. 296.

94 *Ibid.*, p. 290.

95 Hawke, *op. cit.*, p. 146. Although there were doubtless individual cases of high weight loss by unthrifty cattle, such animals perhaps attracted the attention of the witnesses quoted by Hawke who refers primarily to cattle driven in Ireland, or from Scotland to Norfolk and London.

96 *Ibid.*, pp. 145-146.

97 *Ibid.*, p. 140. Within his ten companies Hawke did not include any returns from Welsh railways.

98 *Farmers Magazine*, January 1847, p. 46. The drover at this time travelled free with his charges.

99 Hawke, *op. cit.*, p. 141. Hawke used $5^1/_2$d. per truck-mile to calculate his estimates.

100 *Farmers Magazine*, January 1847, p. 46.

101 *J.R.A.S.E.* Ser iii, VI, 1895, p. 71.

102 B.P.P. XVI. 1866, pp. 11-12.

103 Hawke, *op. cit.*, p. 147. Although the evidence would suggest that railway usage reduced the overhead costs of cattle transit, the familiar expenses of beer, board, gates and forage occur in the inventories above. These costs were incurred in taking cattle to the railhead and also in the movement of animals between fairs in the Midland counties.

104 *First Report of the Royal Commission on Market Rights and Tolls*, I, 1889, B.P.P. LIII. Appendix.

105 D Howell, *Agriculture in Wales in the Nineteenth Century*, p. 10. (Text of paper delivered to Hist. Geog. Assn. Aberystwyth, 1973).

106 R. Phillips, "The last of the Drovers", *Trans. Cymm.*, 1968. Pt. I, passim. Other drovers from the Llanddewibrefi region regularly drove both cattle and sheep to Brecon Fair during the years before World War II. (Personal Communication: Mr. G. Davies, Llanddewibrefi.)

107 T. Bowstead "Report on the British and foreign cattle exhibited at Kilburn", *J.R.A.S.E.*, Ser ii., XV, 1879, p. 603. He maintained that the cost of transporting animals to Kilburn Show ranged from $4^1/_2$d. per mile for calves to 1s. per mile for bulls. These charges it appears, were somewhat inflated owing to the necessity of disinfecting carriages and renewing wear and tear of the padded fabric of the interior of the carriage.

108 B.P.P. XLI. p. 501.

109 *Ibid.*, Final Report, pp. 131-39. The situation had been exacerbated by the *Railway and Canal Traffic Act* of 1888, under the terms of which the traditional free railway passes for drovers were withdrawn, except for cattle travelling to the Royal and other shows. The railway companies argued that the free pass system had long been abused to the extent that friends of drovers and even women had been seen to travel on free passes. This, however, was vehemently denied by John Campbell, farmer and sometime drover of Gwernarglwydd near Rhayader. (B.P.P. XL. p. 968.)

DROVERS ROUTES IN CENTRAL & SOUTH WEST WALES

5

Manuscript material relating to the location of drovers' routes to the English border is extremely sparse. The several drovers' account books discussed previously, together with isolated comments and peripheral references contained in the diaries and travel journals of nineteenth century farmers and antiquarians constitute the bulk of the source material available. During the nineteen thirties the late Dr. R.T. Jenkins published his *"Y Ffordd yng Nghymru"*, a book for younger readers, which contained a limited amount of information on the drovers and their itineraries.[1] In addition, among the Jenkins papers deposited in the library of the University College of North Wales are several pages of manuscript notes concerned, in very general terms, with some of the routes taken by the drovers from the northern and southern counties of Wales to the English borders. The author readily acknowledges that these notes, compiled by Jenkins largely on the basis of the reminiscences of local people, have been to a considerable extent the foundation of this chapter.[2] However, the Jenkins notes, although an invaluable "launching pad", provided little more than an outline sketch, and it was clear from the outset that to compile a detailed account of the principal trade routes it would be necessary to employ cartographic sources and local information in addition to undertaking a considerable amount of fieldwork.

The first approach to the problem involved a review of the parish histories (where available) of those localities mentioned by Jenkins as lying in close proximity to a drove route. In general terms this proved to be a rather barren exercise, many of the histories being written in the late nineteenth and early twentieth centuries when local historians tended to be concerned more with the antiquarian than the socio-economic aspects of the history of their parishes. The second approach was effected by means of a series of circular and personal letters to the incumbents and schoolmasters of parishes believed to be connected in some way with the cattle trade. Recipients of such letters, in which information was sought regarding the location of drovers' inns and shoeing compounds, together with details of the routes themselves, were requested to pass on the letter to other local residents if they were personally unable to help. This postal appeal was reinforced by a brief broadcast on B.B.C. Wales Radio 4 in February 1971. The combination of the postal appeal and the broadcast elicited an encouraging response, indicating the very considerable interest both in England and Wales in the saga of the drovers. Many respondents were subsequently contacted during the course of the fieldwork and their assistance in establishing the position of the drove routes often proved invaluable. By means of a combination of the Jenkins notes, the postal appeal and the account books, it was possible to establish the general directional movements of the drovers. It soon became clear that it would be quite impossible, owing to time limitations, to undertake the fieldwork necessary to compile a detailed description of the complete drove routes from west Wales to the English border. Accordingly it was decided to limit the detailed study to the county of Cardigan and the northern and central regions of Carmarthenshire. Nevertheless, the "continuation" routes from these counties to the principal points of exit from Wales were traced and will be described subsequently, although in rather less detail than those for Cardiganshire and Carmarthenshire.

It was necessary, before beginning the fieldwork, to attempt to obtain further knowledge of the routes by studying the available cartographic material. The principal cartographic sources used were the first editions of the 1in Ordnance Survey Maps compiled in the eighteen thirties, together with the first edition 6in maps published in the eighties and nineties of the 19th century. Also Thomas Kitchen's map of Cardiganshire (1754), Singer's map of the same county engraved by Carey in 1803, and Emmanuel Bowen's map of South Wales (1760) provided useful details. This material was supplemented by a detailed search of the Tithe Maps and Apportionments for the parishes of Cardiganshire and Carmarthenshire as a means of establishing the location of field and place names which may have been linked with the cattle trade. In particular the Tithe Apportionments were searched for names containing *"sais"* and *"saeson"* elements as it was hypothesised that such nomenclature as *"Rhyd sais"*, and *"Cae saeson"* may have derived from the activities of the English drovers and dealers who frequently visited Wales. Marshall noted that Leicestershire graziers:

"draw cattle from almost all quarters of the kingdom, sometimes going... to the very seacoast of Wales to buy them, posting from fair to fair for a week or a fortnight before returning home" [3]

Similarly the Bulkeley diaries testify to the presence of English buyers at the fairs of North Wales. Thus in 1741:

"Three Northamptonshire graziers being now come to the country were content with the leavings of our country drovers," and again in 1749, *"Bangor Fair today proved a very good one and a great many English dealers in it."* [4]

Upon plotting the distribution of these *"sais"* elements there appeared to be a strong correlation between their location and the passage of a drove route. A similar relationship appeared to exist for the location of place names containing a *"London"* type element, such as *"Smithfield"*, *"Piccadilly"*, *"Holborn"* and *"Little London."* It was further hypothesised that the distribution of fields or enclosures containing the elements *"pound"* or *"ffald"* in their names might perhaps be linked with both the drovers' routes and the geographical location of cattle fairs throughout Cardiganshire and Carmarthenshire. This, however, was shown not to be the case, and that apart from local village pounds, spread of *"Cae Pound"* or *"Cae Ffald"* names tends to occur in a virtually random fashion. The final stage in the research involved taking to the field armed with the evidence accumulated from the above sources, and by a combination of interviews with elderly local residents and careful observation on the ground, attempting to assemble a record of the drovers' routes as they existed in the 1970s.

It is probable that the general direction taken by cattle drovers in their north-south and west-east wanderings in the nineteenth century was as old as the trade itself, although enclosure, turnpiking and other landscape changes might have necessitated minor deviations. There remained opportunities for broad meandering across open upland moorlands, yet the capacity to strike across lowland country and create new routeways was severely limited by the mid-sixteenth century since most of England south of the Trent was under cultivation and increasingly subject to enclosure. The evolution of the turnpike system from the later seventeenth century onwards both created problems and afforded opportunities. Clearly, the turnpiking of a road in regular use by drovers would add significantly to their costs, to which extant account books bear ample witness. On the other hand, turnpiking and the general development of lowland communications and the bridging of rivers could be advantageous in terms of timeliness of marketing, in addition to which shod cattle travelling along a decently-maintained turnpike would often arrive at the point of sale in superior condition to those arriving by way of lengthy and sinuous detours. It was, then, a matter of fine judgement for a particular drover to balance out the comparative advantages and disadvantages. Among the letters of Lord Fitzwilliam of Milton in Northamptonshire and his steward, Francis Guybon, are references to an interesting case of a shift of route as a consequence of the imposition of tolls. In a lengthy and somewhat tortuous dispute concerning the repair of a 'chaise highway' (i.e. a drove road) on a certain common used (and much damaged by) drovers en route to the eastern Fens, it was eventually agreed that if the highway were to be maintained by the townships through which it passed, tolls should be levied. The response of the Lincolnshire drovers was immediately to re-route via the toll-free local lanes and tracks, to the considerable satisfaction of Fitzwilliam who appreciated only too well the damage to common grazing wrought by drovers of cattle and sheep. [5]

If many drove roads in lowland England and Wales are now incorporated in the modern road

system, and those in the uplands obscured by forestry, manuscript sources, local tradition and assidu-
ous fieldwork enable stretches of earlier routes to be identified. This is especially so in the hills and
uplands where early drove routes tended to follow open mountain thereby to avoid the necessity of
fording major rivers and of negotiating enclosed lowland. By adopting ridge-top tracks and terraces,
many of which were of prehistoric origin, drovers were afforded extensive views of open country and
prior warning of attack by thieves, besides which they had ample time to divert their animals in the
event of meeting another drove. The ancient Kerry Ridgeway, visible as a deep green track through
the rushes and bracken of the Kerry Hills on the Radnorshire-Shropshire border is a typical
example.Here, the deeply-sunken grass track characterises the situation where stock were confined to
a relatively restricted area. Elsewhere, as for example, on Aberedw Hill near Builth Wells, less con-
finement occurred and routes are identified as broad turf lanes which still remain largely bracken-free
as a consequence of many generations of treading by cattle. In wet conditions, of course, a track
would soon become pocked and rutted, if not impassable. After a while this would be avoided and an
alternative route taken with the result that drove tracks over many open hills comprise a series of
adjacent bracken-free parallels often between sixty and ninety feet in width. Occasionally these
routeways have been incorporated into modern cultivation systems. In the late nineteen seventies, for
example, it was possible to define the line of the '*Rhyd y Biswal*' drove road between Talerddig and
Rhyd in Montgomeryshire by means of the differential growth of both sward and bracken on the
newly-reseeded hill.

Whereas these routeways, most of them of indeterminate origin, were primarily used by drovers
from medieval times onwards, they were frequently intersected by transhumance routes and, moreover,
were regularly used by farmers and other members of the community who resorted to the hills for
bracken, peat and other natural products. Equally, since parallel tracks and hollow ways across hills
also define prehistoric trackways, one can never be absolutely certain that a specific roadline is a well-
defined drovers' route unless place/field names and other collateral evidence is available. This sort of
evidence is equally valuable when it comes to identifying drove roads in lowland country where
physical characteristics vary widely according to the nature of the landscape traversed. Throughout
much of northern Britain the drove road appears as a green lane flanked by stone walls, sometimes
petering out into a grassy corrugation across open country. In enclosed landscape elsewhere drove
roads follow farm or estate boundaries or provide direct links between local fairs, in which case they
tend to occur as deep, narrow lanes between hedged embankments. Other droveways, formerly through
open field, have become part of the modern road system where they are characterised by extra-wide
grass verges bordering the tarmac road surface. Some care is needed to differentiate between such
roads and later enclosure roads which also have wide verges. As a general rule, former drove roads
tend to be anything up to twice the width between hedges as the roadlines laid out by enclosure
commissioners, concurrently being sinuous rather than straight. Even where central parts of enclosure
roads were surfaced with stone, widths of 45 to 50 feet were necessary to allow detours around
stretches which became impassable in winter in the years before Metcalf and McAdam developed
techniques to provide all-weather surfacing. The drove road, on the other hand, having developed
from a series of adjacent parallel tracks formed by herded cattle, is often more than a hundred feet
from hedge to hedge.

Drove routes through Cardiganshire and Carmarthenshire

For the sake of simplicity in the discussion of the principal routes through Cardiganshire and
Carmarthenshire, the region has been divided broadly into four areas:
1. The mountain mass to the east of Llanddewibrefi, Tregaron, Ffair Rhos and Cwmystwyth (Map 2).
2. The area to the east of Carmarthen and the south of Lampeter (Map 3).
3. The area to the south of Cardigan and the north of the Whitland – Carmarthen turnpike (Map 4).

4. The area to the south of Aberystwyth and the north of a line between Llangranog and Llanfair Clydogau (Map 5).

These four areas will be discussed separately, while reference will be made from time-to-time to Map 1, compiled exclusively from the Jonathan and Roderick accounts. On all maps, broken lines are employed where details of the route are not clear.

The mountain routes from the centres of Tregaron, Ffair Rhos, Cwmystwyth, Llanddewibrefi and Pontrhydfendigaid (Bont) represented perhaps the most arduous and taxing sections of the long trail to England. Apart from the ruggedness of the terrain, these routes, in the main, traversed unfenced open hill country which doubtless accentuated the problems of controlling large droves of cattle. The centralised location of Tregaron, the last lowland station before the mountain route for Abergwesyn and Beulah and thence through Radnorshire into England, led to the growth of the town as an important assembly point for droves of cattle from west Cardiganshire and north Carmarthenshire (Map 2). Local information collected in Tregaron provides support for Rees's contention that cattle converging on the town were gathered in Pen Pica, the enclosure lying behind the present Talbot Hotel, whence they were driven across the Tygwyn Fields towards Cwmberwyn, the first "halt" on the route.[6] Besides being frequently mentioned in the itineraries set out in the Jonathan accounts, Cwmberwyn was used as an overnight station by the sheep drover Dafydd Isaac during the early years of the 20th century.[7] Moreover, it was from the farm of Cwmberwyn that Jenkin Williams, (the dealer of Deri-garon), would look back upon Tregaron and declare, somewhat uncharitably:

"Mae Tregaron fach yn mwgi   "Little Tregaron smokes
Nid oes fater ta hi'n llosgi   It does not matter if it burns
Os bydd newydd drwg ar gered   If there's bad news about
Yn Nhregaron cewch ei glywed"[8].   It's in Tregaron it will be heard."

While some drovers were accommodated at Cwmberwyn, others stayed at nearby Diffwys.[9] Diffwys is no longer a farm, yet the remains of numerous small enclosures on the open hill are still visible and may well have been used as temporary holding paddocks for droves of both sheep and cattle. From Cwmberwyn and Diffwys, the route continued in the direction of Nantystalwyn, for the most part following the existing road. Occasionally however, it diverges from the modern tarmac road, such divergences being clearly visible from aerial photographs of the locality and also detectable as sunken lanes which tend to cut across the bends in the modern road. There are two major divergences, the first of which occurs approximately half a mile above Diffwys, while the second is to be found before Nant-y-Gerwyn one mile west of Nantystalwyn. At Nantystalwyn the main route was joined by a further trail used by drovers bringing cattle from the fairs of Pontrhydfendigaid and Ffair Rhos. Unlike the Tregaron-Abergwesyn route, that linking Pontrhydfendigaid with Nantystalwyn is indicated on neither the Kitchen nor Bowen maps. However, Nantystalwyn is prominently marked on Singer's map of 1803, suggesting that by this time the farm had achieved some importance. The map also pinpoints the location of the drovers' road passing from Pontrhydfendigaid by Strata Florida, Pantyfedwen, Blaengasffrwd and Moel Prysgau to Nantystalwyn. This road is still clearly visible between Nantystalwyn and Moel Prysgau, although its course has been substantially obscured by the activities of the Forestry Commission between Strata Florida and Pantyfedwen.

An informant in Llanddewibrefi contended that both cattle and sheep were driven from Nantystalwyn across the Drygarn to Rhayader via the Rhiwnant and Elan, a contention reinforced by the comments of other local residents.[10] However, neither aerial photographs nor the cartographic sources indicate the existence of an established track over the Drygarn, although fieldwork revealed several deeply sunken tracks leading from Nantystalwyn in the direction of that mountain. Two of these lanes, some ten feet wide, may be readily followed to the top of Bryn Crwn where they gradually disappear. The botanical composition of the sward of these "green lanes" eliminates the possibility of their being dried-up water courses, while their considerable width suggests that they are not sheep tracks. This leaves two possible alternatives; either the tracks represent drift ways by which cattle from the Nantystalwyn farm were driven for grazing on the open mountain, or they comprise regular drove roads to join the *"Rhiw y Porthmyn,"* which, according to the Nanteos Estate Map of 1819, left the road from Moel Prysgau half a mile before Nantystalwyn and traversed the hill towards Llannerch-yrfa.

Both the droves from Nantystalwyn and Tregaron continued past Llannerch-yrfa, fording the Irfon three times and following the course of that river to the hamlet of Abergwesyn, where they would have been likely to meet cattle converging on the village from Llanddewibrefi via Soar-y-Mynydd. In addition to providing accommodation and refreshment, the Grouse Inn (Pentwyn) at Abergwesyn, mentioned in the Jonathan itineraries, was also an important cattle shoeing centre, the enclosure behind the inn being used for this purpose.[11] The route from Abergwesyn to Beulah did not follow the present county road. Instead, the drovers crossed the fields in front of the Grouse Inn, forded the Gwesyn and followed the ancient hill track known as the *"Cefn Cardis"* by which they eventually arrived at Beulah via Aber Annell.

Reference has been briefly made to the drove route connecting Abergwesyn with Soar-y-Mynydd which was concerned, in the main, with animals from the Llanddewibrefi area. The trail passed from Llanddewibrefi by Cwmdulas and past Bryn Caregog to Bronbyrfe. The entry in the Jonathan accounts of 1839 which mentions the expenditure of five shillings at "Cwmdulas House", lends support to the strong local tradition that there existed an old tavern on the mountains above the present Cwm Dulas. The remains of this tavern have been located, but it is not recorded on the Llanddewibrefi Tithe apportionment. However, the first edition of the O.S. 6in Map indicates "ruins" on this site, implying that if this "tavern" had been erected for the use of the drovers in the 1840s (i.e. after the drawing up of the Tithe Apportionments), it had become redundant by the closing decades of the century. At Bronbyrfe the drovers' road branched. The principal branch passed Blaendoethie to Soar-y-Mynydd after which the Tywi was forded at Pantllwydiau. The drovers then continued via the Rhydgoch to Abergwesyn, entering that hamlet by Penybryn. The second branch of the route headed in a southerly direction past Pysgotwr where it left the existing road and continued beyond Bryn Glas to the foot of Hafod Las on the Pysgotwr Fach. Here it connected with another trail crossing Esgair Maen from Cwmdulas. This route is visible from Bronbyrfe and can also be detected leaving the junction with the main route at Hafod Las. Elderly residents in the locality speak of the one time existence of a tavern at this junction. The Llanddewibrefi Tithe Apportionment indicates the presence of "ruins" at the junction, although these "ruins" do not appear on the first edition 6in map of the area. Inspection of the site revealed a series of grass mounds which appeared to be the remains of the stone walls of a substantial building. By virtue of its isolated location on a drovers' route, this ruin almost certainly comprises the remains of the tavern, the memory of which is enshrined in local folk memory. The trail from Hafod Las continues past Penyraglangwynt, along the outskirts of what is now Coed Penrhiwar, eventually joining the Cwrt-y-Cadno to Rhandir-mwyn road opposite Troedrhiwbeynon.

Map 2 also illustrates two other important routes across the mountains of mid-Cardiganshire. These routes, from Cwmystwyth and Ffair Rhos, were used respectively by droves destined either for the north Midlands via Shrewsbury, or for the southern counties via Worcestershire. Initially the droves converged upon Cwmystwyth, whence they followed the turnpike road along the Ystwyth valley to Tyllwyd. On several occasions David Jonathan records expenditure upon "bread and ale" at Tyllwyd, thereby confirming the view of the present occupier that Tyllwyd was originally a farm-cum-tavern.[12] Several hundred yards beyond Tyllwyd the drovers would have encountered the Blaenycwm tollgate. Whether they passed through this gate or managed to circumvent it is not altogether clear from evidence on the ground, although it is perhaps significant that no entries for payments of toll at Blaenycwm appear in the Jonathan accounts. It is clear, however, from both the Jenkins notes and local information, that beyond the Blaenycwm gate the drovers no longer followed the turnpike to Rhayader. Instead, they continued in a north-easterly direction across Yr Allt, fording the River Diluw by Lluestdolgwiail and thence across Esgair Ychion to Llangurig. This route is marked on the 1st Edition of the Ordnance Survey One-inch map.

MAP 2 Drovers' Routes across the Central Cardiganshire Hills

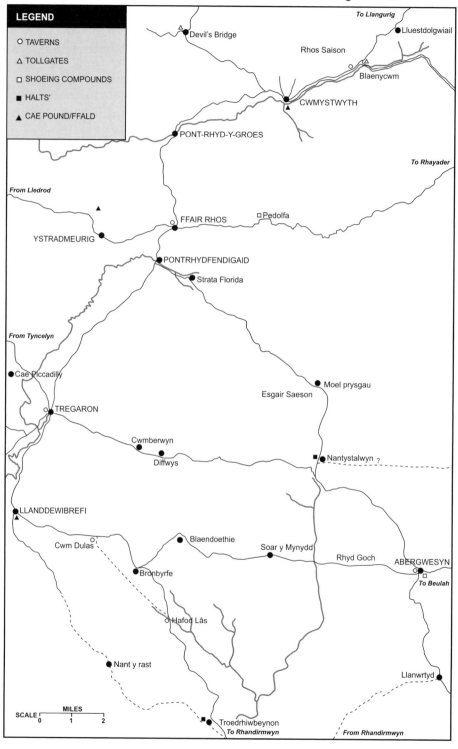

LEGEND

○ TAVERNS

△ TOLLGATES

□ SHOEING COMPOUNDS

■ HALTS'

▲ CAE POUND/FFALD

To Llangurig

Devil's Bridge

Lluestdolgwiail

Rhos Saison

Blaenycwm

CWMYSTWYTH

PONT-RHYD-Y-GROES

To Rhayader

From Lledrod

□ Pedolfa

FFAIR RHOS

YSTRADMEURIG

PONTRHYDFENDIGAID

Strata Florida

From Tyncelyn

Cae Piccadilly

Moel prysgau

Esgair Saeson

TREGARON

Cwmberwyn

Nantystalwyn ?

Diffwys

LLANDDEWIBREFI

Blaendoethie

Cwm Dulas

Soar y Mynydd

Rhyd Goch

ABERGWESYN

Bronbyrfe

To Beulah

Hafod Lâs

Nant y rast

Llanwrtyd

SCALE

MILES

0   1   2

Troedrhiwbeynon

To Rhandirmwyn

From Rhandirmwyn

MAP 3 Drovers Routes in North Carmarthenshire

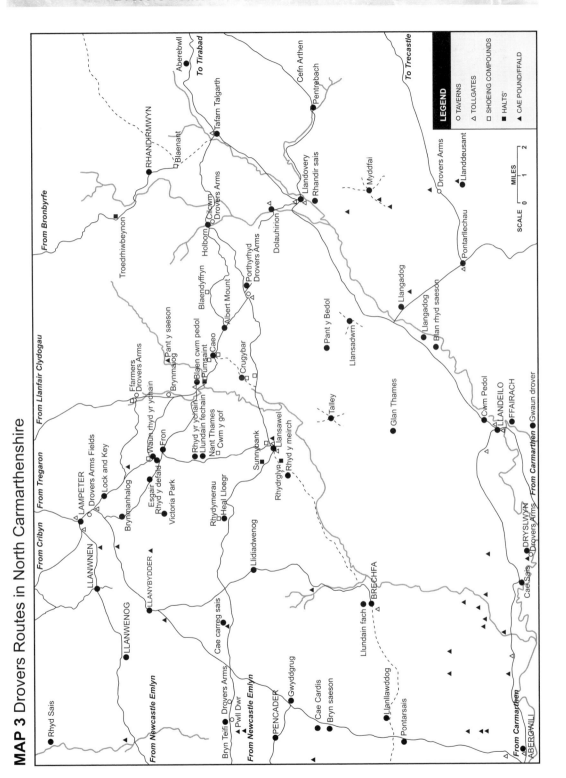

LEGEND

○ TAVERNS
△ TOLLGATES
□ SHOEING COMPOUNDS
■ HALTS'
▲ CAE POUND/FFALD

SCALE
MILES
0 1 2

To Trecastle

To Tirabad

Aberebwll
Pentrebach
Cefn Arthen

Tafarn Talgarth

RHANDIRMWYN
Blaenant

From Bronbyrfe

Llanddeusant
Drovers Arms
Myddfai
Llandovery
Rhandir sais

Troedrhiwbeynon

Holborn
Chicwm
Drovers Arms

Porthyrhyd
Drovers Arms
Dolauhirion

Pontarllechau

Blaendyffryn
Albert Mount
Pant y saeson

From Llanfair Clydogau

Ffarmers
Drovers Arms

Blaen cwm pedol
Pumsaint
Caeo
Brynmalog

Llangadog
Blan rhyd saeson
Llangadog

Pant y Bedol

Crugybar

Llansadwrn

From Tregaron

Waun rhyd yr ychain
Fron
Rhyd yr ychain
Llundain fechain
Nant Thames
Cwm y gof

Talley

Glan Thames

Cwm Pedol
LLANDEILO
FFAIRACH
Gwaun drover

LAMPETER
Drovers Arms Fields
Lock and Key

Esgair
Rhyd y defaid
Victoria Park

Rhydymerau
Heol Lloegr

Sunnybank

Llansawel

Rhydrglyn
Rhyd y meirch

From Cribyn

LLANWNEN

Brynmanhalog

Llidiadwenog

From Carmarthen
DRYSLWYN
Drovers Arms
Cae Sais

Rhyd Sais

LLANWENOG

LLANYBYDDER

Cae carreg sais

BRECHFA
Llundain fach

Bryn Teifi
Drovers Arms
Pwll Dwr

From Newcastle Emlyn

PENCADER
Gwyddgrug
Cae Cardis
Bryn saeson

Llanllawddog
Pontarsais

From Carmarthen
ABEROWILL

From Newcastle Emlyn

The second route, which linked the fair of Ffair Rhos with Rhayader and hence with the southern Midland counties was used extensively by drovers purchasing cattle in the Llangwyryfon-Lledrod area who arrived at Ffair Rhos via Ystrad Meurig.[13] The route passed through the several fair fields of Ffair Rhos, past Tafarn-ty-uchaf and the nearby toll-house and thence into the mountains to Pedolfa, the shoeing point above the Teifi Pools. From here it continued across open mountain, fording the Claerddu and branching in a north-westerly direction approximately one mile before Claerwen. Subsequently the drove forded the Claerwen and joined the Cwmystwyth-Rhayader turnpike at Aberhenllan above Pont ar Elan whence it continued to Rhayader via Llansantffraed.

Attention has already been drawn to the existence of a route linking Rhandir-mwyn and Llanddewibrefi via Bronbyrfe. The continuation of this route to Rhandir-mwyn is shown on Map 3, as are other important routes in mid-Carmarthenshire.[14] The multiplicity of routes which passed through the central part of the county ultimately coalesced at Llandovery or Tafarn Talgarth, whence the route to England was the well-trodden track over the Epynt via Tafarn y Mynydd. While cattle droves from the fairs of mid-Cardiganshire passed through Tregaron before crossing the mountains, those from the southern fairs of Dihewyd, Capel Sain Silin, Talsarn and Newcastle Emlyn converged upon Lampeter. References to Lampeter occur time and again in the Jonathan accounts, while the Tithe Apportionments mention "Drover's Lane" and "Drover's Arms Fields" as lying alongside the Teifi, suggesting a strong connection between the cattle trade and the town. Generally, droves moving through Lampeter were destined either for Llandovery or other towns in the Tywi Vale or alternatively for Cilycwm and the Epynt trail to the River Wye at Erwood (Y Rhyd). In either case there were several alternative routes. The principal route was through Cwmann, where the numerous taverns, including the "Ram" and the "Lock and Key" would have provided sustenance for the journey.[15] That the Lampeter-Llandovery turnpike comprised at least part of the route is clear from entries in the Jonathan accounts which record payment of toll at the Cwmann gate and also at the Pentre-Davies gate above Pumsaint. However, J. E. Lloyd, writing in 1909, maintained that the drovers travelled along the turnpike and through the Pentre-Davies gate before branching in an easterly direction for Caeo, thus avoiding further toll.[16] Although the Jonathans used the Caeo route, their accounts, together with those of Roderick Roderick, mention toll charges at Dolauhirion, thereby indicating the use of the turnpike for the remainder of the journey from Pumsaint to Llandovery. Local enquiry revealed that having passed through Cwmann gate to Treherbert, some drovers followed the narrow lane past King's Park and Penbryn, eventually rejoining the turnpike at Mountain Cottage where there was reputedly a shoeing forge. However, the first edition 6in map does not locate a smithy at this point, nor is there any evidence on the ground of the enclosures normally associated with a cattle shoeing forge. Nevertheless the Tithe Apportionment lists several field names in the proximity of this junction which may have "droving" connotations. In particular, "*Waun rhyd yr ychain*", "*Cil yr ychain*" and "*Rhyd y defaid*" are worthy of mention in this context.

The route from Lampeter to Pumsaint described above, tended to follow the course of existing roads. Fieldwork in the Lampeter area, however, revealed a further drift road connecting Cwmann with Pumsaint. This is in the form of a lane which leaves the county road at Brynmanhalog, some 1½ miles to the south of Cwmann and heads in a south-easterly direction towards Fron on the Esgerdawe-Lampeter road. This lane possesses all the characteristics of a drove road. It cannot be readily traced along the whole of its course past Caer Pencarreg to Fron, but the lane may be followed from Esgair Farm to Fron where it linked with the parish road joining the turnpike below the Pentre-Davies gate at Pumsaint. While it has not been possible to corroborate the field evidence with field name and cartographic clues, this lane certainly appears to have been a drovers' road. Moreover, given the enthusiasm of the drovers to avoid a tollgate wherever possible, the orientation of the lane would suggest that it was used for the avoidance of gates both at Pumsaint and Cwmann. Some 1½ miles to the south of Fron, on the outskirts of Esgerdawe, is the farm of Llundain Fechan, through which flows the Nant Thames. This farm is reputed to have been the first overnight resting place of the Cardiganshire drovers en route for England, and was of sufficient importance in the mid-eighteenth century to feature prominently on the maps of both Bowen and Kitchen.[17] It has been contended elsewhere that the drover and hymnologist Dafydd Jones of Caeo settled at Llundain Fechan and was responsible for so naming the farm.[18] This, however, is not feasible as Llundain Fechan appears in an indenture of 1708 relating to turf cutting on nearby Panaugleision.[19] A further link between the cattle trade and the Esgerdawe area is provided by the local tradition that Cardiganshire cattle were shod at Cwm y gof, a glen on Pwllau Farm not far from Llundain Fechan. [20]

The village of Pumsaint lies directly on the main drovers' route for Llandovery and the Epynt, but enquiry among local residents yielded little in the way of information regarding the activities of the drovers, while the only field name suggesting a link with the trade is that of "*Blaen cwm pedol*" on the outskirts of the village. [21] Having crossed the Cothi at Pumsaint, the drovers left the turnpike road and turned down the parish highway past the Ogofau mines and thence into Caeo village.[22] Here was one of the largest cattle trading centres in Wales, fairs being held on May 30th and October 6th, these dates being chosen to coincide with the seasonal movements of the drovers to England.[23] Given the importance of Caeo as a trading centre and of its position on a principal drove route, it might reasonably be expected that there would have been cattle shoeing forges within the proximity of the village. However, despite the local contention that cattle were shod at Gornoethle and also in the paddocks behind the church, there is little field evidence of such activities. Both Lloyd and the R.T. Jenkins manuscripts contend that the drovers' route from Caeo followed the parish road to Albert Mount and thence via Blaendyffryn (reputedly a shoeing centre) over Pen Lifau and past Cwmfranfawr to Cilycwm. Local information collected during the course of the fieldwork endorses these conclusions. [24] Moreover, the location on the Cilycwm Tithe Map of "Holborn Fields" lying alongside the lane from Cwmfranfawr as it enters the village, and of the "Drovers' Arms" tavern, suggests a further positive link between Cilycwm and the cattle trade.

A second route to Cilycwm from Albert Mount passed through the village of Porthyrhyd. This route, in common with the direct route by way of Blaendyffryn, did not follow the existing road, except for some quarter of a mile beyond Albert Mount. Here, at Aberbowlan, where the present road deviates towards Maestwynog, the drovers forded the Dulais stream and crossed the hills to Porthyrhyd, entering the village by Llynglas opposite the former Drovers' Arms (now a dwelling house). This trail through Caeo, Porthyrhyd and thence to Cilycwm, was used by Roderick Roderick in 1839, while David Jonathan often visited the Drovers' Arms at Porthyrhyd en route for Llandovery. Payments of toll at the Dolauhirion gate above Llandovery are recorded in the Roderick and Jonathan papers, suggesting that both these dealers followed the turnpike road between Porthyrhyd and Llandovery. However, there are no records of toll payments at the Porthyrhyd gate in either set of accounts and it might therefore be concluded that means were available by which this gate could be circumvented.[25] From Cilycwm the drovers' route continued eastwards to ford the Tywi approximately one mile outside the village. Subsequently it crossed the Forest Bank by way of the road past Pendrynllwyn to Tafarn Talgarth in the Brân valley.[26] Tafarn Talgarth, (currently the Glanbrane Arms) represented a junction of some importance for it was here that several routes from Cardiganshire, Pembrokeshire and Carmarthenshire merged. Moreover, Tafarn Talgarth lay at the beginning of the ancient track, the Cefn Llwydlo.[27] Passing along the Cefn Llwydlo for rather more than two miles, the drovers forked in an easterly direction past Aberebwll and Spite Inn to Llanddulas, where they may have been joined by further droves of cattle from Llandovery. The route taken by the latter involved passing through the Felindre toll gate to the east of the town and thence along the Brecon turnpike to Pentrebach where they left the turnpike, crossed the Gwydderig stream and followed the highway over Cefn Arthen and Trelaeth Hill to Llanddulas.[28]

At Porthyrhyd, the route to the Epynt linked with a much used trail from the Newcastle Emlyn area, passing over Mynydd Llanllwni and Mynydd Llanybydder to Rhydcymerau, Llansawel and thence to Porthyrhyd. This route followed the course of the present B4336 road from Pengraigwen south of Llandysul to cross the B4459 at Bryn Teifi. Local enquiry in Llanfihangel-ar-arth revealed that the public house at this crossing was regularly used by the drovers. The inn was originally known

The shoeing compound behind the Talbot Hotel, Tregaron

Jenkin Williams's view back towards Tregaron

as *"Pwll Dwr"*, a name deriving from the pond in front of the inn from which the droves of cattle could freely drink. The Tithe Apportionments reveal another tavern, the "Drovers' Arms", approximately one mile to the west of the junction of this route with the Carmarthen-Llanybydder turnpike. This tavern, however, is now a private residence.[29]

That the route past the "Drovers' Arms" across Mynydd Llanybydder and Mynydd Llanllwni followed the course of the existing road is clear from both local information and nomenclature. The road is known locally along part of its course by the evocative *"Rhyd y Biswal"*, while the section from Pentop Llanllwni to Rhydcymerau is still referred to as *"Heol Lloegr."*[30] The village of Rhydcymerau no doubt comprised a convenient and welcome "halt" for the drovers after the long journey across the open mountain via the *"Rhyd y Biswal"*. The village possessed a pair of smithies, and a nearby tavern, which although a barn today, is recorded on the first edition 6in map as the "Cart and Horses."

The section of the route between Rhydcymerau and Llansawel did not follow the course of the existing B4337. Instead, drovers turned left at the "Cart and Horses" and continued in the direction of Post Carreg where they joined the old drift road which ran above Cwmcoedifor and Cwm Hywel Farms, eventually joining the B4337 at Sunnybank Farm approximately half a mile to the west of Llansawel. This road is clearly marked on the first edition 6in map. There is a strong local tradition of the existence of a cattle shoeing enclosure (*Cwm yr efail bach*) along the course of the drift road above Cwmcoedifor, although there is no indication of such an enclosure either on the ground or in the Tithe Apportionment for the area.[31]

Sunnybank Farm, which lies at the end of the old road, together with Rhydyglyn Farm on the Llansawel-Abergorlech road, were both regularly used by the drovers for the overnight corralling of cattle, while animals were being shod in Llwyn Felfryn field in Llansawel village as recently as the mid-1880s.[32] Leaving Llansawel, the drovers crossed the Cothi above Glanyrannell Park and continued thence either to Caeo via Crugybar or to Porthyrhyd. The details of the actual route taken from Glanyrannell to Porthyrhyd are not clear. Intensive enquiry in the area did not yield any positive information while the map and manuscript sources provided few clues. However, the absence on the ground of any obvious drift roads and lanes suggests that the drovers followed the course of the existing road linking Llansawel with Porthyrhyd via Maestwynog.

In addition to these principal west-east trails, Map 3 illustrates certain other routes which appear to have been used by the drovers. The Jenkins notes draw attention to the "parallel roads" along the Tywi valley being exploited by drovers from Pembrokeshire on the way to Llandovery and the Epynt trail, while Lloyd records that drovers from north Pembrokeshire met at Llandovery before joining the route from Cardiganshire at Llanddulas.[33] This view echoes that of H.T. Evans, who specifically mentions drovers moving up the Tywi valley to Llandovery.[34] Although the Jonathans travelled with their droves from Haverfordwest along the turnpike to Carmarthen, they usually passed through the Glangwili gate and continued northwards to Lampeter.[35] Thus their accounts do not provide any evidence for the use of the turnpike to Llandeilo and Llandovery. Nevertheless, there is no indication on the ground of nineteenth century drovers travelling up the north side of the Tywi Valley by any means other than the turnpike road. A study of contemporary maps of the area tends to the same conclusion.

It has long been held that a track over the moors above Ystradgynlais and Cwm-twrch formed part of an ancient line of communication by which cattle were driven from Glamorgan to the Tywi Vale.[36] Perhaps this may have approximated to the direction taken by the existing road across the Black Mountains from Brynamman to Llangadog. Certainly the numerous *pedol* type names in the Brynamman district suggest a link with the trade. Hence *"Nant Pedol"*, *"Cwm Pedol"*, *"Blaen Pedol"*, *"Foel deg ar bedol"* and *"Bryn pedol"* all occur on the hills to the north-east of Brynamman. At Pontarllechau on the Brynamman-Llangadog road the Tithe Map indicates a track heading in an easterly direction past the Drovers' Arms above Llanddeusant and across the open mountain to Trecastle and Brecon via Pont-ar-Hydfer. It is generally believed in the Llanddeusant area that this was one of the principal drove routes along which cattle and sheep were driven from Glamorgan and the Gower Peninsula for sale at Brecon Fair.

Map 4 illustrates some of the directions taken through south Cardiganshire and western Carmarthenshire by drovers purchasing cattle at the Pembrokeshire fairs. Essentially the routes move in an easterly direction eventually linking with one of the important junctions of Llandovery, Llansawel or Lampeter, as shown in Map 3. In the interests of speed and efficiency many drovers from the Narberth and Haverfordwest areas travelled along the Whitland–St. Clears turnpike for Carmarthen and thence up the Tywi Vale to Llandovery. It has been mentioned previously, and is illustrated on Map 1, that the Jonathans generally made use of the turnpike to Carmarthen as evidenced by the payments of toll at the Narberth and St. Clears gates. However, having passed through Carmarthen, the Jonathans, instead of continuing to Llandovery, almost invariably turned northwards at Abergwili and thence to Lampeter. The coastal turnpike passing through Cardigan from Pembrokeshire was also used by the Jonathans for the transfer of cattle from the Pembrokeshire fairs to their home farm at Dihewyd, or, by the eighteen sixties, to the Aberystwyth railhead.

Many drovers of course, were anxious to avoid toll payments wherever possible, and provided time was not an absolutely vital factor, attempts were also made to avoid the commotion which inevitably arose from driving large herds of cattle through towns like Carmarthen and Llandovery. Accordingly, alternative routes avoiding these centres were sought. One such route passed through the village of Llanboidy, having left the Whitland turnpike by way of the road opposite the Commercial Inn, Llanddewi Velfrey. At the junction of this latter route with the turnpike, the Tithe Apportionments reveal the fields of *"Banc"* and *"Cwm Saison"*, while *"Cwm pedol"* and *"Pen clippin"* occur close to the village of Hiraeth. The close association of these *"Cwm"* and *"Parc"*, *"pedol"* and *"clippin"* names with known shoeing centres suggests that the isolated occurrence of these names may indicate that cattle were shod in the locality. Local enquiry revealed that shoeing took place at either Cefn brafle (Cross Hands) or the nearby farm of Cilgynydd uchaf alongside the Llanfallteg-Llanboidy road.

There is some difference of opinion as to which of these sites comprised the shoeing centre, and unfortunately neither the map sources nor evidence on the ground permits the resolution of this problem.[37] However, the *"Cwm pedol"* field which occurs above Bryn Hill and Carmenau Fawr north of the Narberth–Clynderwen road, was unquestionably associated with the activities at Carmenau Fawr, where one of the most westerly cattle shoeing enclosures in South Wales was located.[38] The cattle shoes, it appears, were forged at the Bryn Hill smithy and taken to Carmenau Fawr where they were nailed to the beasts. The Carmenau Fawr facilities were normally used by drovers coming from south Pembrokeshire via Narberth. Penblewin Farm, which lies on the junction of the Narberth-Clynderwen road with the Carmarthen turnpike, was, until the early decades of the present century, an inn, known rather optimistically as "The Speculation." This inn was used by the drovers as an overnight halt prior to shoeing at Carmenau Fawr, the cattle being corralled in nearby Parc yr efail.[39]

The importance of the village of Llanboidy in the eastwards movement of cattle across mid Carmarthenshire is emphasised by the presence of three centres in the parish believed locally to have been used for the shoeing of cattle. These shoeing centres were located at Caerlleon on the Meidrim road, Bancyllain, one mile to the south-east of the village and at Waun rhiwau in the village itself. The eastern route from Llanboidy followed the course of the existing road to Meidrim, passing by the farm of Trafel yr ych approximately one half mile to the east of the village. The name *"Trafel yr ych"* suggests that this farm may have been involved in the cattle trade, perhaps as an overnight halt, although local enquiry yielded no information in support of this possibility. Nevertheless, this farm was clearly of some importance during the eighteenth century as it is recorded on both the Bowen and Kitchen maps. From Meidrim the route passed by Rhydaberwern, Pantycendy and Cynwyl Elved to the hamlet of Esgair, where the trail branched, continuing either to Pencader or heading due east for Brechfa via Llanpumsaint and Llanllawddog.[40] While this would seem a logical enough route, avoiding the Carmarthen turnpike and ultimately linking with the Epynt crossing, the map sources reveal nothing in the way of place and field names suggestive of drove movements.

Drovers taking cattle from south Pembrokeshire to the fairs of Henfeddau, Newcastle Emlyn and Lampeter left Llanboidy via Cwmfelyn Mynach (where they probably refreshed themselves at the

Map 4 Drovers' Routes in South Cardiganshire and West Carmarthenshire

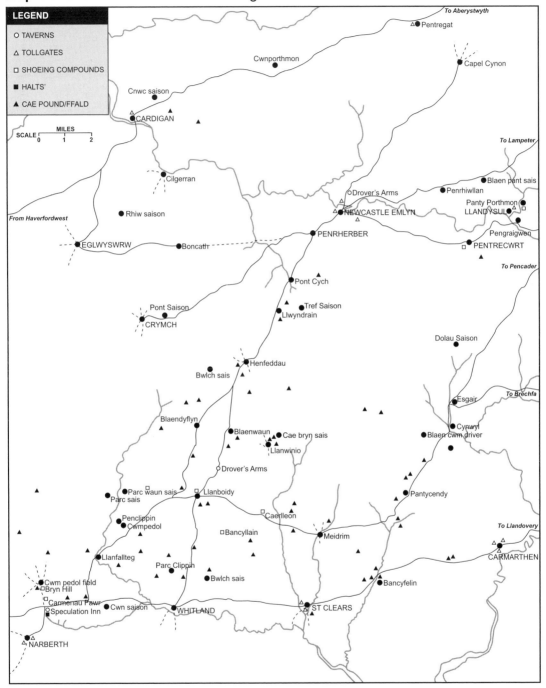

LEGEND

○ TAVERNS
△ TOLLGATES
□ SHOEING COMPOUNDS
■ HALTS'
▲ CAE POUND/FFALD

SCALE
MILES
0 1 2

To Aberystwyth

△● Pentregat

Cwnporthmon

● Capel Cynon

Cnwc saison ●

● CARDIGAN

To Lampeter

Cilgerran ●

● Blaen pant sais

○ Drover's Arms

● Penrhiwllan

Panty Porthmon ●
LLANDYSUL ●

△ NEWCASTLE EMLYN

From Haverfordwest

● Rhiw saison

● PENRHERBER

Pengraigwen
□ PENTRECWRT

● EGLWYSWRW   ● Boncath

To Pencader

● Pont Cych

Pont Saison
● Tref Saison
● Llwyndrain
● CRYMCH

Dolau Saison

To Brechfa

● Henfeddau

Bwlch sais

● Esgair

Blaendyflyn

● Cynwyl
● Blaen cwm driver

● Blaenwaun
● Cae bryn sais
● Llanwinio

○ Drover's Arms

□ Parc waun sais
Parc sais ●

□ Llanboidy

● Pantycendy

Penclippin
● Cwmpedol

□ Caerlleon

To Llandovery

□ Bancyllain

● Meidrim

Llanfallteg

Parc Clippin ●

● Bwlch sais

△ CARMARTHEN

Cwm pedol field
△ □ Bryn Hill
□ Carmenau Fawr   ● Cwn saison
□ Speculation Inn

● WHITLAND

△ ST CLEARS

● Bancyfelin

△ NARBERTH

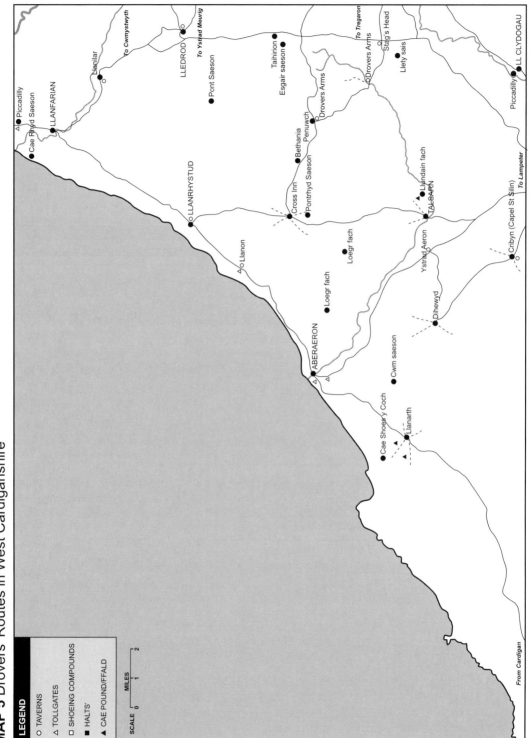

MAP 5 Drovers' Routes in West Cardiganshire

LEGEND
○ TAVERNS
△ TOLLGATES
▢ SHOEING COMPOUNDS
■ HALTS'
▲ CAE POUND/FFALD

SCALE

MILES
0   1   2

Piccadilly
Cae Rhyd Saeson
LLANFARIAN
Llecilar
To Cwmystwyth
LLEDROD
To Ystrad Meurig
Pont Saeson
Taihirion
Esgair saeson
To Tregaron
Drovers Arms
Stag's Head
Llety sais
Drovers Arms
Piccadilly
LL CLYDOGAU
LLANRHYSTUD
Bethania
Penuwch
Pontrhyd Saeson
Cross Inn
Llundain fach
TALSARN
To Lampeter
Llanon
Loegr fach
Cribyn (Capel St Silin)
Loegr fach
Ystrad Aeron
ABERAERON
Dihewyd
Cwm saeson
Cae Shoes'y Coch
Llanarth
From Cardigan

Drovers' Arms), continuing past Blaenwaun and Llanwinio Common to Henfeddau. From Henfeddau they followed the county road past Llwyndrain, across the Cych at Pont Cych and thence to Penyrherber which represented a junction with those routes taken by cattle purchased at Eglwyswrw and Crymych and destined for Newcastle Emlyn and the eastern route to England.[41] Droves which were eventually to be driven to England by way of the Abergwesyn trail, passed through Newcastle Emlyn and Llanwnen to Lampeter. This road was regularly taken by the Jonathans, who recorded having recourse to the good offices of the taverns at Garreg, Rhydowen and Penpontbren at various stages of the journey (Map 1). As an alternative, cattle entering England by way of the Epynt route travelled from Newcastle Emlyn to Pentrecwrt where the farm of Geulanfelen provided hospitality.[42] From this point the drovers took the road past Cwrt and forded the Tyweli below Pengraigwen outside Llandysul, whence they passed through Bryn Teifi to join the "*Rhyd y Biswal*" for Rhydcymerau.[43]

The use by the Jonathans of the turnpike road linking Cardigan and Aberystwyth for the transmission of cattle purchased in south Cardiganshire and Pembrokeshire, to the Shrewsbury and later the Aberystwyth railhead, has been previously mentioned. During the pre-railway era, however, animals bought in mid-Cardiganshire were generally driven across the mountains via the Cwmystwyth and Ffair Rhos routes (Map 2). Alternatively, they converged upon Tregaron and Lampeter and thence by the Abergwesyn or Epynt routes to England. Map 5 shows that the routes through the area tend eventually to link up with these above-mentioned centres. From Aberystwyth, beasts were driven through Llanfarian, past the Llanilar tavern (mentioned so often by the Jonathans) and thence to Lledrod. Lledrod was not only an important disposal centre, the fair being held in a field opposite the King's Arms Inn, but it also possessed facilities for cattle shoeing, either at the forge near Lledrod Mill, or at Rhydyrefail to the south of the village.[44]

From Lledrod there were three regularly used itineraries. The first of these connected with either the Ffair Rhos or Nantystalwyn routes via Ystrad Meurig, while the second passed by Tynygraig to Ysbytty Ystwyth to join the Rhayader turnpike at Cwmystwyth. The third route, to the townships of Lampeter and Tregaron, left Lledrod in a southerly direction and followed the Sarn Helen Roman road through Bronnant and past Taihirion to Tyncelyn where it traversed the track taken by cattle from the Penuwch and Cross Inn areas. At Tyncelyn the drovers either turned eastwards for Tregaron, or continued down the Sarn Helen to the Stag's Head Inn, a tavern visited from time-to-time by the Jonathans. The crossroads at Stag's Head was a junction with a local drove route from Penuwch and Llangeitho which entered Tregaron via Deri-garon.[45] The main route, however, passed down the Sarn Helen to Llanio where it joined the turnpike to Lampeter or alternatively branched for Llanddewibrefi.

It is readily accepted that while Maps 1-5 show the principal routes taken by the drovers, they do not represent a completely exhaustive charting of the drove roads in the areas covered. Undoubtedly, following enclosure both of the uplands and lowlands, there were a multiplicity of drift roads linking villages and local fairs which have subsequently disappeared as a result of modern agricultural activities. Indeed, had this book been produced fifty, or perhaps sixty years ago, not only would the fieldwork have been relatively simple, but also "first hand" local information would have enabled more satisfactory corroboration of the evidence for the location of drove routes than has been possible in the present study. Even so the information collected during the course of the fieldwork in most cases supported similar "verbal" information accumulated by Jenkins in the nineteen-thirties. This to some extent justifies the method of approach, while at the same time being a testament to the length and accuracy of folk memory in rural Wales.

A feature common to the majority of the routes described above is the tendency, where possible, to follow the open mountain and thus to avoid the enclosed lowlands and river valleys. Despite the inadequacy of pre-eighteenth century cartographic sources, it seems possible, given the known antiquity of the Welsh cattle trade, that some of these routes across the hills were themselves of great antiquity. It is well known that the Neolithic ridgeways across the chalk downs of southern England permitted the development of more rapid and less hazardous lines of communication than the forging of tracks through the densely wooded vales. Similarly in Wales, prior to the clearance and enclosure

Ty'ncornel Youth Hostel on the drovers' road from Blaendoethie to Soar-y-Mynydd

The drovers' road descending to a ford beyond Ty'ncornel Youth Hostel

The drovers' road between Llansawel and Porthyrhyd, west of the B4302

of much of the lower-lying land, the movement of cattle across open hill would have enabled drovers not only to avoid the very real problems of fording the major rivers, but also to establish direct west-east trails towards the English border. The development of lowland communications and the bridging of the major rivers in the sixteenth and seventeenth centuries would have offered little benefit to the drovers. Clearance and enclosure of the lowland vales, although accompanied by the improvement of communications links between villages and towns, would not have provided any more direct cattle routes than the existing hill tracks. Furthermore, enclosure *per se* would have reduced the availability of wayside forage for droves of cattle. However, the subsequent evolution of the turnpike roads, which tended in general to follow the river valleys, provided a rapid and relatively efficient road network which was exploited by many of the larger drovers. Others, preferring to avoid the burden of tolls associated with the turnpikes, continued to use the ancient hill trails across Cardiganshire and Carmarthenshire which linked with the English border by way of the routes discussed below.

Drove routes from the Cardiganshire and Carmarthenshire Borders

The network of routes linking the borders of Carmarthenshire and Cardiganshire with the counties of Shropshire and Hereford is illustrated on Map 6. The northern routes to Shrewsbury and Leebotwood represent the direction taken by droves from north Cardiganshire, Merionethshire and Montgomeryshire, although as Map 1 shows, the Jonathans frequently followed the northern routes with cattle driven from central Cardiganshire, particularly after the establishment of the Shrewsbury railhead. The routes from Aberystwyth and Abergwesyn to Ludlow and Leominster were also taken by droves from mid-Cardiganshire, while the trail across the Epynt to the River Wye and thence to Herefordshire connected with the drove roads from Carmarthenshire and Pembrokeshire. Welsh cattle

The road from Newchurch to Glascwm

The former Drovers' Arms, Porthyrhyd

MAP 6 Drovers' Routes from the Carmarthenshire and Cardiganshire Borders

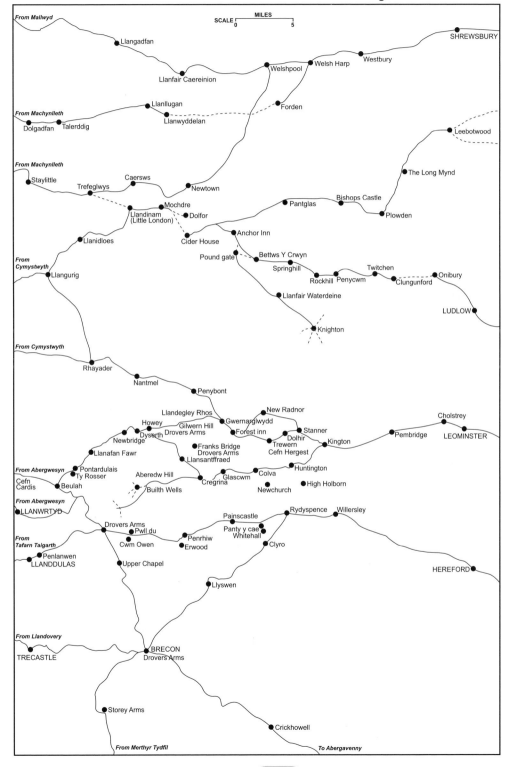

SCALE MILES 0 5

From Mallwyd

Llangadfan

SHREWSBURY

Welshpool · Welsh Harp · Westbury

Llanfair Caereinion

Llanllugan · Forden

From Machynlleth

Dolgadfan · Talerddig · Llanwyddelan

Leebotwood

From Machynlleth

Staylittle

The Long Mynd

Trefeglwys · Caersws · Newtown

Mochdre · Pantglas · Bishops Castle

Llandinam (Little London) · Dolfor · Plowden

Llanidloes · Cider House · Anchor Inn

From Cymystwyth

Llangurig · Pound gate · Bettws Y Crwyn · Twitchen · Onibury

Springhill · Rockhill · Penycwm · Clungunford

Llanfair Waterdeine

LUDLOW

Knighton

From Cymystwyth

Rhayader · Nantmel · Penybont

Llandegley Rhos · New Radnor · Cholstrey

Howey · Gilwern Hill · Gwernarglwydd · Stanner · Pembridge · LEOMINSTER

Newbridge · Dyserth · Drovers Arms · Forest inn · Dolhir · Kington

Franks Bridge · Trewern · Cefn Hergest

Llanafan Fawr · Drovers Arms · Llansantffraed

From Abergwesyn

Pontardulais · Aberedw Hill · Glascwm · Colva · Huntington

Cefn Cardis · Ty Rosser · Cregrina · High Holborn

Beulah · Builth Wells · Newchurch

From Abergwesyn

LLANWRTYD

Drovers Arms · Painscastle · Rydyspence · Willersley

Pwll du · Panty y cae · Whitehall

From Tafarn Taigarth

Penrhiw · Clyro

Cwm Owen · Erwood

Penlanwen · LLANDDULAS · Upper Chapel

Llyswen

HEREFORD

From Llandovery

BRECON · Drovers Arms

TRECASTLE

Storey Arms

Crickhowell

From Merthyr Tydfil · To Abergavenny

The former Drovers' Arms north of Llanddeusant. It was rebuilt, in 1890, as the Cross Inn

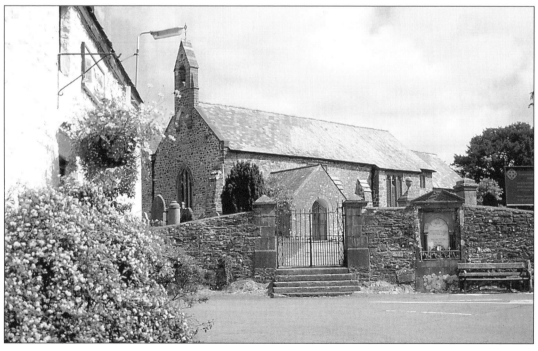

The Plough Inn and Church, Myddfai, south of Llandovery. This village is recorded as having a Drovers' Arms

The Cwmystwyth to Rhayader road at Craig Goch Reservoir

for sale in the south-western counties of Gloucestershire, Wiltshire, Somerset and Devon passed through Llandovery and Brecon to cross the River Severn via the Aust ferry which was reached by way of the Crickhowell-Abergavenny road. In 1797, Warner's progress was:

"frequently retarded by numerous droves of black cattle from Pembrokeshire and Carmarthenshire travelling towards the Passage to be transported across the Severn and driven towards the markets of Bristol and the other large towns of Somerset, Gloucestershire and Wiltshire." [46]

In the first part of this chapter mention was made of the importance of Tafarn Talgarth as a junction of the routes taken by drovers from Llandovery and the Lampeter-Llansawel region.[47] From Tafarn Talgarth the route followed the course of the existing road past Aberebwll and Spite Inn to Llanddulas. At Penlanwen, a farm approximately one mile beyond Llanddulas, the drovers' road diverted from the present road towards Cross Inn, a final port of call before the ascent of the Epynt.[48] The track up the Epynt from Cross Inn joined the Tricrugiau trail at Tafarn y Mynydd where it traversed the Epynt to the Drovers Arms on the Garth-Brecon road and continued across the open mountain towards Cwm Owen. By-passing Cwm Owen slightly to the north, the drovers travelled past Pwll du to join the Twmpath at Cefn Hirwaun above Gwenddwr and thus to descend the Epynt and to meet the River Wye to the north of Erwood (Y Rhyd).[49] The Wye was forded at a point approximately one hundred yards to the south of the present bridge where, despite the width of the river, a smooth rocky bed provided ideal fording conditions. The house *"Glanyrafon"* which stands on the Radnorshire side of the river is marked on the 2½ inch O.S. map (1904 ed.) as *"Cafn Twm bach."* It would appear that at some time the name was corrupted to *"Caban Twm Bach"*, for the present owner of the house has in his possession a wooden signboard on which the name appears in this form.[50] If the original *"cafn"* is taken as its obsolete meaning of "boat", the local tradition of a ferry at this point along the river is sustained. Whether *"Twm bach"* actually ferried cattle across the Wye at times when the ford was not negotiable is not clear. However, his services would have been required by neither drovers nor travellers after the late eighteen sixties when the iron bridge which occupied the site of the present structure was erected.

Having crossed the Wye, the drovers continued by Penrhiw and Penpreselly Hill to Painscastle and thence across Clyro Hill to Rhydyspence and on to the turnpike road for Hereford. The Rev. Francis Kilvert mentioned in his diaries that on one occasion he ascended Clyro Hill past Whitehall Cottage and Pantycae in an attempt to locate the site of the "Coldbrook" and "Black Ox", two hostelries reputed to have been frequented by the drovers.[51] The Clyro Tithe Map reveals that the "Coldbrook" was located close to the present Whitehall Cottage. Although it is not indicated on the Tithe Map, the tradition of the "Black Ox" on Clyro Hill is still part of local folk memory. It is possible that as well as passing over the hill, cattle drovers also visited the village of Clyro itself. This would apply particularly to drovers from Glamorgan and south Breconshire destined for Herefordshire via Brecon.[52]

If Erwood was the principal crossing point on the River Wye, several authorities have drawn attention to the existence of a route which crossed the hills below Builth Wells and followed the course of the River Duhonw to its confluence with the Wye which was forded before traversing Aberedw Hill.[53] The ascent of Aberedw Hill via the Rhiw Rhystyn continued past Ffynnonau above which, according to local tradition, was an inn, the Tafarn Mynydd.[54] An isolated block of enclosed land on the open hill suggests that there may have been a habitation of some description on the site, although inspection of the Aberedw Tithe Map and the 1st Edition 6in Map (1891) provides no further clues. From the "Tafarn Mynydd" the drovers' route descended Aberedw Hill to Cregrina, continuing from here along the existing road to Colva and thence via Newchurch to Rhydyspence.[55,56] The hamlet of Cregrina lay on another important route which represented a continuation of the Cefn Cardis, the hill route connecting Abergwesyn and Beulah. The Cefn Cardis met what is now the Beulah–Abergwesyn road at Aber Annell, passing from here to Newbridge-on-Wye along the road past Pontardulais, Ty Rosser and Llanafan fawr.[57] Field evidence and local enquiry suggests that the first part of the journey from Aber Annell did not follow the existing road, instead of which it crossed Beulah bridge and continued past Tynewydd and Pencrug to link with the road at Pontardulais.[58] Arriving at Newbridge, the drovers were accommodated at the aptly named "Mid-Wales" inn (now a private residence), ample grazing for their animals being available between the inn and the banks of the Wye. Beyond Newbridge, the route forded the River Irfon at Dyserth and crossed the Builth-Llandrindod turnpike at Crossgate below the village of Howey, whence it meandered across the southern slopes of Gilwern Hill to Cregrina on the River Edw. Here facilities were available for the reshoeing of casualties.[59]

Subsequently the drovers followed the valley of the Clas Brook to Glascwm and thence across open hill country to the hamlet of Colva and to the border at Huntington. The Jonathans passed through Colva from time-to-time en route both for Hereford via Willersley and for Worcester by way of Gladestry and Kington. While they followed the route from Abergwesyn to Beulah, they did not continue from Beulah along the route described, preferring the more direct, and no doubt quicker road through Lanafan Fechan (Map 1). Together with the drovers' road linking Dyserth and Kington via Cregrina, there was a somewhat shorter route which left Howey, crossed Gilwern Hill and Rhos Llandegley to join the Rhayader turnpike near the farm of Gwernarglwydd whence it continued along the turnpike for two miles, to join the Builth Wells road at the Forest Inn tollgate. After several hundred yards it left this road for the lane passing Trewern and Cefn Hergest eventually arriving at Kington.[60] This diversion from the Rhayader turnpike conveniently avoided toll payments at the New Radnor, Knapp and Walton gates.

By comparison with the considerable network of routes to the English border illustrated on the southern half of Map 6, there were only two major itineraries through the northern part of the area. Essentially these connected Shrewsbury with the collecting centres of Machynlleth, Dinas Mawddwy and Mallwyd. The first was a "highway route", following the turnpike from Mallwyd to Welshpool via Llangadfan, Llanerfyl and Llanfair Caereinion. Through the latter town, according to one observer, there passed daily "great herds of cattle" which were shod in the Wynnstay fields.[61] The accounts of the Jonathan family contain references to the payment of toll at "3 gates Pool to Salop",

The ford across the River Wye (in the foreground) at Newbridge

The A470, the old drovers' road to Dinas Mawddwy, near the Cross Foxes Inn

revealing that these dealers continued to follow the turnpike as far as Shrewsbury. There is evidence, however, that the more "cost-conscious" operators avoided the Welshpool-Shrewsbury turnpike by crossing the meadows to the east of Welshpool, fording the Severn and ascending the Long Mountain to the Welsh Harp Inn along the course of the Roman road which traversed Offa's Dyke at Forden. This road eventually linked with Shrewsbury via Westbury. In his evidence to the Select Committee of 1853 which considered the establishment of the Montgomeryshire Railway, Joseph Dickenson indicated that:

> "*a great proportion of the cattle from Welshpool goes through Westbury which is adjoining the Ree Valley, to avoid the toll on the other roads.*" [62]

At Forden the Westbury-Shrewsbury route was joined by droves of cattle from the Machynlleth area which had arrived by means of a route designed to avoid toll payments at the gates of Penybont and Caersws on the Machynlleth-Newtown turnpike.[63] These gates were bypassed by way of a track which left the turnpike at Tainewyddion, Penegoes, and continued across country via Talywern and Bwlch Glynmynydd, and through Pont Dolgadfan to Talerddig, where it once again met the turnpike road. Passing through the Talerddig gate the drovers left the turnpike several hundred yards south of the village to join the old drift road running past Caeauduon and Blaenglanhanog to Rhyd. This road, clearly marked on the first edition Ordnance Survey map, is now only discernable by means of differential crop patterns, although towards Rhyd it may be located as an overgrown "double-hedged" track. At Rhyd, however, the track joins the metalled road for Llanwyddelan and Llanllugan, this road being identified, rather appropriately, on the first edition of the Ordnance Survey 1 inch map as the "*Rhyd y Biswal.*"

A second route from Machynlleth also avoided the turnpike road by traversing the open mountain via Forge and Staylittle to Trefeglwys. This route, though, did not entirely follow the existing road to Staylittle. Instead of passing through Dylife and Rhosgoch, the drovers left the present road above Rhyd y Porthmyn pool and travelled past Rhyd y Porthmyn and Rhiw Defeitty Fawr to Staylittle by means of a track which is still discernible. [64] Drovers using the route from Machynlleth to Trefeglwys would be destined either for Shrewsbury via Welshpool, or perhaps for Ludlow. Although it is known that the ridgeway across the Kerry Hills comprised part of the Ludlow route, the details of the direction taken to the ridgeway are uncertain. According to the Jenkins notes, drovers arriving at Llangurig from Cwmystwyth joined the ridgeway at Cider House on the Dolfor-Beguildy road south of Newtown, while it would also seem logical that cattle heading for southern Shropshire and Herefordshire from the Trefeglwys region would also follow this route. It is unlikely that drovers intent upon taking the Kerry Hill ridgeway either from Trefeglwys or Llangurig would have travelled to Newtown and then moved south to meet the ridgeway at Cider House. This suggests that a more direct route may have been forged, although neither field work nor map evidence has enabled the determination of the precise location of such a route.

At Kerry Pole, three miles along the ridgeway from Cider House, there occurred a branch in the drovers' route, the main branch continuing via the ridgeway across the Kerry Hills towards the farm of Pantglas some three-quarters of a mile beyond which it traversed Offa's Dyke. Although Fox maintains that the original opening in the Dyke for trade purposes was slightly to the south of the existing gap, there is every possibility that drovers following the ridgeway in the nineteenth century were treading a path which had been in regular use for eleven centuries and indeed, may well have been a trade route prior to the construction of the Dyke.[65] Having crossed the Dyke, the drovers continued by way of Bishop's Moat to Bishop's Castle, entering that village on the Welsh Street. Subsequently they followed the course of the existing B4384 road through Eyton to the hamlet of Plowden where they ascended the Long Mynd via the ancient Port Way, eventually joining the road to Woolstaston and Leebotwood.

The second branch in the route left the ridge way at Kerry Pole and followed the lane for Anchor Inn across the Rhuddwr Brook. The fields adjacent to the Anchor Inn, renowned as a port of call for the drovers, may have accommodated cattle overnight prior to their being shod at the shoeing com-

Towards Cwmystwyth

pound at Poundgate Farm, two miles south of the Anchor.[66] The name "poundgate", when considered in association with the complex network of sunken trackways leading to the farm, suggests that this farm may have originally served as a marshalling centre for local droves before proceeding to Ludlow and the south Midlands. From Anchor Inn and Poundgate the drovers passed to the south of Betws-y-Crwyn and ascended Dowke Hill to Stonypound Farm, beyond which the route joined the ridgeway along the level plateau of Spoad Hill, crossing Offa's Dyke at Springhill.[67] While Fox argues that there is no ground evidence to suggest the existence of an original opening in the Dyke at Springhill, he does not discount the possibility of the modern road occupying the site of such an opening.[68] Having traversed Spoad Hill, the route ascended Clun Hill to Penycwm where it left the existing Clun-Bucknell road to cross Black Hill and to re-join the Clun road at Twitchen, and thence via the "Green Lane" to Onibury and into England.

FOOTNOTES FOR CHAPTER 5

1   R.T. Jenkins, *Y Ffordd yng Nghymru*, Wrexham, 1933, pp. 75-87.
2   U.C.N.W. MSS. 22286-22287.
3   Marshall. *op. cit.*, p. 302.
4.   G. Nesta Evans. *op. cit.*, pp. 120-1, 123.
5   D.R. Hainsworth and C. Walker, *The correspondance of Lord Fitzwilliam of Milton and Francis Guybon, his steward, 1697–1709*, Northants Record Society, 1990.
6   D.C. Rees, *Tregaron, Historical and Antiquarian*, Llandysul, 1936, p. 39.
7   Phillips. *op. cit.*, p. 116.
8   D.C. Rees. *op. cit.*, p. 123.
9   Personal Communication: Mr. R.T. Hughes, Cwmberwyn.
10   Personal Communication. Mr. G. Davies, Llanddewibrefi.
11   The late Mr. John Hope Rees informed me that the last "long distance" drover to use the Abergwesyn route was William Evans of Tynllan who died on April 3rd 1899 at the age of 87 years. Evans, who frequently caroused in the Grouse Inn with the landlord, Jac Pentwyn, is buried in Pantycelyn Chapel between Abergwesyn and Beulah.
12   Personal Communication: Mrs. Raw, Tyllwyd.
13   Personal Communication: Mr. D. Jones, Bronnant.
14   My attention has been drawn by several informants, particularly Mr. Gwilym Price, Blaenant, Rhandir-mwyn, to the existence of a shoeing centre at Blaenant to the south of Rhandir-mwyn. The cattle shoes were forged at the Blaenant smithy, while in a nearby field a circular enclosure, surrounded by banks which are now between two and three feet high, is reputed to have been used for the shoeing process.
15   Reference was made in Chapter 3 to the "Lock and Key" at Smithfield, from which the Lampeter inn may have derived its name.
16   J.E.J. Lloyd, *The Black Cattle Droves*, Historical Memo. of Breconshire 1, 1909, pp. 53-59.
17   N.L.W. Brigstocke MS.18 (*A History of Caeo*, 1904).
18   E.O. James, "Sources for the Welsh Droves" *Carms. Loc. Hist. Mag.*, 1-2, 1961-2, p. 40.
19   N.L.W. Sir Marmaduke Lloyd MS. B.56.
20   Personal Communication: Mrs L Parry-Jones, Rhydcymerau.
21   However, a plaque in the vestry of the church at Pumsaint commemorates Jane Evans of Tyn y waun who went with Florence Nightingale to the Crimea, having previously found employment in London through the agency of the drovers (E.O. James, *op. cit.*, p. 39).
22   Lloyd. *op. cit.*, p. 56.
23   N.L.W. Brigstocke MS. 18.
24   I am particularly grateful to Miss F. Morgan of Albert Mount who kindly introduced me to several local people who showed me various sections of this route. The drovers' road to Cilycwm may still be followed by motor car, although not without considerable difficulty in places.
25   Local residents in Porthyrhyd tell of the discovery, some years ago, of large quantities of cattle shoes in a field alongside the junction of the turnpike with the Cilycwm parish road. This may indicate the one-time location of a shoeing compound at this site.
26   Lloyd, *op. cit.*, p. 54.
27   The Rev. Price of Prestatyn wrote, during the mid 19th century, of drovers travelling from "Talgarth fach via Llwydlo" (N.L.W. 2369C).
28   Lloyd, *op. cit.*, p. 56. After passing through the Felindre gate and the Llanfair-ar-y-bryn gate above Tafarn Talgarth, the drovers could travel toll-free across Brecknockshire until they reached Willersley on the Herefordshire border.
29   Frequent payments at the Glangwili and Alltwalis gates indicate that the Carmarthen-Llanybydder turnpike was used by the Jonathans en route for Lampeter and Tregaron. Moreover, the field name "*Cae cardis*" suggests a possible link between this road and its use by the drovers.

30 I am grateful to Mrs. L. Parry Jones for much of the information concerning the drove roads around Rhydcymerau and Llansawel.

31 Personal Communication: Occupier of Cwmcoedifor, to whom l am grateful for pointing out the supposed location of this 'compound'.

32 Personal Communication: Mr. Ivor Davies, Llansawel.

33 Lloyd, *op. cit.*, p. 57.

34 H.T. Evans, *op. cit.*, pp. 17-19.

35 In 1842 cattle dealers from Carmarthenshire issued a broadsheet on which they declared that they would attend Cilgerran Fair on June 14th... "being the day following Haverfordwest Fair and on their way from Haverfordwest to Newcastle Emlyn without unnecessary expense. (N.L. W. Prints Box XHF).

36 "H.L.J", *Arch. Camb.*, XV, 1869, p. 84.

37 Personal Communication: Mr. W. Goodwin, Llanboidy.

38 Personal Communication: Mrs. W. Lewis, Carmenau Fawr, Mr. W Rogers, Narberth.

39 Personal Communication: The Occupier, Penblewin Farm.

40 Personal Communication: Mr. W. Goodwin, Llanboidy.

41 U.C.N.W. MS. 22287.

42 D.E.Jones, *Hanes plwyfi Llangeler a Penboyr,* Llandysul, 1899, p. 372. I am indebted to Mr. A.T. Lewis for drawing my attention to this reference.

43 Mr. A.T. Lewis informs me that cattle were shod at Pontweli close to Pantyporthmon Farm outside Llandysul. Moreover, there is a strong local tradition that cattle were enclosed, prior to shoeing, on a glen at Pantyporthmon Farm.

44 It was past Rhydyrefail that the drover Dafydd Isaac took his sheep, having bypassed Lledrod via Tyncoed (Phillips, *op. cit.*, p. 116). It is the opinion of Mr. D. Jones of Bronnant that cattle were also shod in the fields behind Tynporth and Tynllan, Lledrod. Other local residents inform me that accommodation for drovers was available at the farm of Tyncoed.

45 The routes from Penuwch and Llangeitho are marked on Singer's map, while the "Drovers Arms" at Penuwch is shown on the first edition 6in map.

46 R. Warner, *A Walk through Wales in August 1797*, Bath, 1798, p. 31.

47 Among the letters of the Rev. Price of Prestatyn who described the route across the Epynt to Whitney "Tafarn Talgarth" is referred to as "Talgarth fach." (N.L.W. MS 2369C).

48 It is maintained locally that Spite Inn was built at the request of the drovers to "spite" the occupiers of Cross Inn!

49 Lloyd, *op. cit.*, pp. 53-7.

50 Personal Communication: Lord Swansea, Glanyrafon.

51 W. Plomer, *Selections from the Diary of the Rev. Francis Kilvert*, Vol. I, London, 1938, p. 122.

52 The accounts of Roderick Roderick reveal that although this dealer did not pass through Clyro, he paid toll at the gates of Talgarth and Hay en route for Hereford via Bredwardine (Map 1).

53 Particularly, Anon., *"The Trail of the Black Ox,"* privately printed, Builth Wells.

54 Personal Communication: Mrs. Davies, Llastio, Cregina.

55 *Brecon and Radnor Express*, 17 Jan., 1935.

56 W. Howse, *Radnorshire*, Hereford, 1949, p. 229.

57 N.L.W. MS. 2369C.

58 Personal Communication: Rev. J. Coutts. Newbridge–on–Wye.

59 Anon., (Black Ox), *op. cit.*, p. 4.

60 W. Howse, *op. cit.*, p. 229.

61 C. Humphreys, "The Trades and Industries of Llanfair Caereinion a hundred years ago," *Mont. Coll.*, 46, 1939-40, pp. 104-l05.

62 H.L.R.O.H of C.60, 1853, p. 167(Montgomeryshire Railway). The Jenkins MSS. also list Forden village among the centres lying on the Shrewsbury route.

63 OS. 1st Ed. 1 inch 1836 (Sheet 60), The Jonathans, en route for Newtown, recorded paying toll at the Llanbrynmair (Penybont) gate although there are no entries for disbursements at Talerddig and Caersws.
64 OS. 1st Ed. 1in 1836 (Sheet 60). 1st Ed. 6in 1891.
65 Fox, *op. cit.*, p. 113.
66 This compound was estimated by the late Professor E.G. Bowen to date back to the mid-fourteenth century.
67 Despite its rather interesting name, there is apparently no evidence to link Stonypound Farm with the cattle trade.
68 Fox *op. cit.*, p. 135.

The chapel at Soar-y-Mynydd

THE WELSH DROVERS IN ENGLAND

6

Maps 7 and 8, which detail some of the routes taken by the Welsh drovers through the Midland and Home Counties, have in the main been compiled from the Jonathan, Roderick and Davies accounts. There is in addition abundant evidence, both in manuscript and in printed sources, to show that by the nineteenth century the drovers travelled widely throughout central and south-eastern England (Map 9).[1]

The northern route from Shrewsbury to Northampton and thence to Bedford and the south east has been abstracted from the Jonathan account books. Other sources also indicate that this was a widely-used route for cattle being driven from both the central and northern counties of Wales. That it was essentially a highway route, following the course of the Watling Street turnpike is clear from the large number of tollgate payments recorded in the Jonathan papers. The accounts refer, together with the localities marked upon the map, to Ivetsey Bank, Norton Canes and Brownhills, thereby indicating that the route continued to follow Watling Street across Cannock Chase from Oakengates. An elderly resident of Norton Canes, who died at the age of 92, remembered the Welsh drovers stopping at the Fleur de Lys Inn at Norton Canes, which he described as "a good pull-up for drovers".[2]

Beyond Norton Canes, the regular drovers' route branched at the Rising Sun public house near Brownhills. Thus, while drovers travelling to Leicester, Market Harborough and Northampton continued to follow Watling Street, those going towards London and the Home Counties headed in a southerly direction for Castle Bromwich, Coleshill and Meriden where they would take refreshment at the "George in the Tree".[3] The Jonathans, whose cattle sales in the first instance were made in the fairs of the grazing counties, did not take this southern route, but followed Watling Street to Hinckley and Lutterworth whence they dispersed to the various market towns of Northamptonshire and Leicestershire.[4] The southern route continued past Meriden and Berkeswell to Kenilworth, eventually passing to Buckingham, Leighton Buzzard, Dunstable and London. The route follows the course of what is still known as the "Welsh Road".

Although the "Welsh Road" was apparently not used by the Jonathans or Roderick Roderick, it is frequently mentioned in the accounts of the sheep drover, Robert Jones of Eisteddfa, Criccieth. Heading for Wendover Fair, for example, Jones passed via Shrewsbury through Norton Canes, Brownhills, Coleshill, Kenilworth, Southam, down the "Welsh Road" to Buckingham and thence to Winslow, Aylesbury and Wendover (Map 10).[5] The Welsh Road, is a typical example of an existing country road possessing all the characteristics of an old drovers' route; the wide grass verges, the abundance of local tales concerning the drovers and the numerous "Welsh" field and place names readily identify the original purpose of the lane.[6] There occur for example, Welsh Road Farm, Welsh Road Gorse, Welsh Ridge and Welsh Road Meadow between the villages of Offchurch and Prior's Hardwick. The occurrence of "London" elements in place names along the Welsh Road, such as "London End" in the villages of Prior's Hardwick and Upper Boddington would tend to support the argument advanced in an earlier chapter that farms, fields and hamlets containing a London/ *Llundain* element in their names may well have been so named by the drovers after the metropolis to which they were frequent visitors.

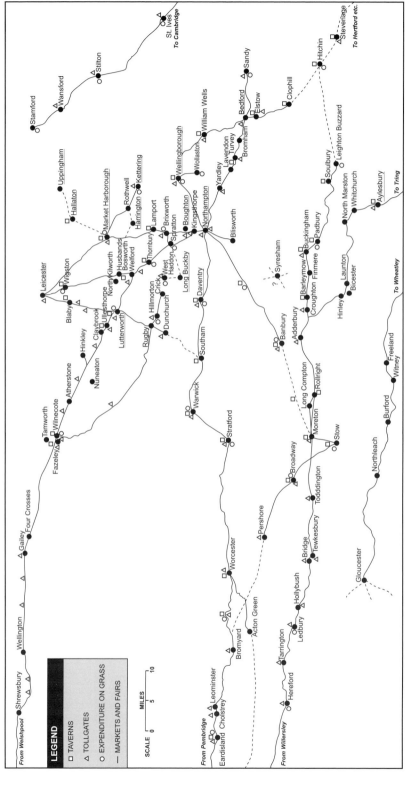

MAP 7 Drovers' Routes in the Midland Counties

LEGEND

□ TAVERNS
△ TOLLGATES
○ EXPENDITURE ON GRASS
— MARKETS AND FAIRS

SCALE

MILES

0   5   10

It is not coincidental, therefore, that these "London" elements seem to occur very frequently in localities visited by the Welsh drovers. A study of the first edition of the 6" Ordnance Survey maps reveals "London" elements at Lechlade, Staunton and Huntley in Gloucestershire and also at Silverstone in Northamptonshire and Thame in Buckinghamshire, all known to have been associated with the Welsh cattle trade. Isolated examples also occur of corruptions of the Welsh language being incorporated into field and place names along established droving routes. A particular instance is found in the village of Prior's Hardwick which lies on the Welsh Road. Local tradition contends that drovers passing Prior's Hardwick watered their cattle at a pond known locally as "cowpool". Superficially there is nothing particularly unusual about this name. However, a pond or water-filled hollow in this locality was almost invariably termed a "pit" and thus an isolated occurrence of the word "pool" would seem to indicate a non-local derivation of this term. The similarity in pronunciation between the Welsh "*pwll*" and English "pool" suggests that perhaps the name "cowpool" may have derived from a corruption of the Welsh name given to the pond during the droving era.

The fact that the course of the "Welsh Road" often represents a manorial boundary is a reflection of its considerable antiquity. In the early fifteenth century, the Warwickshire farmer John Broome of Baddesley Clinton purchased oxen from "Gruff Hope Wallace" from a drove en route from Birmingham to the midland pastures and which may well have passed down the "Welsh Road."[7] By the late seventeenth century, the road was definitely being used for the passage of Welsh cattle. Thus it is recorded among the Constable's accounts in the parish records of Helmdon that in 1687 a sum of money was given:

"to a poor Welshman who fell sick on his journey driving beasts to London".[8]

As Map 10 shows, the "Welsh Road" passed through the village of Syresham in south Northamptonshire. This village is mentioned on one occasion in the Jonathan papers, although it is not clear from the context whether the Jonathans were passing in a southerly direction down the "Welsh Road" or in an easterly direction along the Brackley-Towcester road. Eventually the "Welsh Road" passed to Buckingham and subsequently to Leighton Buzzard via Thornborough, Stewkley and Mursley. Although he did not directly follow this section of the road, the dealer Roderick Roderick records taking refreshment at Soulbury en route for Leighton Buzzard via Buckingham (Map 7).

Prior to doing so, he would perhaps have spent the night at the New Inn, Padbury, a renowned drovers' house to the south of Buckingham. In a manuscript in the Northamptonshire Records Office, Miss Joan Wake noted, in 1925, the recollections of an 85 year old resident of Weston Turville near Aylesbury, one Mrs. Van Bar. As a small child Mrs. Van Bar had lived with Mr. and Mrs. Webb, licencees of the New Inn at Padbury. She recalled that each year two mounted dealers named Walters and Davies arrived at the New Inn to arrange accommodation for their drovers and cattle. Webb, apparently, was always willing to accommodate the drovers as he attached considerable value to the manure which the cattle would leave on his pasture. The dealer David Jonathan eventually hired accommodation land for his beasts at the village of Spratton in Northamptonshire. In this respect, the recollections of an elderly Aylesbury resident are of some interest.[9] This person recalled staying at Manor Farm, Padbury, as a young man, in the company of one Jimmy Janes. Janes was a retired dealer or drover whose uncle Rees Rees purchased this farm in order to fatten any cattle remaining unsold between west Wales and Padbury. The Padbury farm represented the end of the last stage of the journey for Rees's cattle, only ponies being taken further for sale at Barnet Fair.

Roderick Roderick, travelling to the fairs of Hitchin, Barnet and Hertford did not record details of his route between Leighton Buzzard and Hitchin. He may, however, have moved in the direction of Dunstable, bypassing the town via the ancient green way which traversed the common land on its outskirts, and thence along the by-ways to Hitchin.[10] Within the Dunstable area there is ample evidence of the activities of the drovers. Between Dunstable and the village of Ivinghoe on the Icknield Way, for example, is a deep hollow in the chalk known locally as Coombe Hole. There is a strong tradition that this coomb, which provides a natural cattle fold, was used as an overnight resting place for droves of Welsh cattle en route for Barnet Fair.[11] Bull Farm, in the parish of Tilsworth abutting on to Watling Street near Dunstable, also has strong links with the cattle trade. Adjoining the farm, which up to the late nineteenth century was also an inn, are a series of small enclosures ranging in size from two to three acres. These enclosures, in existence prior to the local Enclosure Act of 1768, were apparently used for corralling cattle while their drovers took refreshment at the farmhouse. Moreover, it is believed locally that cattle joining Watling Street from Leighton Buzzard were shod at Bull Farm before proceeding to London.[12] While this may have been so with local cattle, beasts from Wales would invariably have been shod at an earlier stage of the journey so that if Welsh beasts were in fact shod at this point they would have been animals which had either become lame or had lost their original set of shoes.

At Culworth, between Prior's Hardwick and Syresham, the "Welsh Road" is traversed by the ancient Banbury Lane linking the Iron Age camp at Hunsbury Hill on the outskirts of Northampton with the old market town of Banbury. The Jonathan accounts reveal that the Banbury Lane was a regular route to Northampton for droves entering the Midlands by way of the Cotswolds. In 1914, the lane was still for the most part a grassy track between high hedges.[13] Today, however, it more or less follows the existing 'B' road through Pattishall and Cold Higham to Thenford Mill, after which it coalesces with the main Banbury-Brackley road. To the south west of Banbury, the lane no doubt connected with the many ancient routes across the Cotswolds reputed to have been used by the Welsh drovers.

The drove routes across Herefordshire and Shropshire are linked to four principal points of entry for drovers from southern Wales. Animals being driven from the Builth and Rhayader areas tended either to converge on Kington and thence into England via Pembridge and Leominster, or by way of Rhydyspence where they crossed the Wye and followed the Willersley turnpike to Hereford. Drovers from Brecknockshire and Glamorgan moved towards Monmouth to cross the Severn at Arlingham. More usually, however, particularly for cattle being taken to the south-western counties, the Aust and Redwick passages across the Severn estuary were used. Both the Leominster and Hereford routes were used by the Jonathans, either on the way to Northampton via Warwick and Southam or to the Home Counties by way of Aylesbury and Tring. In both cases, the course of the turnpike road was followed, as indicated by payments for toll in the accounts. At the town of Bromyard on the Leominster-Worcester turnpike, the route divided. Having rested overnight at Bringsty Common on the Bromyard Downs, drovers would either continue to head for Worcester or alternatively across Linley Green to Malvern.[14] From here they travelled through the village of Welland to Upton-on-Severn, eventually crossing the Avon below the toll house at Pershore before arriving at Broadway.[15] This was the general direction of the route taken by the Jonathans with sheep for sale at Stow-on-the-Wold. More often, however, they continued from Broadway along the turnpike to Worcester and thence to Stratford along a road free of toll. Having rested their beasts at Warwick, they proceeded along the highway to Southam and thence to Daventry or Northampton. Alternatively they travelled from Southam to Rugby via Dunchurch if they wanted to commence selling at the fairs of Leicester, Market Harborough and Rugby rather than Northampton.

The important route from Willersley to Hereford and through the Cotswolds to Buckingham and the Home Counties is well illustrated in the Roderick accounts and included on Map 7. Other drovers entering England via Rhydyspence, particularly those wishing eventually to sell cattle in Gloucester and the fairs of southern Gloucestershire and Wiltshire, made for Gloucester by way of Mordiford, Newent and Maisemore.[16] The Roderick route, however, meandered its way across the Cotswolds to the Adderbury toll gate and then along the Buckingham road either to Leighton Buzzard or Padbury and Aylesbury. Another route, avoiding the payment of toll at the Croughton and Buckingham gates, was taken by the Jonathans to Aylesbury en route for Uxbridge. This involved leaving the Adderbury-Buckingham road beyond Aynho and following the by-lanes to Launton (thereby circumventing Bicester) and North Marston, to join the main Aylesbury road at Whitchurch.

Reference was made above to drovers converging on the city of Gloucester. From here there were two principal routes to London and the south-eastern counties. The first route left Gloucester via

MAP 8 Drovers' Routes in the Home Counties

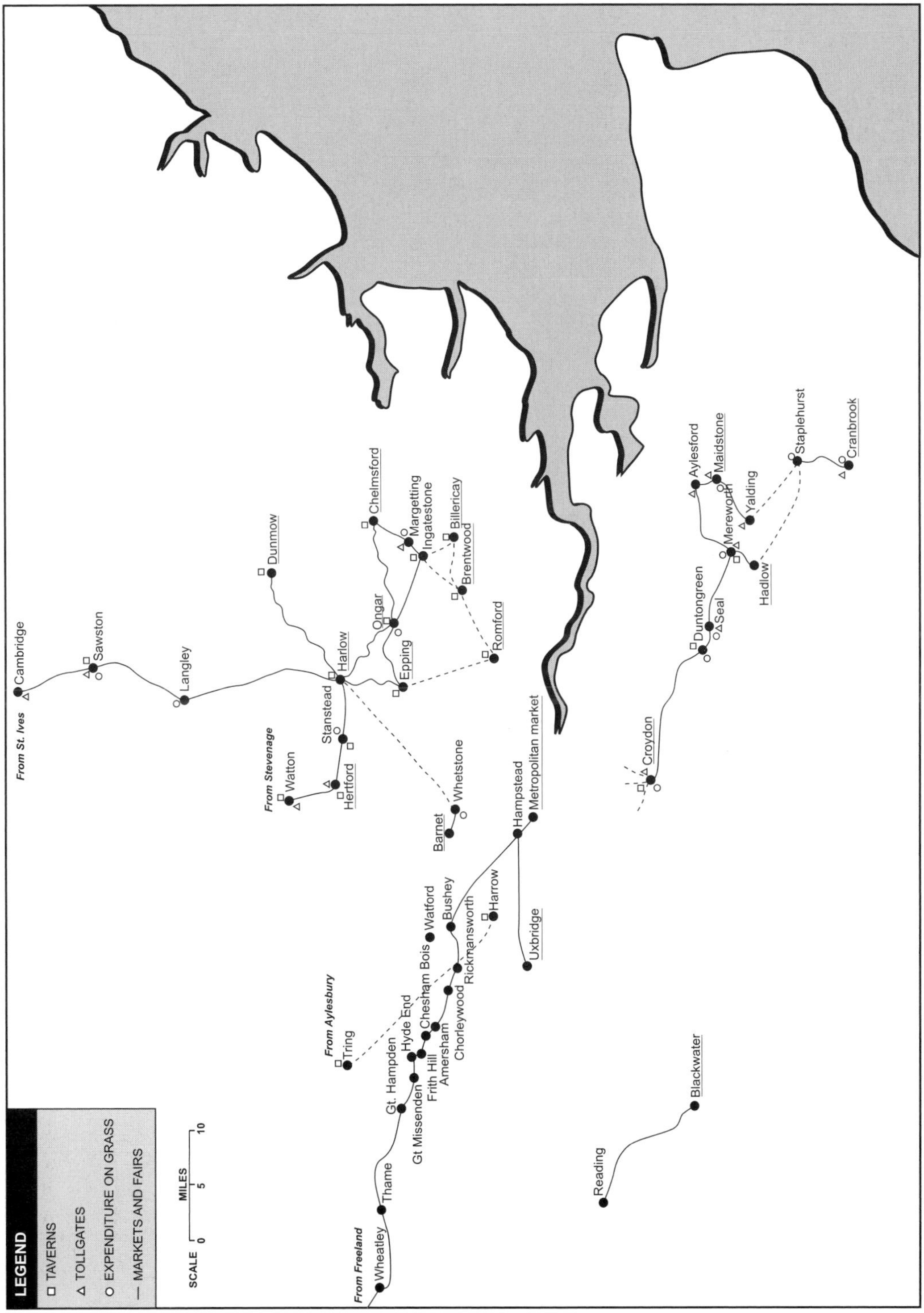

LEGEND

- □ TAVERNS
- △ TOLLGATES
- ○ EXPENDITURE ON GRASS
- — MARKETS AND FAIRS

SCALE

MILES

0   5   10

From St. Ives Cambridge

Sawston

Langley

Dunmow

Chelmsford

Margetting

Ingatestone

Billericay

Brentwood

Ongar

Harlow

Epping

Romford

From Stevenage

Watton

Stanstead

Hertford

Whetstone

Barnet

Hampstead

Metropolitan market

From Aylesbury

Tring

Watford

Bushey

Chesham Bois

Hyde End

Frith Hill

Amersham

Chorleywood

Rickmansworth

Harrow

Uxbridge

Gt. Hampden

Gt Missenden

From Freeland

Wheatley

Thame

Reading

Blackwater

Croydon

Duntongreen

Seal

Aylesford

Maidstone

Merewoyth

Yalding

Staplehurst

Cranbrook

Hadlow

Birdlip Hill and followed the Ermine Street to Cirencester and Cricklade. Beyond Cricklade the drovers mounted the Berkshire Ridgeway at Liddington along which they could travel unimpeded by tollgates. Along the course of the Ridgeway they would frequently be joined by other drovers who had crossed the Aust or Redwick passages and travelled by way of Chipping Sodbury and Chippenham or Bristol and Bath to meet the Ridgeway at Liddington.[17] As an alternative to passing through Cirencester, droves from Gloucester could leave the Ermine Street by Darley Farm some three miles north of Cirencester and join the by-road known today as the "Welsh Way". This lane, which runs through Perrott's Brook, Barnsley and Ready Token to Fairford and Lechlade, was used also by droves of cattle which had crossed the Severn at Arlingham and traversed the uplands above Stroud and the Frome Valley (Map 11).[18] From Lechlade, droves following the "Welsh Way" would continue along the highway to Faringdon and Wantage, to meet cattle from the Berkshire Ridgeway before the great fair of East Ilsley.[19] At Lechlade, marking the end of the "Welsh Way", droves which had crossed to Winchcombe from Worcester and had made their way to Northleach and Coln St. Aldwyn, joined the main route to London and the south-east.[20] Although Bonser indicates that the droves passed through Northleach, local tradition asserts that the town was in fact circumvented by means of a track known locally as the Green Lane. This track followed the level ground above Northleach and thereby avoided the steep slope into the town and, incidentally, the payment of toll-gate charges. It left the Gloucester-Northleach road beyond the Puesdown Inn and ran to the north of Hampnett where it joined the road linking Hampnett with Haselton. The Green Lane ultimately rejoined the road out of Northleach by Bedwell Farm at the top of the hill leaving the town.[21]

The route on Map 7 linking Gloucester with the Metropolitan Market is that taken by George Edmonds who died in Chesham in January 1935 and who drove both sheep and cattle from Wales to London in the eighteen eighties.[22] The route, which followed the existing highway from Gloucester, passed via Witney and then diverged through Freeland village to avoid payment of toll on the old Oxford-Witney road. At various stages this route was traversed or joined by drove lanes from central Oxfordshire. Woodstock, for example, lay on the "Grene Way", an ancient track known to have been used by the Welsh drovers during the pre-turnpike era.[23] The orientation of the "Grene Way" suggests that it was used by droves which had passed through the north Midlands on the way to the Surrey fairs of Blackwater and Farnham.

These fairs, held respectively on the 8th and 10th November, were the venue of many Welsh drovers. The Jonathans often attended Blackwater, as did Jenkin Williams of Tregaron.[24] Williams' fellow townsman, David Davies, accompanied his master's cattle by rail from Aberystwyth to London's Barnet Fair. Animals remaining unsold after Barnet Fair were then driven to the fairs of Reigate, Kingston, Harley Row, Blackwater and Horsham.[25,26] Generally speaking, cattle arriving at these Surrey fairs did so either by way of the Hog's back to Guildford or alternatively via the Upper Thames Valley and through Goring and Reading. Droves which were merely passing through Guildford towards the Kent fairs were taken through Albury and Dorking, while Horsham was reached via the "Drove Road" which passed over Albury Heath and Shere Heath to Ewehurst and thence to Horsham.[27]

George Edmonds' route across the Chilterns to Hampstead and the Metropolitan Market ran almost parallel to another London route from Lechlade through Abingdon, West Wycombe, Beaconsfield and Gerrard's Cross. Writing in 1934, Harmon drew attention to the regret felt by the elderly residents of West Wycombe at the disappearance, as a result of road widening, of the village roadside stream. This stream had provided water for droves of Welsh animals within the memory of persons living at that time.[28] A correspondent asserts that the Welsh drovers were accommodated at the King's Head at Hotspur outside Beaconsfield, until recently an inn-cum-farm in possession of accommodation land.[29] Robert Jones of Eisteddfa often travelled through Beaconsfield en route for Barnet and Uxbridge fairs in the eighteen twenties.[30] Having moved down the "Welsh Road" through the Midlands, Jones passed via Padbury, Winslow, Wendover, Beaconsfield, Hillingdon and then through the Pinner gate to Uxbridge and on to Barnet.

Barnet Fair, besides being a pleasure fair, was perhaps the most important sale centre in the Home

The butter market at Llanidloes, on the drovers' road from the Aberystwyth area to England

Counties from the point of view of the Welsh drovers. Not only was it a very large fair, but it catered also for goods other than livestock, thus giving the drovers an opportunity to collect "pin money" for their wives by selling Welsh lace and other household products. A delightful, if slightly exaggerated account of the fair appeared in the *Farmer's Magazine* of 1856. This account, written by an Englishman, refers in a rather uncomplimentary manner to the Welsh drovers and provides some indication of the disdain in which the unfortunate drovers were held. It is worth quoting at length:

> "*Imagine some hundreds of bullocks like an immense forest of horns, propelled hurriedly towards you amid the hideous and uproarious shouting of a set of semi-barbarous drovers who value a restive bullock far beyond the life of a human being, driving their mad and noisy herds over every person they meet if not fortunate enough to get out of their way; closely followed by a drove of unbroken wild Welsh ponies, fresh from their native hills all of them loose and unrestrained as the oxen that precede them; kicking, rearing and biting each other amid the unintelligible anathemas of their inhuman attendants... the noisy "hurrahs" of lots of "un- English speaking" Welshmen who may have just sold some of their native bovine stock whilst they are to be seen throwing up their long-worn shapeless hats high in the air, as a type of Taffy's delight, uttering at the same time a tirade of gibberish which no one can understand but themselves.*"* [31]

Map 8 sets out the movements of the Jonathans, Roderick Roderick and David Davies in the Home Counties and southern Kent. John Bannister emphasised the importance of Welsh cattle in the economy of both grazing and arable farms in Essex and Kent. Cattle remaining after Barnet Fair were driven into the southern Counties:

> "*Particularly Kent and Essex... where there are fed a greater number of Welsh cattle than in any other part of the kingdom, the graziers giving their preference to this breed.*" [32]

The evidence contained in the drovers' accounts is supplemented by contemporary farmers'

MAP 9 References to Welsh Dealers & Drovers in the Central & Southern Counties of England

accounts and diaries, many of which refer to Welsh cattle. Typically such entries as "13 Welsh heifers bought at Epping Fair" (1776) and "cost and expense of 20 Welsh calves" occur, while among the toll returns of the Brentwood Cattle Fair of 1780 appear the names of Evan Thomas, Cadwalladr, William Williams and Griffith Williams.[33,34,35,36] Some of these drovers, like their compatriots in the midland counties, eventually purchased or rented property and settled in Essex. The Spitty family of Hurlock, for example, is descended from a cattle drover whose original home was Ysbytty Ystwyth in Card iganshire, from which village the family derives its name.[37]

Welsh drovers and dealers may also have settled in Kent where Welsh cattle (particularly the Castlemartins from Pembrokeshire and the red cattle of Glamorgan) were highly esteemed. Marshall saw Welsh cattle being driven along the roads around Maidstone during the Autumn of 1798, while as Map 8 shows, Roderick Roderick passed through Aylesford village where he met drovers from Glamorgan for whom Aylesford Fair was an important venue.[38] Among the other Kentish fairs attended by the Welsh drovers, those of Chilham, Challock and Baddlesmere are mentioned by Bannister, while a letter from Canterbury written by a Welsh drover in the early nineteenth century indicates that that city also witnessed the presence of the drovers. [39,40] The Welsh drovers were well acquainted with Sussex, their presence having been noted at the fairs of Nailsham, Findon, East Grinstead, Shoreham, Howe, Seaford, Selsey and Steyning.

It will be clear from the above discussion that the Welsh cattle drovers and their beasts travelled widely throughout central and southern England. The accounts of one family of dealers, the Jonathans of Dihewyd, are sufficiently comprehensive to enable their activities at the fairs of Northamptonshire and Leicestershire to be traced in some detail. Throughout the whole period covered by the accounts, the principal market outlets appear to have been Northampton, Leicester, and Market Harborough, cattle not disposed of at these and other local fairs being driven through the Home Counties for sale at Harlow, Chelmsford, Romford, Epping, Brentwood and other Essex fairs. Thus animals from a particular drove could have been purchased by the Welland Valley grazier, the grass fattener from the Essex marshes, and the yard and stall feeder from the heavy clays of mid-Essex. From Northampton the route to Essex passed via the Bedford turnpike to Clophill and thence through Hertfordshire by means of a route which cannot be determined from the accounts. Occasionally, when cattle were being sold at Wellingborough Fair, Bedford was approached by a less direct route (see Map 7). After 1864, however, cattle were no longer driven from Northampton to the Essex fairs. By this time the railhead at nearby Blisworth was being exploited and the cattle, together with their drovers, travelled to Brentwood by rail.

Usually, the first market centre to be visited was that of Northampton, either by way of Daventry or Lutterworth. On occasions, however, sales would be made initially at Leicester or Market Harborough. In either case the Welford and Market Harborough turnpikes linking Northampton with Leicester were used for the movement of stock between the fairs. Together with these principal market centres, the Jonathans sold cattle at several other fairs identified on Map 7. This was particularly so during the late fifties and early sixties when increasing numbers of cattle were being sold at the fairs of Rugby and Boughton Green. The village of Spratton, first mentioned in the 1840s, features frequently in the account books and appears to have been used as a collecting point for droves of cattle destined for the various Midland markets. It was ideally suited to this purpose by virtue of its close proximity to the major market centres.

The importance of Spratton increased further in the mid 1860s when the dealers took 149 acres of grazing land near the village at a rental of £450 per annum. The possession of this land provided them with an opportunity to hold cattle during low price periods and to await the advent of more profitable markets without being forced to buy expensive grass keeping. Furthermore, it enabled them to avoid the trouble and expense of attending the smaller market centres by providing a "fall-back" area for cattle which remained unsold after the principal markets. In this context it is significant that the dealers' visits to the smaller fairs of Hallaton and Rothwell became less frequent after the acquisition of the Spratton land. Finally, this holding land permitted the Jonathans to graze the better quality

Map 10 The Welsh Road and Banbury Lane

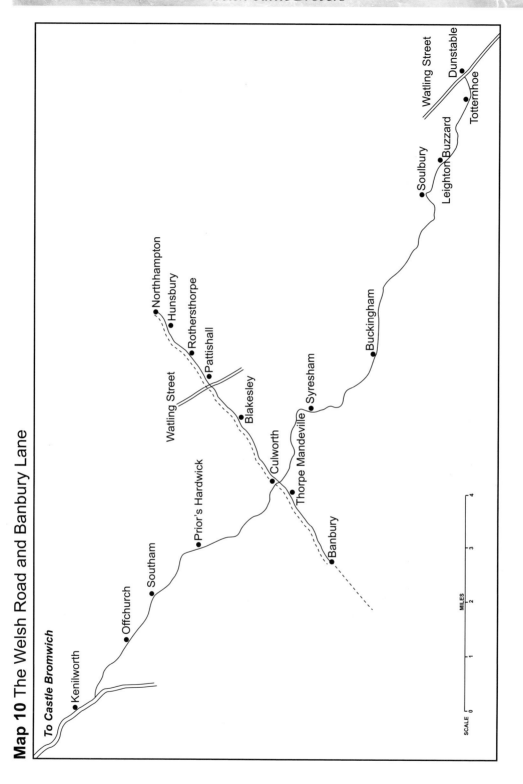

To Castle Bromwich

Kenilworth

Offchurch

Southam

Prior's Hardwick

Northhampton
Hunsbury
Rothersthorpe
Pattishall
Watling Street
Blakesley
Culworth
Thorpe Mandeville
Syresham
Banbury

Buckingham

Soulbury
Leighton Buzzard
Totternhoe
Watling Street
Dunstable

SCALE
0   1   2   3   4
MILES

beasts which remained after the autumn sales, and eventually to drive these animals to Essex and the southern counties for stall-feeding to slaughter weight over the winter months.

Figure IX sets out the distribution of the mean percentage of sales of the Jonathan cattle at the various centres within the Midland grazing region. The histogram does not relate to total sales, for in many cases, the name of an individual purchaser rather than the locality of sale appears in the accounts. Nonetheless, the importance of the principal markets and fairs of Northampton, Leicester and Market Harborough is clearly emphasised. The account books suggest that the dealers usually attended at these centres in the first instance, only moving to the smaller fairs when demand was particularly favourable. Moreover, close inspection of the entries for individual years reveals that there was no consistent increase or decrease in sales at a given centre over the period covered by the accounts. It is possible, for the period 1856/69 where the accounts are particularly detailed, to trace the monthly pattern of cattle sales at the various outlets shown in the histogram. (Table XIV).

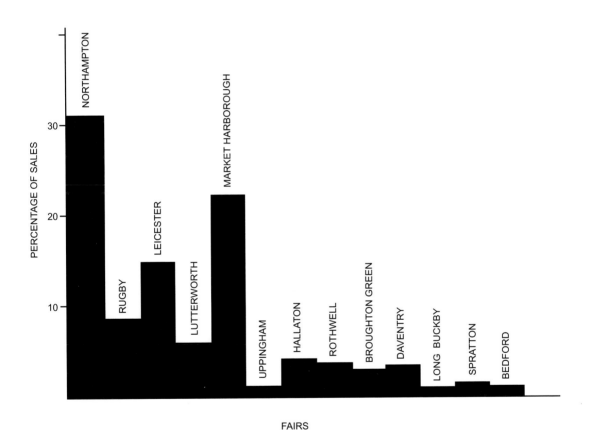

Figure IX. Percentage of Sales 1832-89 (Jonathan Accounts)

Table XIV
Percentage of sales in Midland Markets and Fairs per month (Jonathan Accounts)

Centre	Jan %	Feb %	Mar %	Apr %	May %	June %	July %	Aug %	Sept %	Oct %	Nov %	Dec %	Total cattle sold
Northampton			19	19	25	8	1	4	1	16	7		2453
Rugby				21	7	9	2	2	4	26	29		614
Leicester			13	40	27	9	2	2		3	4		1949
Lutterworth			15	40	30	1		7	4		3		392
Market Harborough			9	34	20	6	1	3	2	12	13		1648
Uppingham			8	4	23	44	6	15					110
Hallaton				31	68	1							219
Rothwell				40	60								234
Boughton Green			2	1	23	74							212
Daventry			1	0	6	13	3	5	9	63			261
Long Buckby			46	25	29								28
Spratton				33		67							117

This exercise underlines the great importance of spring sales in the midland area, more than two-thirds of the total annual sales in Northamptonshire and Leicestershire being made between April and June at a time when demand from graziers would be at its peak. Subsequently the volume of sales declined, only to increase again in October, thereby reflecting the demand for beasts for autumn depasturing. A large proportion of the animals sold in the grazing counties at this latter end of the year were disposed of at Rugby and Market Harborough which lay deep in the heart of the "fattening pasture" country, where farmers were particularly insistent that their fields were grazed bare before the onset of the winter frosts. Nevertheless, despite this demand for "scavenger" animals, the great majority of Welsh cattle driven to England during the late autumn months were sold in the densely-populated eastern and home counties where they would be stall-fattened for the Christmas or early spring markets of London and the other rapidly growing towns of south-eastern England.

FOOTNOTES FOR CHAPTER 6

1   However, the Chancery and Exchequer proceedings for the early seventeeth century suggest that of the large numbers of cattle driven from Wales to England, the majority were sold in the Midlands, with only small numbers infiltrating the southern counties. (A. Everitt in *The Agrarian History of England and Wales 1500-1640*, IV, Cambridge, 1967, p. 515).

2   Personal Communication: Rev. D. Skelding, Norton Canes.

3   Skeel, *op. cit.*, p. 148, quoting W. Duignan, *Warwickshire Place Names*. London, 1912. The existence of several "Welsh" names in this locality provides further evidence of the movements of the drovers. Hence "Welshman's Hill" near Castle Bromwich (*V.C.H. Worcs.*, iv. p. 304) and "Welsh Meadow" at Frankley (*V.C.H. Worcs.*, III p. 12).

4   From time to time the Jonathan papers mention "Three Potes". This no doubt refers to the Three Potes Inn near Hinckley, well known as a drovers' retreat.

5   R.T. Jenkins, *op. cit.*, pp. 52-3.

6   J. Drew, "The Welsh Road and the Drovers" *Trans. Birmingham Arch. Soc.*, 82, pp. 38-43.

7   C. Dyer, "A small Landowner in the fifteenth century, "*Midland History*", 1(3), 1972, p. 7.

8   I am indebted to Mr. E.G. Parry of Brackley for this reference. The Welsh Road is also mentioned as such in the Priors Marston Enclosure Award of 1758.

9   These recollections were gathered by Miss P. Bell, Archivist, Bedford County R.O. who communicated them to me.

10 This grassy track, between Dunstable Downs and Totternhoe Knobs is known as "Drover's Way."

11 Personal Communication: Mrs. J. Durley, Aylesbury. Although the downland herbage now provides abundant grazing, it is likely that during the nineteenth century, prior to downland pasture improvement, forage for droves crossing the chalk downs for the eastern counties may have been in short supply. This would apply particularly during a period of drought.

12 Personal Communication: Mr. L. Matthews, Dunstable.
    It is interesting to compare the reputed method of shoeing, which involved using cut horsehoes, with the use of purpose forged "*ciws*" described in Chapter IV.

13 C. Markham, "Banbury Lane", *Jour. Northants. Nat. Hist. Soc. & Field Club*. XVII, 1914, p. 120.

14 Personal Communication: Miss E.D. Pearson, Bromyard.

15 Personal Communication: Mr. F. Stratton, Pershore.

16 Finberg, *op. cit.*, p. 13.

17 Bonser, *op. cit.*, p. 186.

18 T. Sawyer, "Roads in Gloucestershire", *Trans. Bristol & Glos. Arch. Soc.*, XX, 1895. p. 249.
    The activities of the Welsh drovers in the locality of East Ilsey is provided by the presence of several "Welshman's Ponds" in the area.

19 Personal Communication: Mr. F. Underhill, Didcot.

20 Bonser, *op. cit.*, p. 186.

21 I am indebted to the Rev. R. Walker of Northleach for drawing my attention to the existence of this Green Way.

22 Personal Communication: Mr. A. Stratford, Chesham.

23 E. Marshall, "The Early History of Woodstock Manor in its Environs", 1873; Personal Communication: Mr. M. Ashton.

24 D.L. Rees, *op. cit.*, p. 123.

25 Personal Communication: Mrs. A. Davies, Tregaron.

26 In 1864, the Jonathan accounts record that cattle were taken by rail to Reading, whence they were driven to Horsham, Cross-in-Hand and East Grinstead. This is the only occasion when the latter three places are mentioned.

27 O.M. Heath, *Walks around Albury*, Surrey, 1950.

28 H. Harmon, *Notes on West Wycombe*, Blandford, 1934, p. 22.

29 Personal Communication: Mr. K.B. Holden, Beaconsfield.

30 U.C.N.W. Bangor MS. 8441.

31 *Farmer's Magazine*, 1856, p. 57. Writing from London to Eben Fardd in 1858, S. P. Tregelles explained that he had met a dozen Welshmen who were returning home to the Teifi area after selling cattle at Barnet Fair. They intended to travel to Hereford by rail and to complete the remainder of the journey on foot. They told Tregelles of the Welsh preachers who held services at the fair which were regularly attended by their fellow countrymen. (N.L.W. Cwrt Mawr MS 73 f. 103. I am indebted to Mr. MacDonald of the MSS. Department of the National Library of Wales for this reference).

32 Bannister, *op. cit.*, p. 327.

33 Essex. R.O.D / DBE A8.

34 Essex. R.O.D / DDC A28 f 79.

35 Essex. R.O.D / DTW A4.

36 Eliza Vaughan relates a tale of two Welsh drovers, John Jones and Robert Ellis, who sold cattle at Bardfield Fair near Braintree in 1790. Jones murdered Ellis on the return from Braintree for which he was eventually tried and executed at Chelmsford. (*The Essex village in days gone by*, Colchester, 1930, pp. 19-26).

37 Glyn H. Morgan, *The Romance of Essex Inns*, Letchworth, 1967, p. 94.

38 P.G. Hughes, "Porthmona ym Morgannwg", *Trans. Cymm.* 1946-7, pp. 250-70.

39 Bannister, *op. cit.*, p. 327.

40 U.C.N.W. MS. 9881.

Map 11 The Welsh Way

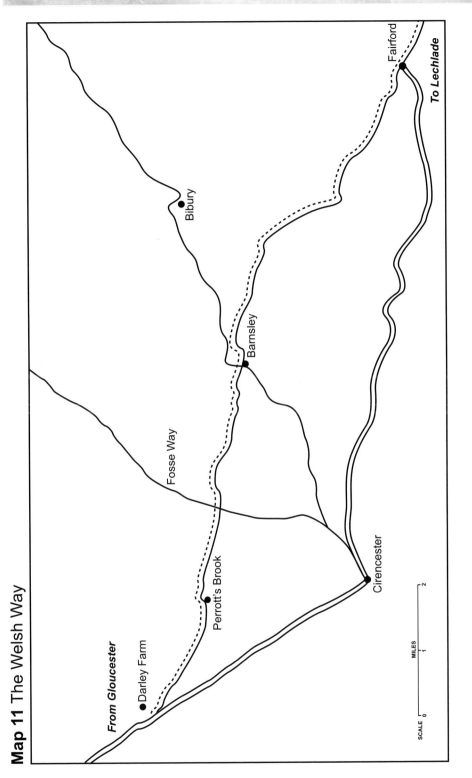

From Gloucester

Darley Farm

Perrott's Brook

Fosse Way

Bibury

Barnsley

Cirencester

Fairford

To Lechlade

SCALE

MILES

0   1   2

EPILOGUE

The saga of the long-distance drover came to an end as local fairs and markets in Wales tended to be concentrated in close proximity to the railways. However, in the period before the development of motorised cattle transport the local drover still played a prominent part in the conduct of the cattle trade, farmers and dealers requiring his services for the safe delivery of cattle to the fairs and also for loading of beasts into railway trucks. Thus, although Edmund Hyde Hall's "distinguished persons in the history of this country's economy" had all but disappeared before the nineteenth century drew to a close, the skills of "the art and mystery" of droving were preserved among the district drovers of Wales. The Jonathans, whose farming expertise generated the initial capital to enable them to embark on cattle dealing, finally returned to farming in the closing decades of the century, having accumulated sufficient funds to settle other members of the family on farms throughout Cardiganshire. It would be pleasant to think that other cattle dealers were able to spend their declining years farming in their native Wales after long, arduous and often frustrating years of trading. In the final analysis, however, any survey of the activities of the drovers must leave this and many other questions unanswered due simply to the fact that the majority of them left no written record of their doings. They were, in effect, shadowy figures who loomed large in the lore of the countryside and to whose sociocultural importance contemporary observers bore witness.

Diarists, travellers and topographers were noticeably silent, however, on the subject of the possible contribution of the drovers to the development of Welsh agriculture, and although it is not difficult to imagine local drovers and their farmer friends passing the long winter evenings discussing English farming methods over mugs of *"cwrw"*, such notebooks and diaries extant shed little light upon this matter. Until the discovery of further manuscript material provides us with more explicit information on the possible link between the movements of the drovers and the dissemination of new agricultural knowledge through Wales, this must remain a matter for intelligent speculation and perhaps for local studies. The possibility that Welsh drovers and dealers may have settled in parts of the Midland and Home Counties also suggests a potentially fertile field of research for local historians. In the rich grazing counties of Northamptonshire and Leicestershire, for example, numerous Welsh names occur among the occupiers and owners of land. While many of these people emigrated from Wales in the nineteen thirties, it is not inconceivable that some of them are the descendants of drovers who abandoned the Welsh hills to farm in this lush Canaan.

Tales of the exploits of men like the Jonathans, their contemporaries and forebears, have become enshrined in the rich tradition of Welsh folk memory. In the Midlands also, the Welsh drovers and dealers are still spoken of with a certain amount of awe by elderly villagers and their descendants, while the element of continuity finds expression in the soft Carmarthenshire accents which still may be heard today among the dealers attending the markets of Northampton or Market Harborough.

APPENDIX I

Weather Conditions in Summer (1816-41).
From *The Welshman*, December 10th, 1841.

1816 Extremely cold and wet, one of the worst harvests known.
1817 Cold and wet in July and August, fine in September.
1818 Intensely hot and dry (temperature often above 80^0 F).
1819 Fine and hot August very hot no thunder.
1820 Fine and very productive.
1821 Mostly cold and showery. Some hot days. Rains (immense) damaged harvest.
1822 Hot and dry, occasional storms; good harvest.
1823 Cold and showery. Rained every day in July except 24th.
1824 Fine and warm, never too hot, nice September.
1825 Very hot temperature at 90^0F on July 18th.
1826 Hottest and driest summer known.
1827 Hot and dry but not as much as 1826.
1828 Immense rains beginning July 9th; large floods July 16th and 30th. Bad harvest.
1829 Cold and stormy; heavy rains in September.
1830 Cold and wet especially in June.
1831 Warm, gleamy, showery and electrical. A sickly summer; great number of insects, especially house flies.
1832 Moderate.
1833 Very fine, particularly the early part, abundant harvest.
1834 Fine and hot; heavy rain in July, early and productive harvest.
1835 Hot and dry; abundant harvest.
1836 Very dry in the Midlands, almost entire destruction of the turnip crop by the fly.
1837 Severe spring, hot summer, deficient harvest.
1838 Cold and wet, late unproductive harvest.
1839 Almost unceasing rains; harvest not unproductive, but damaged.
1840 Fine warm summer, very hot. August feed deficient.
1841 Fine and warm in May and June; wet and cold in July and beginning of August. Fine harvest weather at the end of August and September.

APPENDIX II

Sample Probate Inventories of Welsh farmers, 1820-50.
Source: Wills and Administrations, National Library of Wales.

1820 Thomas Hughes, Penmynydd, Anglesey

	£.	s.	d.
Wearing apparel	2	0	0
Bridle and saddle	1	5	0
Kitchen furniture	1	0	0
Dairy furniture		15	0
Parlour furniture	13	0	0
One bed and bedclothes	1	0	0
Another bed and bedclothes	1	5	0
Two chests	2	0	0
Three chests	1	0	0
Cupboard		15	0
Twelve sacks	1	10	0
Chest in the barn	2	0	0
Stack of upland hay	9	0	0
Meadow hay	1	0	0
Stack of Pollard's oats	12	0	0
Part of stack of barley	6	0	0
Potatoes	3	0	0
Two horses	10	0	0
Four cows	32	0	0
Four calves	7	0	0
Four pigs	5	0	0
Cart and gears	5	0	0
Plough and harrow		10	0
Pitch fork and other small articles		15	0
	£118	15	0

1830 John Thomas, Llanfairfechan, Caernarvonshire

One bedchamber containing bed with chairs	5	0	0
Kitchen furniture	6	0	0
Bedchamber upstairs with beds, etc.	20	0	0
Three cows, two heifers, two calves	18	0	0
A horse and pony	12	0	0
Twenty sheep	6	0	0
Hay and corn	6	0	0
Implements for husbandry and an old saddle	2	0	0
Cash out at interest	100	0	0
	£175	0	0

1830 John Williams, Edern, Caernarvonshire

	£.	s.	d.
Wearing apparel	5	0	0
Household furniture	112	0	0
Horses	130	10	0
Cattle	212	15	0
Pigs	21	12	0
Sheep	45	10	0
Implements of husbandry	60	5	0
Corn growing	112	0	0
Hay growing	73	0	0
Potatoes growing	26	10	0
Shares in a vessel	130	0	0
Credits	24	18	0
	£954	0	0

1840 David Roberts, Llanegwad, Carmarthenshire

Wearing apparel	3	0	0
Cash in house	1	0	0
Household furniture	10	0	0
Implements of husbandry	4	0	0
Four horses	10	0	0
Six cows	30	0	0
Three two year olds	6	15	0
Four yearlings	4	16	0
Two pigs	1	10	0
Potatoes		6	0
Corn	21	10	0
	£92	17	0

1840 Thomas Morgan, Llanfihangel Towymynydd, Monmouthshire

	£.	s.	d.
Three cows	28	10	0
Two heifers and calves	18	18	0
In calf heifers	9	9	0
Five calves	5	5	0
Four steers and four heifers	43	0	0
Six yearlings	17	0	0
Eighteen sheep	16	4	0
One calf	8	0	0
One pony	4	10	0
Nine pigs	9	9	0
Three horses	20	0	0
Implements	15	0	0
Harness	4	0	0
Wheat and straw	21	0	0
	£220	5	0

1850 David Jones, Beddgelert, Merioneth

	£	s.	d.
Wearing apparel	3	0	0
Furniture	14	0	0
Implements of husbandry	16	0	0
Horse and gears	14	0	0
Hay and corn	11	0	0
Sixteen cattle	41	0	0
Cash in house	10	0	0
Cash at interest	180	0	0
	£289	0	0

1850 Henry Lloyd, Llanrhaidr, Denbighshire

Two cart horses	25	10	0
Two colts	10	0	0
Three milk cows	15	0	0
Two heifers	5	0	0
Two calves	2	10	0
Pigs	2	10	0
Implements of husbandry	15	0	0
Furniture	8	0	0
Tools	4	0	0
	£87	10	0

1850 Richard David, Bodedern, Anglesey

Horses and gears	39	0	0
Cattle	125	0	0
Sheep and Lambs	20	4	0
Swine	6	10	0
Poultry		5	0
Corn and hay	40	0	0
Implements of husbandry	20	5	0
Clothes	4	0	0
Furniture	25	0	0
	£280	4	0

1850 John Morgan, Llanafan fawr, Brecknockshire

Purse and apparel	20	10	0
Horses and gearing	15	0	0
Cattle	15	10	0
Sheep	10	0	0
Pigs	1	10	0
Poultry		7	6
Furniture	17	0	0
Cash	20	0	0
	£99	17	6

1850 Nathan Jones, Llanbister, Radnorshire

	£.	s.	d.
Cattle	151	0	0
Sheep	56	0	0
Horses	55	10	0
Hay and corn	117	0	0
Implements	20	0	0
Furniture	29	0	0
Cash and securities	577	0	0
	£1005	10	0

1850 William Price, Llandeilo graban, Radnorshire

Purse and apparel	10	0	0
Horses	45	0	0
Cattle	50	0	0
Sheep	30	0	0
Pigs	7	0	0
Poultry		15	0
Implements of husbandry	15	0	0
Furniture	12	0	0
Corn in barn	60	0	0
Growing corn	20	0	0
	£249	15	0

1850 Hugh Hughes, Clynnog, Caernarvonshire

Wearing apparel	5	0	0
Furniture	20	2	6
Four cows	10	0	0
Yearling calf	1	10	0
Two horses	12	0	0
Five pigs	5	0	0
Hay	3	0	0
Corn	4	0	0
Implements of husbandry	5	7	0
Gears	1	6	0
	£67	5	6

1850 Owen Jones, Amlwch, Anglesey

Purse and apparel	15	0	0
Furniture	106	15	0
Hay and corn	81	10	0
Potatoes	3	15	0
Horses	111	0	0
Cattle	401	18	0
Implements of husbandry	89	0	0
Cash at bank	652	0	0
Money out at interest	346	0	0
	£1806	18	0

1850 Bryan Bound, Llanddewy Ystradenny, Radnorshire

	£.	s.	d.
Purse and apparel	14	1	4
Horses and gearing	99	0	0
Horned cattle	180	0	0
Sheep	64	0	0
Pigs	5	0	0
Poultry		16	8
Household goods	40	0	0
Growing corn	6	0	0
Hay	5	0	0
Implements of husbandry	20	0	0
Debts due to deceased	10	0	0
	£443	18	0

1850 John Ebbsworth, Laugharne, Carmarthenshire

Nine cows	36	0	0
Two bullocks	11	0	0
Six three year olds	15	0	0
Nine two year olds	13	10	0
Eight yearlings	6	0	0
Five horses	20	4	0
One hundred and nineteen mountain sheep	21	16	0
Cash at interest	401	0	0
	£524	10	0

1850 William Rees, Bedwas, Monmouthshire

Forty wethers	80	0	0
Ninety mountain sheep (Yearling)	22	10	0
One hundred ewes	35	0	0
Five cows	35	0	0
Six yearlings	12	0	0
Five two year olds	17	10	0
Two steers	13	5	0
Three feeding cows	18	0	0
Household furniture	18	0	0
	£251	5	0

1850 William Lewis, New Moat, Pembrokeshire

Eight two year olds	32	0	0
Eight yearlings	12	0	0
Eight calves	4	0	0
Eight cows	40	0	0
Four sheep	2	0	0
Five horses	20	0	0
Implements of husbandry	8	0	0
Furniture	15	0	0
	£133	0	0

APPENDIX III

ADVICE TO DROVERS BY VICAR PRICHARD (1549-1644).

Cyngor i'r Porthmon

Advice to Drovers

Os 'dwyt borthmon *dela'n onest,*
  Tâl yn gywir am y gefaist;
Cadw d'air, na thorr addewid;
  Gwell nag aur mewn côd *yw credid.*

If you are a drover, deal honestly
Pay a fair price for what you have
Keep your word, do not break promises,
Better than gold, is a code of ethics.

Na chais ddala'r tlawd wrth angen,
  Na thrachwanta ormod fargen:
Na fargenna â charn lladron,
  Ni ddaw rhad o ddim a feddon,

Do not attempt to take advantage of the poor,
Do not greed for over profit,
Do not deal with notorious thieves,
Nothing of theirs is of value.

Gochel brynu mawr yn echwyn,
  Pawb ar air a werth yn 'sgymmun;
Prynu'n echwyn a wna i borthmon,
  Ado'r wlad a myn'd i'r 'Werddon.

Beware of buying too much on credit,
Do not take people at their word
Buying on credit will cause a drover
To leave the country and flee to Ireland.

Gochel dwyllo dy fargenwyr.
  Duw sydd Farnwr ar y twyliwyr;
Pe dihangit tu hwnt i'r 'Werddon
  Duw fyn ddial twyll y porthmon.

Beware of cheating your bargainer,
God will judge you for deceiving.
Even if you flee beyond Ireland,
God will avenge a dealer's cheating.

Byth ni rostia un o'r twyllwyr,
  'Rhyn a heliant, medd y 'Sgrythur;
Ni ddaw twyll i neb yn ennill,
  Fe rêd ymaith fel trwy'r rhidill.

Do not shield the ones who cheat,
All they collect, say the scriptures
Will not benefit them
But will vanish as through a sieve.

Gochel feddwi wrth borthmonna,
  Gwîn hel borthmon i gardotta;
Os y porthmon a fydd meddw,
  F'a'r holl *stoc* i brynu'r cwrw.

Beware of drinking while you're droving,
Wine will reduce the drover to a beggar,
If the drover is a drunkard,
All his stock will buy his beer.

Dela'n union, carca d'enaid;
  Na ddiflanna â dâ gwirioniaid:
Pe diflannit i'r Low Cwntres,
  Dial Duw a fyn d'orddiwes.

Deal honestly, save your soul,
Do not steal the cattle of the simple
Even if you disappear to the "Low Countries"
God is sworn to avenge you in the end.

Rhys Prichard, *Canwyll y Cymry,* (1807 ed.) Carmarthen 1807, pp. 148-149.

BIBLIOGRAPHY

In the Bibliography, the following abbreviations have been adopted:

J.R.A.S.E.:	The Journal of the Royal Agricultural Society of England.
Ag. Hist.:	Agricultural History.
Ag. Hist. Rev.:	The Agricultural History Review.
Econ. Hist. Rev.:	The Economic History Review.
N.L.W. Journal:	Journal of the National Library of Wales.

PART A
PRIMARY SOURCES
MANUSCRIPT MATERIAL

National Library of Wales (N.L.W.)
Chirk Castle MSS. E223, E1098, E2812, E3367, E6297, F7174.
Llanllyr MSS. 112-125, Transactions of Talsarn Fair (1802-1837).
Brigstocke MS. 18, Ms. History of Caeo, Carmarthenshire (1904).
Broadhead Evans MSS. 32, 33, 102, Correspondence and notes of John Evans, Anglesey (late C19th).
G.E. Owen MSS. 7266-67, Cardiganshire Great Sessions case (1793).
Dynevor Deeds and Documents, 4, Carmarthen Fair regulations (mid C18th).
Glynne of Hawarden MS. 6606, Premia for turnip crops (Early C19th).
Harcourt Powell MSS. (Unnumbered),Cattle Sales at Narberth Fair (Early C19th).
Ellis MS. 2068, Edward Williams to T.E. Ellis re. rents in North Wales in "Great Depression".
Sir Marmaduke Lloyd MS. B.56, Indenture relating to turf cutting in Paneugleision, Carms. (1708).
Cwrt Mawr MS. 73, S.P. Tregelles to Eben Fardd (1855).
Glansevern MSS. Jones Correspondence (early C19th).
Evans (Aberglasney) MS. 181741, Cardiganshire Quarter Sessions case (1814).
D.T.M Jones MSS. 7808, 9365. 9100, 1187, 8820.
Miscellaneous N. L. W. MSS.
N.L.W . MSS. 9600-9614, Notes and accounts of David Jonathan of Dihewyd, Cardiganshire (1839-82).
N.L.W. MS. 6733, Ms. Recollections (mid C19th).
N.L.W. MS. 17927A, Accounts of a Trawsfynydd dealer (1822).
N.L.W. MS. 11706A, Accounts of Roderick Roderick of Porthyrhyd (1838-9).
N.L.W. MS. 2719C, Ms. Essay on Welsh Farming (late C19th).
N.L.W. MS. 13147A, Iolo Morganwg MSS.
N.L.W. MS. 1659 Ms. Notes of Walter Davies.
N.L.W. MS. 1769C, Notes of the Rev. J. Jenkins of Kerry (mid C19th).
N.L.W. 1695B, Weights of Radnorshire Cattle (1800).
N.L.W. MS. 2639C, Notes of the Rev. Price of Prestatyn.

University College of North Wales (U.C.N.W.)
Porthyraur MS. 33281, Caernarvonshire Great Sessions case (1806).
Mostyn MSS. 6607; 6572, Letter concerning furze growing (early C19th); Welsh cattle weights (1827).
Gwredog MSS. 2, 35, Notes and accounts of Elias Jones.
Miscellaneous U.C.N.W. MSS.
U.C.N.W. MS. 6938, Traffic returns for Menai Bridge 1830-1846.
U.C.N.W. MS. 9881, Letter from a drover in Canterbury (early Cl9th).
U.C.N.W. MS. 18607, Notes of Rev. J.E. Vincent.
U.C.N.W. MS. 22286-22287, Notes and MSS of Dr. R.T. Jenkins.
U.C.N.W. MS. 8441, Accounts of Robert Jones of Eisteddfa (c.1820).

Additional Manuscript Material used in compiling Graphs of Price Movements.
National Library of Wales.
Harpton Court MSS. 2122-2124.
Falcondale MS. 25.
Tredegar Park MS. 45/277.
Glynllivon MS. 4878.
Colby MS. 4878.
Llwyngwair MSS. 19, 20.
Broom Hall MSS. 49, 51, 52.
Penpont MS. 3494.
N.L.W. MS. 10346B.
N.L.W. MS. 1910B.
N.L.W. MS. E2.A20.
N.L.W. MS. 11701A.
N.L.W. MS. 3110A.
N.L.W. MS. 31116.
N.L.W. MS. 15051E.

University College of North Wales (U.C.N.W.)
Penrhyn MS. 1740 (3).
Gwredog MSS. 2, 35.
Vaynol MS. 4585.
U.C.N.W. MS. 1017.

Welsh County Records Offices
Caernarvonshire R.O. Vaynol MSS. 3110, 3074, 3075, Correspondence re. rentals on Vaynol estate during "Great Depression".
Carmarthenshire R.O. Cawdor MS. 260, Fines payable to drovers "misbehaving" while in charge of cattle.
Carmarthenshire R.O. Castell Gorfod MS. B. 178, Letter from Lord Cawdor, 1879.
Carmarthenshire R.O. MS. T.T. Box V10.
Merionethshire R.O. MS. D/ T. 66 Accounts of David Davies (1838).
Merionethshire R.O. MS. D/0/543/6, Notes and Accounts of J.B. Annwyl.
Merionethshire Quarter Sessions, Michealmas 1884 (9), Trinity 1806(14), Hilary 1814 (31).
Monmouthshire R.O. MS. W. and T.M./ B.27, Petition to Treasury complaining of forestalling at Newport Fair (1843).
Monmouthshire R.O. MS. D156/32, Proclamation against forestalling Usk Fair (1852).
Pembrokeshire R.O. MS. DX/ 130/7, Notes and accounts of a Pembrokeshire farmer (C19th).
Pembrokeshire R.O. MS. D/ RTP, Narberth Fair Transactions (1833).

English Records Offices and other Depositories
Northamptonshire R.O.I.L. 1961, Drover committed to gaol for stealing (1634).
Essex R.O.D/DBE A8, Welsh Drovers in Essex (C18th-C19th).
Essex R.O.D/DDC A 28 f.79, Welsh Drovers in Essex (C18th-C19th).
Essex R.O.D/DTW A4. Welsh Drovers in Essex (C18th-C19th).
University of Nottingham Library NeC 8659(a), J. Lown, to Duke of Newcastle (1837).
Shropshire R.O. Quarter Sessions Order Books.
Public Records Office; H.O. 73(1); P.C. 8/71; 5879. Material concerning Cattle Plague in Kent, 1865.
City of London R.O. MS. 407A, Metropolitan Market Convictions Books. Cl9th.
City of London R.O. MS. 3, Ordinance curtailing city drovers activities. Cl9th.
Middlesex R.O. MJ/SBR/, Quarter Sessions Order Book (1752).
Middlesex R.O. MJ/ OC/, Privy Council ban on cattle movements (1746).
Bodleian Library MS. Ridley A III c. 14, Accounts of John Jackson, Easington, Oxfordshire (1766-1799).
House of Lords R.O. 14, H of C, 24, 1863 p. 4 (Pembrokeshire and Tenby Railway).
H.L.R.O. H. of L., 8, 1859, p. 6 (Vale of Llangollen Railway).
H.L.R.O. H. of L., 1, 1861, p. 311 (Aberystwyth and Welsh Coast Railway).
H.L.R.O. H. of L., 62, 1872, p. 3 (Teifiside Railway).
H.L.R.O. H. of L., 60, 1853, p. 667 (Montgomeryshire Railway).

OFFICIAL PUBLICATIONS

Board of Agriculture, The Agricultural State of the Kingdom in February, March and April 1816, B.P.P.1.

Report and Minutes of Evidence of the Select Committee of the House of Commons on Agriculture in the United Kingdom, 1821, B.P.P. 11.

Report and Minutes of Evidence of the Select Committee on Agricultural Distress, 1836, B.P.P. VIII.

Report and Minutes of Evidence of the Select Committee on the Bank of England Charter, 1831-2, B.P.P. VI.

Report and Minutes of Evidence of the Select Committee on Commons Inclosure, 1844, B.P.P. VII.

Report and Minutes of Evidence of the Commission of Inquiry for South Wales, 1844, B.P.P. XVI.

Report and Minutes of Evidence of the Commission of Inquiry into the State of Education in Wales, 1847, B.P.P. XXVII.

Report and Minutes of Evidence of the Select Committee on Agricultural Customs, 1847-8, B.P.P. VIII.

Report and Minutes of Evidence of the Select Committee on Smithfield Market, 1847, B.P.P. VIII.

Report and Minutes of Evidence of the Select Committee on the Trade in Animals, 1866, B.P.P. XVI.

Report of the Royal Commission on the Employment of Women and Children in Agriculture, 1830, B.P.P. III.

First Report of the Royal Commission on Market Rights and Tolls, 1889, B.P.P. LIII.

Royal Commission on the Depressed state of the Agricultural Interest, 1882, (Assistant Commissioners' Reports) B.P.P. XV.

Report and Minutes of Evidence of the Royal Commission on the Agricultural Depression, 1881-7, B.P.P. XV-XVII.

Reports and Minutes of Evidence of the Royal Commission on Land in Wales and Monmouthshire, 1894-96, B.P.P. XXXVI - XLI.

STATUTES OF THE REALM

3 & 4 Ed.VI c.18, 19 (1551-2)	An Act for the buying of rother Beasts and Cattle.
5 & 6 Ed.VI c.14, 21(1552)	An Act against Regrators, Forestallers and Engrossers.
27 Hen.VIII c.7, (1535-6)	An Act for the Abuses in the Forests of Wales.
34 & 35 Hen. VIII c.26, (1542-3)	An Act for certain Ordinances in the King's Majesty's Dominion and Principality of Wales.
5 Eliz.I c.12, (1562)	An Act Touching Badgers of Corn and Drovers of cattle to be licenced.
3 Chas.I c.1, (1627)	An Act for the further Reformation of sundry abuses committed on the Lord's Day, commonly called Sunday.
15 Chas.II c.8, (1662)	An Act to prevent the selling of live fat cattle by Butchers.
22 & 23 Chas. II c.19, (1670)	An Act to prevent frauds in the Buying and Selling of Cattle at Smithfield and elsewhere.
29 Chas.II c.7, (1676)	An Act for the better observation of the Lord's Day, commonly called Sunday.
6 Anne c.22, (1706)	An Act to explain and amend an Act of the last session of Parliament, for preventing frauds frequently committed by bankrupts.
19 Geo.II c.5, (1746)	An Act to enable His Majesty to make Rules, Orders and Regulations, more effectually to prevent the spreading of the distemper which now rages amongst the horned cattle of this Kingdom.
12 Geo.III c.71, (1772)	An Act for repealing several laws therein mentioned against Badgers, Engrossers, Forestallers and Regrators, and for indemnifying Persons against Prosecutions for Offences committed against the said Acts.
7 & 8 Vict. c.24, (1844)	An Act for abolishing the Offences of forestalling, regrating and engrossing and for repealing certain statutes passed in restraint of Trade.
29 & 30 Vict. c.2, (1866)	An Act to amend the law relating to Contagious or Infectious Diseases in Cattle and other Animals.
30 & 31 Vict. c.134, (1867)	An Act for regulating the traffic in the Metropolis, and for making Provision for the greater security of Persons passing through the Streets and for other Purposes.
35 & 36 Vict. c.94, (1872)	An Act for regulating the Sale of Intoxicating Liquors.
57 & 58 Vict. c.97, (1894)	An Act to consolidate the Contagious Diseases (Animals) Acts 1878 to 1893.

PART B
SECONDARY SOURCES BOOKS

Addison, W., *English Markets and Fairs*, Batsford, 1953.

A Dictionary of Welsh Biography, London, 1959.

Anon., *The Trail of the Black Ox,* privately printed, Builth Wells, (no date).

Ashby. A.W. and Evans, I.L., *The Agriculture of Wales and Monmouthshire*, Cardiff, 1944.

Ashton, T.S., *An Economic History of England, The Eighteenth Century*, London, 1955.

Ashworth, W., *An Economic History of England, 1870-1939*, London, 1970.

Bannister, J., *A Synopsis of Husbandry*, London, 1799.

Beever, W., *Notes on fields and cattle*, London, 1870.

Bingley, A., *Memoirs of British Quadrupeds*, London, 1809.

Bonser, K., *The drovers, who they were and where they went*, London, 1970.

Calendar of Close Rolls, Ed.II, 1309-13.

Calendar of Treasury Books, LVIII, 1743.

Calendar of Wynn Papers, 1515-1690, N. L. W. Aberystwyth, 1926.

Calendar of the Records of the Borough of Haverfordwest, 1539-1660, B. C.S. No.24.

Carey, J., *A delineation of the Turnpike roads of England and Wales*, London, 1806.

Chambers, J.D., and Mingay, G.E., *The Agricultural Revolution, 1750-1880*, London, 1966.

Clapham, J.H., *An Economic History of Modern Britain, 1850-1886*, Cambridge, 1952.

Clark, J.,*General View of the Agriculture of Brecknockshire*, London, 1794.

Clark, J., *General View of the Agriculture of Radnorshire*, London, 1797.

Cobbett, W., *Rural Rides,* Penguin edn., 1967.

Coleman, J., *The Cattle, Sheep and Pigs of Britain*, London, 1887.

Cox, R., *The Green Roads of England*, London, 1914.

Crosswood Deeds and Documents, N. L. W., Aberystwyth, 1927.

Davies, D.G., *Welsh Agriculture during the "Great Depression" 1873-96*, Unpublished M.Sc.(Econ). Thesis, University of Wales, 1973.

Davies, H.R., *The Conway and Menai Ferries*, B. C.S. No.8.

Davies, T., *Dinas Mawddwy*, 1893.

Davies, W., *A General View of the Agriculture and domestic economy of North Wales*, London, 1810.

Davies, W., *A General View of the Agriculture and domestic economy of South Wales*, London, 1815.

Deane, P. and Cole. W., *British Economic Growth 1688-1959*, Cambridge, 1962.

Defoe, D., *A Tour through England and Wales*, Everyman Edn., 1946.

Dixon, J., *Practical Agriculture*, London, 1805.

Dodd, A.H., *A History of Caernarvonshire, 1284-1900*, Denbigh, 1968.

Eames, A., *Ships and Seamen of Anglesey, 1558-1918*, Denbigh, 1973.

Edwards I, *Star Chamber Proceedings in Wales*, Cardiff, 1929.

Eliot, G. *Silas Marner*, Penguin Books, 1967.

Ernle, Lord, *English Farming Past and Present*, 6th Edn., London, 1961.

Evans, G.N., *Social Life in mid-eighteenth century Anglesey*, Cardiff, 1935.

Evans, H., *The Gorse Glen*, Liverpool, 1948.

Evans, J.E., *Letters written through ... South Wales*, London, 1804.

Everitt, A.M., *In The Agrarian History of England and Wales, IV, 1500-1640*, Cambridge, 1967.

Fox, C., *Offa's Dyke*, London, 1955.

Gayer, A., Rostow, W., and Schwartz, A., *The Growth and Fluctuation of the British Economy 1790-1850*, Oxford, 1953.

Gibson, J., *Agriculture in Wales*, London, 1879.

Gregg, P., *A Social and Economic History of Britain 1760-1965*, London, 1965.

Haldane, A., *The Drove Roads of Scotland*, London, 1952.

Hainsworth, D.R. and Walker, G. *The Correspondence of Lord Fitzwilliam of Mitton and Francis Guybon, his steward, 1697-1709*, Northants Records Society, 1990.

Halliwell, J.O., (ed.) *The Diary of Dr. John Dee*, Camden Society, 1842.

Halsbury, J., *The Laws of England*, 3rd Edn., London, 1952.

Harmon, A., *Notes on West Wycombe*, Glandford, 1934.

Harris, M.I., *The Railway Network of Wales*, Unpublished M.A. Thesis, University of Wales, 1953.

Hassall, C., *General View of the Agriculture of Carmarthenshire*, London, 1793.

Hassall, C., *General View of the Agriculture of Pembrokeshire*, London, 1794.

Hassall, C., *General View of the Agriculture of Monmouthshire*, London, 1812.

Hawke, G.R., *Railways and Economic Growth in England, 1840-1910*, Oxford, 1970.

Heath, O.M. *Walks around Albury*, Surrey, Guildford, 1950.

Hewitt, J., *Medieval Cheshire, An Economic and Social History of Cheshire during the reigns of the three Edwards*, Manchester, 1928.

Historical Manuscripts Commission, *Duke of Rutland Manuscripts*, Vol. I.

Howell, D., *Agriculture in Wales in the nineteenth century; the impact of railways on Welsh Agricultural Development*, (Text of paper given to Hist. Geog. Assn., Aberystwyth, 1973.)

Howse, W., *Radnorshire*, Hereford, 1949.

Hughes, H.E., *Eminent Men of Denbighshire*, Liverpool, 1946.

Hughes, P.G., *Wales and the Drovers*, London, 1943.

Hyde-Hall, E., *A description of Caernarvonshire 1809-11*, Caern. Hist. Soc., No.2.

Inglis-Jones, E., *Peacocks in Paradise*, Faber and Faber, 1971.

Jenkins, David, *The Agricultural Community in South-West Wales at the turn of the twentieth century*, Cardiff, 1971.

Jenkins, D.E., *The Reverend Thomas Charles of Bala*, Denbigh, 1908.

Jenkins, R.T., *Y Ffordd yn Nghymru*, Wrexham, 1937.

Johnes, T., *A Cardiganshire landlord's advice to his tenants*, Hafod, 1800.

Jones, D.E., *Hanes Plwyfi Llangeler a Penboyr*, Llandysul, 1899.

Jones, E.L. *Seasons and Prices; the role of the weather in English Agricultural History*, London, 1964.

Kay, J., *General View of the Agriculture of Anglesey*, London, 1794.

Kay, J., *General View of the Agriculture of Caernarvonshire*, London, 1794.

Lawrence, J., *A general treatise on cattle*, London, 1805.

Lewis, S., *A Topographical Dictionary of Wales*, London, 1833.

Lleufer Thomas, D., *Digest of the Report of the Welsh Land Commission*, London, 1896.

Lloyd, T., and Turnor, D., *General View of the Agriculture of Cardiganshire*, London, 1794.

Machiavelli, N., *The Prince*, Penguin Books edn. 1963.

Malkin, B., *The Scenery, Antiquities and Biography of South Wales*, London, 1807.

Marshall, E., *The Early History of Woodstock Manor and its environs*, London, 1873.

Marshall, W., *The Rural Economy of the Midland Counties*, London, 1790.

Meyrick, S. R., *The History and Antiquities of Cardigan*, London, 1808.

Mogg, E., *Paterson's Roads,... the direct and principal cross roads in England and Wales*, 18th Edn., London, 1832.

Morgan O., *The Romance of Essex Inns*, Letchworth, 1967.

Orwin, C.S., and Whetham, E., *A History of British Agriculture 1846-1914*, Newton Abbott, 1964.

Parkinson, R., *A treatise on the breeding and management of livestock*, London, 1810.

Parry-Jones, D., *My Own Folk*, Llandysul, 1972.

Perry, P.J., (ed.), *British Agriculture 1875-1914*, London, 1973.

Plomer, W., (ed.), *Selections from the diary of the Reverend Francis Kilvert*, London, 1938.

Price, O., in *The Agrarian History of England and Wales*, Cambridge, 1972, Vol.II.

Prichard, R., *Canwyll y Cymry*, 1807 (edn.), Carmarthen, 1807.

Rees, T., *A Topographical and Historical description of South Wales*, London, 1815.

Roberts, R.O., *Farming in Caernarvonshire around 1800*, Denbigh, 1973.

Roberts, S.R., *Diosg Farm*, Newtown, 1854.

Schedule of Dinas Mawddwy Records, N.L.W. Aberystwyth, 1940.

Smith, L.T., (ed.), *Leland's Itinerary in Wales*, London, 1906.

Sturt, G., *A Farmer's Life*, London, 1927.

Tawney, R., and Porter, W., *Tudor Economic Documents*, London, 1924.

Thomas, D., *Agriculture in Wales during the Napoleonic Wars*, Cardiff, 1963.

Thomas, H., *A History of Wales, 1485-1660*, Cardiff, 1972.

Thompson F.M.L., *English Landed Society in the Nineteenth Century*, London, 1963.

Trow-Smith, R., *A History of British Livestock Production, 1700-1900*, London, 1959.

Tucker, N., *Denbighshire Officers in the Civil War*, Denbigh (n.d.)

Vaughan, E., *The Essex Village in days gone by*, Colchester, 1930.

Victoria County History of Berkshire, London, 1906.

Victoria County History of Worcestershire, London, 1924.

Warner, R., *A Walk through Wales in August 1797*, Bath, 1798.

Webb, S., and B., *English Local Government: The Story of the King's Highway*, London, 1913.

Williams, D., *A History of Modern Wales*, London, 1969.

Williams, D., *The Rebecca Riots*, Cardiff, 1971.

Wilson, J.M., (ed.) *Rural Cyclopedia*, Edinburgh, 1847.

Wynne, E., *Gweledigaethau y Bardd Cwsg*, 1864 ed., Carmarthen.

Youatt, W., *Cattle, their breeds, management and diseases*, London, 1834.

Young, A., *The Farmer's Calendar*, London, 1804.

ARTICLES

Almack, W.B., "On the Agriculture of Norfolk", *J.R.A.S.E.*, Ser i, V, 1849.

Baker, D., "An Eighteenth Century Drover, William Williams of Tan y Bwlch", *Jour. Merion. Hist. and Rec. Soc.*, VI (iv), 1972.

Barns, T., "Derry Ormond, some new evidence", *N.L.W. Journal*, XXII, 1981-82.

Bettey, J.H., "Livestock trade in the West Country in the Seventeenth Century", *Somerset Arch. Nat. Hist.*, 127, 1983.

Bowstead, T., "Report on the British and foreign cattle exhibited at Kilburn", *J.R.A.S.E.*, Ser. ii, XV, 1879. *Bye Gones*, 1889-90, 1904.

Craigie, P.G., "Twenty years changes in our foreign meat supplies", *J.R.A.S.E.*, Ser ii, XXIII, 1887.

Cregeen, E., "Recollections of an Argyllshire drover", *Scottish Studies*, 3 (2), 1959.

Davies, J.L., "The Livestock trade in West Wales in the Nineteenth Century", *Aberystwyth Studies*, 13, 1934.

Dickenson, W., "On the Farming of Cumberland", *J.R.A.S.E.*, Ser, i, XIII, 1852.

Dixon, H.H., "The rise and progress of Shorthorns", *J.R.A.S.E.*, Ser, ii, 1, 1865.

Drew, J., "The Welsh Road and the drovers", *Trans. Birmingham Arch. Soc.*, 82, 1963.

Dyer, C., "A Small Landowner in the fifteenth century", *Midland History*, 1(3), 1972.

Edwards, P.R., "The Cattle Trade of Shropshire in the late Sixteenth and Seventeenth Centuries", *Midland History*, VI, 1981.

Evans, E., "Two Machynlleth Toll Books", *N.L.W. Journal*, VI, 1949-50.

Evans, H., "The Welsh Drovers", *Wales and Monmouthshire*, 8, 1937.

Farmer's Magazine, Sept. 1800, March 1801, Oct. 1801, Jan. 1802, July 1803, Feb. 1816, July 1816, Jan.1817, Feb. 1818, Feb. 1822, Dec. 1828, July 1837, Jan. 1847, Jan. 1849, Jan. 1851, July 1853,

June 1854, Dec. 1854, Jan. 1857, Jan. 1859, May 1859, June 1860, Sept. 1862, Dec. 1864.

Finberg, H.P.R., "An Early Reference to the Welsh Cattle Trade", *Ag. Hist. Rev.* 2, 1954.

Fletcher, T.W. "The Great Depression in English Agriculture" 1873-96, *Econ. Hist. Rev.*, Ser ii, XIII, 1961.

Fussell, G.E., "The size of cattle in the eighteenth century", *Ag. Hist.*, III, 1929.

Gentleman's Magazine, Sept. 1770, Jan. 1800, May 1801, July 1801, Aug. 1801, July 1802.

Gisborne, L., In *Quar. Rev.*, 168, 1849.

Green, F., "Early Banks in West Wales", *Trans. Hist. Soc. West Wales*, 1916.

Grey, C., *Letter to the Bath Society*, X, 1805.

Hughes, P.G., "Porthmona ym Morgannwg," *Trans. Cymmr.*, 1946-7

Humphreys, C., "The trades and industries of Llanfair Caereinion a hundred years ago", *Mont. Coll*, 46,1939-40.

James, E.O., " Sources for the Welsh drovers", *Carms. Local Hist. Mag.*, 1-2, 1961-2.

Jenkins, R.T., "A Drover's Account Book", *Caerns. Hist. Soc. Trans.*, 1-6, 1939-45.

Jones, D.J.V., "More Light on Rhyfel y Sais Bach", *Ceredigion*, 5, 1964-7.

Jones, J.E.J., "Fairs in Cardiganshire", *Card. Antiq. Soc. Trans.*, VIII, 1930-33.

Jones, K.W., "A Drover's Account", *Jour. Merion. Hist. and Rec. Soc.*, 2, 1953-6.

Lloyd, J.E., "The Black Cattle Droves", *Hist. Memo. of Breconshire*, 1, 1909.

Markham, C., "Banbury Lane", *Jour. Northants. Nat. Hist. Soc. and Field Club*, XVII, 1914.

Morgan, J., "The Montgomeryshire Smoky-Faced Cattle", *Powysland Club*, XIX, 1889.

Moore-Colyer, R.J., "Further References to the Welsh Cattle Trade", *N.L.W. Journal*, XXV (3), 1988.

Ibid., "Drove Roads", *Rights of Way Law Review,* October, 1998.

Parry, O., "Financing the Welsh Cattle Trade", *Bull. Board of Celtic Studies*, 8, 1935-7.

Perry, P.J., "A geography of bankruptcies in late Victorian England and Wales", *Ag. Hist. Rev.*, XX, 1972.

Phillips, R., "The last of the drovers", *Trans. Cymmr.*, 1968 Pt. I.

Powell, J. M., "Agriculture in Montgomeryshire in the early nineteenth century", *Mont. Coll.*, LXV, 1969.

Pringle, R.," A review of Irish Agriculture, chiefly with reference to the production of livestock", *J.R.A.S.E.*, Ser ii, VIII, 1872.

Rankin, H.R., "Cattle droving from Wales to England", *Agriculture*, LXII(5), 1955.

Read, C.S., "On the farming of South Wales", *J.R.A.S.E.*, Ser i, X, 1849.

Roberts, R.O., "The Brecon Old Bank 1778-1890", *Brycheiniog*, VII, 1961.

Rowlandson, T., "On the Agriculture of North Wales", *J.R.A.S.E.*, Ser i, VII, 1846.

Saul, S.B., "The myth of the Great Depression 1873-96", In M.W. Flinn (ed.), *Studies in Economic History*, Edinburgh, 1968.

Skeel, C., "The cattle trade between Wales and England from the fifteenth to the nineteenth centuries", *Trans. Roy. Hist. Soc.*, Ser iv, IX, 1926.

Stenton, F.M., "The Road System of Medieval England", *Econ. Hist. Rev.*, Ser iv, VII, 1936-7.

Thomas, S.P., "Twelve Miles a Day, Some Thoughts on the Drovers", *Radnorshire Society Trans.*, LIV, 1984

Thompson, W., "Cattle droving between Scotland and England", *Jour. Brit. Arch. Assn.*, XXX VII, 1932.

Wall, W. B., "The Agriculture of Pembrokeshire", *J.R.A.S.E.*, Ser ii, XXIII, 1887.

Whetham, E.H., "Livestock Prices in Britain, 1851-93", In W. Minchinton (ed.) *Essays in Agrarian History*, II, Newton Abbott, 1968.

Watson, R., "Droving and the Farm Economy in Eighteenth Century Wales: Some documents from the Allt-y-Cadno Papers", *Carmarthenshire Antiquary*, XVII, 1981.

INDEX

GENERAL INDEX

INDEX OF PERSONAL NAMES

INDEX OF PLACES

"GRENE WAY", Woodstock, Oxfordshire. 158.
"GROUSE INN", Abergwesyn, Brecknockshire. 129, 150.
GUILDFORD, Surrey. 158.
GUILSFIELD, Montgomeryshire. 26, 66.
GWENDDWR, Brecknockshire. 145.
GWERNARGLWYDD, Ltandegley, Radnorshire. 146.
HALLATON, Leicestershire. 163.
HAMPNETT, Northleach, Gloucestershire. 158.
HASELTON, Northleach, Gloucestershire. 158.
HAFOD LAS, Llanddewibrefi. 129.
HAVERFORDWEST, Pembrokeshire. 9, 36, 39, 40, 80, 83, 89, 108, 109, 113, 118, 119, 135, 136, 151.
HELMDON, Northamptonshire. 155.
HENFEDDAU, Pembrokeshire. 83, 136.
"HEOL LLOEGR", Rhydcymerau, Carmarthenshire. 135.
HEREFORD. 141, 146, 151, 156, 166.
HERTFORD. 155.
HILLINGDON, Middlesex. 108.
HINCLEY, Leicestershire. 153.
HIRAETH, Llanboidy, Carmarthenshire. 136.
HITCHIN, Hertfordshire. 155.
"HOLBORN FIELDS", Cilycwm, Carmarthenshire. 133.
HOLYWELL, Flintshire. 27.
HORSHAM, Sussex. 158, 165.
HOWEY, Radnorshire. 146.
HUNTINGTON, Herefordshire. 146.
HUNSBURY HILL, Northampton. 156.
HUNTLEY, Gloucestershire. 155.
ICKNIELD WAY, The. 155.
IVETSEY BANK, Norton Canes, Staffordshire. 153.
IVINGHOE, Buckinghamshire. 155.
KENILWORTH, Warwickshire. 153.
"KENT FIELD", Foel, Montgomeryshire. 87.
KERRY RIDGEWAY, The. 127.
"KINGS ARMS", Lledrod, Cardiganshire. 139.
"KINGS HEAD", Ludgate Hill, London. 122.
"KINGS HEAD", Hotspur, Beaconsfield. 158.
"KINGS HEAD", Fleet Street, London. 61.
KINGS PARK, Lampeter, Cardiganshire. 132.
KINGTON. Herefordshire. 146, 156.
KNAPP, Radnorshire, *tollgate at.* 146.
LAMPETER, Cardiganshire. 127, 132, 136, 139, 145, 150.
LAUNTON, Oxfordshire. 156.
LEATHERHEAD, Surrey. 79.
LECHLADE, Gloucestershire. 155, 158.
LEEBOTWOOD, Salop. 141, 148.
LEICESTER. 114, 153, 156, 161, 163.
LEIGHTON BUZZARD, Bedfordshire. 153, 155, 156.
LEOMINSTER. Herefordshire. 141, 156.
LIDDINGTON, Wiltshire. 158.
LINLEY GREEN, Bromyard, Worcestershire. 156.
LLANAFAN FAWR, Bculah, Brecknockshire. 146.
LLANARTHNEY, Carmarthenshire. 90.
LLANBADARN FAWR, Cardiganshire. 83, 85, 92, 118.
LLANBOIDY, Carmarthenshire. 136.
LLAN-CRWYS, 88, 121, 122.
LLANDDEWIBREFI, Cardiganshire. 127-9, 132, 136, 139.
LLANDDEUSANT, Brecknockshire. 135, 144.
LLANDDEWI VELFREY, Carmarthenshire. 136.
LLANDDULAS, Brecknockshire. 133, 135, 145.

LLANDEILO, Carmarthenshire. 109, 135.
LLANDOVERY, Carmarthenshire. 25, 35, 60, 62, 67, 68, 109, 113, 118, 132, 135, 136, 145.
LLANDRINDOD WELLS, Radnorshire. 109, 146.
LLANDYSUL, Cardiganshire. 109, 133.
LLANELLI, Carmarthenshire. 108.
LLANERCH-YRFA, Brecknockshire. 129.
LLANERFYL, Montgomeryshire. 146.
LLANFAIR-AR-Y-BRYN. Carmarthenshire. 150.
LLANFAIR CAEREINION. Montgomeryshire. 76, 146.
LLANFAIR CLYDOGAU, Cardiganshire. 128.
LLANFARIAN, Cardiganshire. 139.
LLANFIHANGEL-AR-ARTH, Carmarthenshire. 133.
LLANGADFAN, Montgomeryshire. 146.
LLANGEITHO, Cardiganshire. 11, 139, 151.
LLANGOLLEN, Denbighshire. 77, 108.
LLANGRANOG, Cardiganshire. 128.
LLANGURIG, Montgomeryshire. 129, 148.
LLANGWYRYFON, Cardiganshire. 132.
LLANIDLOES, Montgomeryshire. 9, 87, 159.
LLANIO, Tregaron. Cardiganshire. 139.
LLANILAR, Cardiganshire. 139.
LLANLLAWDDOG, Carmarthenshire. 136.
LLANLLUGAN, Montgomeryshire. 148.
LLANPUMSAINT, Carmarthenshire. 136.
LLANSAWEL, Carmarthenshire. 133, 135, 136, 141, 145, 151.
LLANTWIT, Glamorgan. 24.
LLANWNEN, Cardiganshire. 139.
LLANWINIO, Carmarthenshire. 139.
LLANWYDDELAN, Montgomeryshire. 148.
LLANYBYDDER, Carmarthenshire. 133, 150.
LLANYCRWYS, Carmarthenshire. 88, 121, 122.
LLEDROD, Cardiganshire. 132, 139, 151.
LLUNDAIN FECHAN, Lampeter. Cardiganshire. 132.
LLUEST-DOLGWIAIL, Montgomeryshire. 129.
LLWYNCELYNBACH, Farmers, Carmarthenshire. 85.
LLWYNDRAIN. Henfeddau, Carmarthenshire. 139.
LLWYN FELFRYN, Llansawel, Carmarthenshire. 135.
LLWYNGWRIL. Merionethshire. 27.
LLYN PENINSULA. 9, 109.
LLYNGLAS, Portyrhyd, Carmarthenshire. 133.
"LOCK AND KEY", Smithdield, London. 132.
LONDON. 150, 153, 155, 156, 158, 164.
LONG MOUNTAIN, The. 148.
LONG MYND, The. 148.
LUDLOW, Salop. 64, 141, 148, 149.
LUTTERWORTH, Leicestershire. 92, 153, 161.
MACHYNLLETH, Montgomeryshire. 75, 80, 83, 87, 109, 113, 121, 146, 148.
MAESTWYNOG, Caeo, Carmarthenshire. 133, 135.
MAIDSTONE, Kent. 161.
MAISEMORE, Gloucestershire. 156.
MALLWYD, Montgomeryshire. 109, 146.
MALVERN, Worcestershire. 156.
MANCHESTER. 59.
MARGAM ESTATE, Glamorgan. 40.
MARKET HARBOROUGH, Leicestershire. 114, 153, 156, 161, 163, 164.
MEIDRIM, Carmarthenshire. 146.
"MID-WALES", Newbridge, Radnorshire. 109.